An Anth
Scottish Fantasy
Literature

COLIN MANLOVE

AN ANTHOLOGY OF SCOTTISH FANTASY LITERATURE

Polygon

EDINBURGH

This edition published by
Polygon
22 George Square
Edinburgh EH8 9LF

ISBN 0 7486 6213 8

A CIP record is available for this title.

The Publishers acknowledge subsidy from the

THE SCOTTISH ARTS COUNCIL

towards the publication of this volume.

Designed by JUSTIN HOWES

Typeset by Combined Arts, Rushden

Printed and bound in Great Britain by
Cromwell Press, Wiltshire

CONTENTS

Introduction	7	
Fairy Tales	19	*Whuppity Stoorie*
	24	*The Black Bull of Norroway*
	27	*The Wal at the Warlds End*
	29	*Thomas Rhymer*
	31	*Tam Lin*
Robert Henryson	37	*The Testament of Cresseid*
William Dunbar	42	*The Goldyn Targe*
	51	*The Dance of the Sevin Deidly Synnis*
Gavin Douglas	55	*The Palice of Honour*
Patrick Gordon	60	*Penardo and Laissa*
James Macpherson	71	*Ossian*
Robert Burns	80	*Tam o' Shanter*
James Hogg	88	*Kilmeny*
	91	*The Three Perils of Man*
	95	*The Private Memoirs and Confessions of a Justified Sinner*
Thomas Carlyle	98	*Sartor Resartus*
George MacDonald	108	*Phantastes*
	114	*The Princess and the Goblin*

James Thomson 118 *The City of Dreadful Night*

Margaret Oliphant 123 *A Beleaguered City*
127 *Old Lady Mary*
130 *The Land of Darkness*

Robert Louis Stevenson 134 *Dr Jekyll and Mr Hyde*
138 *Tod Lapraik*

Andrew Lang 144 *The Gold of Fairnilee*

Fiona Macleod 150 *The Washer of the Ford*

J. M. Barrie 162 *Peter Pan*

David Lindsay 172 *A Voyage to Arcturus*
178 *The Haunted Woman*

Naomi Mitchison 182 *The Corn King and the Spring Queen*

Bruce Marshall 188 *Father Malachy's Miracle*

James Bridie 194 *Mr Bolfry*

Neil Gunn 201 *The Green Isle of the Great Deep*
209 *The Well at the World's End*

George Mackay Brown 213 *Magnus*
219 *An Epiphany Tale*

Alasdair Gray 223 *Lanark*

Liz Lochhead 231 *The Grimm Sisters*

Iain Banks 239 *The Bridge*

Sian Hayton 246 *Cells of Knowledge*

Margaret Elphinstone 254 *Green Man*

James Meek 264 *Some Notes on His Departure*

Sources 271

Acknowledgments 272

INTRODUCTION

COLIN MANLOVE

If asked what Scottish fantasy is, many of us might look first to Scotland's folktales, the stories handed down orally over the centuries and still occasionally being told, both in Gaelic and Scottish traditions. That is where Scotland is distinctive, it may be said: for the English have few such fairy tales. And as if in support of this there have been numerous collections and reprints of Scottish folktales over the past thirty years, since the international vogue for fantasy began. Some of us, however, might also point to individual works such as James Hogg's *Confessions of a Justified Sinner*, R.L.Stevenson's *Dr Jekyll and Mr Hyde* or perhaps Alasdair Gray's *Lanark*, but will often feel uneasy in speaking of them as 'fantasy' in the same terms as the English variety. But many would be reluctant to extend the term 'Scottish fantasy' further, feeling that there are few Scottish equivalents of writers such as Lewis Carroll or J. R. R. Tolkien or Mervyn Peake. For fantasy is often seen as an escape into a world of wonder, and Scotland seems to have few examples of this.

But Scotland does have a fantasy tradition, and one that forms a large part of its literature. If we understand fantasy as 'a fiction involving the supernatural', there is scarcely a major Scots writer from the medieval period to the present who has not been drawn to write it. From Henryson's court of the planetary gods in his *Testament of Cresseid* (c. 1460) to the reincarnation of Cyrano de Bergerac in A. L. Kennedy's *So I Am Glad* (1995), Scots writers have turned again and again in their work to fantasy. Yet this fantasy tradition remains one of Scotland's best-kept secrets. Indeed it represents a whole ignored area of the Scottish creative mind.

I first tried to unlock this secret in my *Scottish Fantasy Literature: A Critical*

Survey (1994), by discussing a range of Scottish fantasy writers. Here the aim is the same, but this time by letting the writers speak for themselves – at least as well as they can in what are often all too brief extracts. But by giving as many examples as possible, I hope something of the variety and power of Scottish fantasy will come over. Here then will be found traditional fairy tales, dream allegories, Spenserian romance, children's stories, travels to other worlds, ghost stories, comic tales, Christian mysteries and postmodernist visions; here too angels and demons, witches, fairies and enchanters, magic mirrors and *doppelgängers*, cities of evil, islands of holiness, planets of corrupt luxuriance and gardens of delight.

Some of the writers and works here will be familiar, some less so; some have been undeservedly forgotten and others are as yet not well-enough known; and one work, Patrick Gordon's *Penardo and Laissa*, appears in print for the first time since 1615. I have tried to select the most striking and diverse examples, but readers will have their own preferences. It need hardly be said that the extracts will only come fully into their own when seen in the works from which they are taken. Further, almost every work is itself only one of several possible examples. For instance, the fairy tales here are a tiny selection from the vast body of Scottish folk tales; Hogg is the author of many other poems and tales of the supernatural; and Alasdair Gray has written much other work of a fantastic character, from *Unlikely Stories, Mostly* (1983) to *Poor Things* (1992). And then there are the authors who are not represented at all – I think particularly of Sir Walter Scott's tales (often anthologised, though), the supernatural fiction of John Buchan, the narrative poetry of D. M. Black, or Emma Tennant's *Hotel De Dream* (1976). And it was tempting to push the boat out and take in writers not normally considered as Scottish, such as Byron, or Angela Carter of the magnificent *The Infernal Desire Machines of Dr Hoffman* (1972) or *The Bloody Chamber* (1979). To this all one can say is, read on.

Mentioning Byron and Carter does raise the wider issue of the Scottishness of the writers and works here, when one considers that most Scottish fantasy between about 1850 and 1930 was written by Scots living in England (usually in London). Precedent in the form of histories and companions of Scottish literature has already claimed them all – 'all' being George MacDonald, James Thomson, Margaret Oliphant, R.L.Stevenson, Andrew Lang, James Barrie and David Lindsay – for Scottish literature, even where, as with Thomson or Lindsay their upbringing was in England and visits to Scotland were at most occasional. We will gladly not argue with that, but there remains the issue of how far their work, written in England, can be said to be Scottish. For example, MacDonald's *Phantastes* is set in a landscape more Home Counties than Scottish; Barrie's *Peter Pan* is thoroughly London-Edwardian in its setting and outlook; and Lindsay's *The Haunted Woman* takes place within polite London society and in an old Saxon-built mansion in Sussex. Yet for all that there are basic features in all three of these works that unite them with other Scottish fantasies. The same however could not be said of, say, the 'South-Eastern' Scot Kenneth Grahame's *The Wind in the Willows* (1908), which is thoroughly English in its social, pastoral, animal-loving and whimsical character. Nor arguably, can it be said of the much more 'international' fantasy of Muriel Spark, in such works as 'The Seraph and the Zambezi' (1951) or *The Hothouse by the East River* (1973), which is not readily identifiable as Scottish. The persistence of these Scottish characteristics in so many writers living in England does however remain marked; and we may note that the work of the only two English-born writers of fantasy to live and write in Scotland – Margaret Elphinstone and Sian Hayton – shows the primary features of Scottish fantasy. And beyond that there is Shakespeare's *Macbeth*, the epitome of a Scottish fantasy penned by the example to all Englishmen …

In what follows here I shall be making quite a few contrasts with English fantasy to bring out the peculiar character of Scotland's. There does seem to be a quite remarkable polarity between the fantasy of the two countries, so extreme as to suggest a kind of fantastic *doppelgänger*, or Jekyll-and-Hyde situation. The reason for this is more the special insularity of English fantasy rather than any cultural inversion process between the two countries: English fantasy as a whole is quite unique in a European context (as I hope to show in a forthcoming book).

So then, what is Scottish fantasy? We can start from that definition of fantasy as 'a fiction involving the supernatural'. This at once distinguishes it from the 'realistic' novel and from science fiction, each of which depends on events within this nature, however remote their possibility. But it does not divide fantasy from dream allegory, ghost story, Gothic novel or postmodernist fiction, as many other modern definitions try to do. This, it might be argued, creates its own problems: for the 'supernatural' in a dream allegory or a postmodernist novel is not the same kind of supernatural, is not believed in, as is that in a Christian fantasy or in a ghost story. But in fact the interest of the supernatural for Scots is as a transgression of reality: they love to show one world of possibility cutting across another. From the appearance of the planetary gods to Cresseid during her swoon in the oratory in Henryson's *The Testament of Cresseid* to the abrupt upending of James Meek's Sandy in 'Some Notes On His Departure' when he idly speculates on how pleasant it would be to walk on the ceiling of his room, this collision of realities is basic to their fantasy. This may partly explain why Scottish fantasy is so often set in this world, because then the supernatural must appear an interruption; whereas if it appears in an 'other' world, one is halfway to the supernatural and does not so readily feel the discrepancy.

But Scots have always been fascinated by the supernatural. That fascination is seen partly in the popularity of the fairy tale, which breathes of a world inhabited by fairies, kelpies, silkies, shape-shifters, witches and devils. But there is also a wildness to the Scottish imagination that leads its writers to 'elrich fantasyis' as Gavin Douglas calls them, a revelling in the grotesque and in the unreasonable that casts aside all restrictions, which is not merely to be seen as a reaction against repression, whether English, bourgeois or religious. Add to that a continuously mystic strain in the Scots' psyche, the sense of a deeper living world beyond or within this one, from Thomas the Rymer's Elfland to David Lindsay's Muspel or Sian Hayton's domain of the giant Usbathaden in tenth-century Strathclyde, and one has impulses creating works that form the hidden side of Scottish literary tradition, and which not infrequently surface in more 'realistic' literature, from the fantastically brutal comedy of Smollett's *Roderick Random* to the terrene mysticism of Lewis Grassic Gibbon's *Sunset Song*. This impulse towards the supernatural may partly explain why Scottish wonder literature is almost always fantasy rather than science fiction, which hardly any Scots have written.

What then of the term 'Scottish'? First of all it may be best to point out what is not exclusively Scottish. The dream allegories of the medieval 'makars' Henryson, Dunbar and Douglas owe much to Chaucer, and to French tradition. Much nineteenth-century Scottish fantasy springs from the Gothic novel, and some from German Romantic *Kunstmärchen*: and several of its features, such as the use of doubles, mirrors and dreams are frequent currency in European fantasy, from Hoffmann to Gogol and from Dostoevsky to Nerval or Lautréamont. On the other hand, Continental (and English) Romanticism itself owes a huge debt to one Scottish fantasy – Macpherson's *Ossian*. The point here is not so much the indebtedness as the kinship of outlook from which it emerges.

This continental kinship is a key to the kind of literature we are considering here. For the continental use of fantasy is generally as a vision of reality: it provides the unusual angle, the grotesque inversion. In England, by contrast, fantasy is often an escape from reality, not another version of it: England is the home of 'secondary world' fantasy, that which creates another imagined realm, such as Zimiamvia, Gormenghast or Middle-earth. Scotland's fantasy is thus inevitably symbolist literature in a way that England's is not. The divided self in Stevenson's *Dr Jekyll and Mr Hyde* is the product of a whole psychic landscape, both Scottish and Victorian; the planet Tormance in Lindsay's *A Voyage to Arcturus* presents in heightened form the strangulation of the spirit in this world; the afterworld of Gray's *Lanark* is in part a surreal vision of Glasgow. In this the kinship is much more with Hoffmann and Kafka than with Lewis or Tolkien. The tendency is more analytic, often satirical: the impulse in English fantasy towards contemplation, pastoral escape and luxuriance of description is rarely found in Scottish fantasy. The most luxuriant Scottish fantasy is Lindsay's *A Voyage to Arcturus* with its continually rich images of the planet Tormance, and yet every one of these descriptions is spurned as a corruption, a devil's device to prevent the soul approaching the true nothingness of the 'sublime'.

But if the Scottish approach to fantasy has a European dimension, there remains a distinctive Scottish voice in it. The use of doubles and of dream structures is pervasive, far beyond the repressive nineteenth century where such things had a certain international currency. Scotland is inherently double, in the division between Lowland and Highland, or between Scottish and Gaelic cultures. And Scottish Calvinism has for centuries sought to abolish half of Scottish human nature. In fantasy, which is the genre for imaginative release, the repressed sides of the Scottish character make themselves peculiarly known. As for dreams and visions, those are part of the mystic bent already remarked; they also emerge from a marked distrust of the intellect and logical structures which may be a reaction to the dominance of those features in other areas of Scottish culture.

Almost every Scottish fantasy looks to a dissolution of conscious structures and identity followed by a dream or nightmare existence. It here seems no accident that so many medieval Scots writers were attracted to the form of dream allegory, and especially to that which involves the supernatural coming in towards the house or place of the dreamer, to create havoc (in Chaucer's and Langland's allegories the dreamer often has to travel to his experience). The world of Macpherson's *Ossian* is that of the wild Highland unconscious; that of George MacDonald's characters, the dreaming imagination which is at root the home of God in man; of Stevenson's Jekyll, the tortured subconscious of the repressed self; of Fiona Macleod's stories, the realm of a dream-like dissolution of all boundaries; in Barrie's *Peter Pan*, the world of thoughtless childhood; while Neil Gunn takes us to the 'great deep' and George Mackay Brown to a sacramental world at once within and beyond common sight.

In Scottish fantasy there is a general sense of things coming in or converging – much more than in the English form. There are few journeys or quests outward to find something, as in Kingsley or Tolkien: any journeys we find, as in MacDonald, Lindsay or Gray, are more wanderings without clear aim. The supernatural is usually hard by, indeed often all too close to everyday life: it is found in a bureau drawer (MacDonald's *Phantastes*), enters the family home (Henryson's *Testament*, Barrie's *Peter Pan*, Bridie's *Mr Bolfry*), comes as a spiritual adviser or as a tempter (Brown), or is found camping by a hiker (Elphinstone). Most Scottish fantasy is set in this world, and usually in the immediate locality, from Burns's Ayrshire to Lang's Borders, Gunn's Highlands or Elphinstone's Galloway. There is frequent symbolism involving houses or enclosures that are penetrated or abandoned, suggesting the removal of the covering of the conscious or normal self. Burns's Tam o' Shanter leaves the social world of the Ayr pub for the dark realm through which he must ride home; Carlyle in *Sartor Resartus* portrays all society and the world as clothing that must be looked through; the heroes in MacDonald's *Phantastes* and *Lilith* begin by leaving symbolic castles of the self; house, doorway and window imagery pervades the fantasy of Mrs Oliphant; Stevenson's Jekyll becomes confined to a room in his house which is finally broken into. In the twentieth century we have the house in Lindsay's *The Haunted Woman* which contains a hidden route to another world, or the institute in Gray's *Lanark* which is left by Lanark and Rima; or the neat order of the bungalow in Margaret Elphinstone's 'Island of Sheep' which is overthrown.

Several Scottish fantasies have the unstructured character of dreams. Dunbar's visions are of often hallucinatory vividness, particularly in 'The Dance of the Sevin Deidly Synnis'. Douglas's *The Palice of Honour* has uncertain direction, frequent changes of scene and images of intermittent starkness. Both these poets use dream allegory with the sense of dreams as fantasy rather than vision, part of human psychology rather than a literary mode. Macpherson's *Ossian* is a shifting world of weather, geography and men embroiled in obscurity. Carlyle's *Sartor Resartus* is a series of disjointed speculations mixed with a bizarre biography. MacDonald's *Phantastes* and *Lilith*, Fiona Macleod's tales, Barrie's *Peter Pan*, Lindsay's *A Voyage to Arcturus*, Gray's *Lanark*, Iain Banks's *The Bridge*, all varyingly have the lack of structure, causality or sequence that we associate with dreams.

Hostility to the conscious self and the intellect is often seen in Scottish fantasy. There is particular dislike of human mental categories being imposed on reality. Throughout his *Confessions of a Justified Sinner*, Hogg is attacking the cold and priggish reason of the Calvinist Robert Wringhim, whose belief in his election bends all reality to suit it. With his self-justification Wringhim denies his own dark nature; and similarly Stevenson's Jekyll is indicted for his denial of Hyde. Carlyle in *Sartor Resartus* assails those habits of mind that reduce what he sees as the fiery mystery of the universe to their own dark limits. For MacDonald the supernatural world is reached only through the imagination: the whole of his *Lilith* is a gradual defeat of the wakeful intellect. The uncontrolled intellect is the evil behind the perverted utopia in Neil Gunn's *The Green Isle of the Great Deep*. Gray's Thaw breaks through all the structures of life into death, and so too his other self Lanark in the life beyond that, until he has so discovered himself at a primal and instinctual level that he can die indeed. We also find in Scottish fantasy a theme of antagonism to respectability and the comfortable and conformist settling of life, in Burns, Hogg, Stevenson, Lindsay, Barrie, Gray and Lochhead. All this is in marked contrast to English fantasy, which often happily uses reason and imagination together, as in Kingsley's or Lewis's or Tolkien's work; which delights in structures, especially the making of worlds or of wit; which revels in rules or laws, whether they are the rules covering magic or a whole world; which, with such exceptions as Lewis Carroll and Robert Holdstock (in *Mythago Wood*), rarely addresses itself to the unconscious; and for which houses are not so much mental symbols as solid homes, places to go to.

The focus of Scottish fantasy is most commonly on an isolated individual. We do not have the kind of corporate or multiple heroes we can find in English fantasy, as in E. R. Eddison, Charles Williams, Tolkien, T. H. White or Richard Adams. English fantasy is often showing the links between many scattered things: examples are Tolkien's Frodo, whose journey to Mordor brings together all the separated parts of Middle-earth, or Robert Holdstock's *Mythago Wood* (1984) where an ancient woodland is a junction of all the myths of the world. When we read an English fantasy we are quite often involved in seeing patterns and making connections; in Scottish fantasy we are learning to disconnect, to stop patterning reality. Being more expansive in character, English fantasies are often longer: Scottish fantasies are on the whole brief, and are often found in the form of the short story. The central figures in Scottish fantasy are often outsiders, or people marked by some oddity or even blight: for example Henryson's Cresseid is a moral and then physical leper, Mrs Oliphant's ghosts are posthumous misfits, Stevenson's Jekyll is a closet monster, Barrie's Peter Pan is an undeveloped child, Brown's Magnus is a sacrificial lamb. In English fantasy the protagonists are often seen gradually to fit in with society: Kingsley's dirty little Victorian sweep Tom in *The*

Water-Babies learns underwater to get on with the other creatures; C. S. Lewis's Cambridge professor Ransom becomes a citizen of the 'Celestial Commonwealth'.

Scottish fantasy seems much less optimistic about society, which often misunderstands or rejects the protagonists. The price of attempted accommodation is seen in *Dr Jekyll and Mr Hyde*, where the central character has to split himself in half in order to remain 'respectable', and even that scheme fails. In Gray's *Lanark*, Duncan Thaw tries to make his way in the world but ends a social outcast and an artistic failure; and in the next world Lanark finds a society that eats its members. Because they are outsiders, unable to relate properly to society, the end for many protagonists of Scottish fantasy is disappearance or death. This is variously seen in the death of Henryson's Cresseid, the disappearance of Carlyle's Professor Teufelsdröckh, James Thomson's invocation of death in *The City of Dreadful Night*, the end of Lindsay's Maskull, the martyrdom of Brown's Magnus or the slow mortality of Sian Hayton's Marighal. The happy ending often found in English fantasy is a less frequent visitor to that of Scotland.

We find that Scottish fantasy frequently involves a steady reduction or stripping, where English fantasy is accretive. English fairy tales (Dick Whittington, the Jacks) and fantasies (Tom the sweep; Frodo, the Wart in White's *The Once and Future King*) often portray the small-time entrepreneur made good. Hogg's Justified Sinner is steadily hollowed out until his certainties are in rags; similar patterns are seen in the work of Stevenson, Macleod, Lindsay, Gunn, Elphinstone and Hayton. MacDonald's characters have to unlearn, to become like children, to see. The sense is often one of analysis: 'this, at root, is what the world is like'. Carlyle takes the world's clothes off; James Thomson reduces life to a city of dreadful night; David Lindsay's Maskull has to go on rejecting the world until the bare sublime that is Muspel may be reached; Neil Gunn's Hector is denuded of self until he finds his God. This reductive, backwards process is often mirrored in a habit in Scottish fantasy of reversing things, turning them upside-down – whether names (such as Naomi Mitchison's Erif Der), opposite selves such as Hogg's Gil-Martin, Stevenson's Hyde or Lindsay's Nightspore, or inverted places (MacDonald's mirror-regions, Thomson's dark city, Gunn's Green Isle, Gray's Unthank).

Together with this there is a pattern of 'levelling down' in Scottish fantasy: identities that jut out are worn away. In contrast to English fantasy there are few kings, queens and earls. The heroes of Scottish fantasy, if heroes they may be called, learn to be less rather than more;

weakness and worldly failure are more valued than success or power. A theme frequent in the more moral nineteenth-century Scottish fantasy is the removal of pride, as in Hogg's Wringhim, MacDonald's Anodos and Vane, Stevenson's Jekyll and Macleod's Torcall; and in the twentieth-century form the defeat of intellectual arrogance, as in the work of Gunn, Gray, Elphinstone or Hayton. No great victories are won, such as that of Tolkien's Fellowship of the Ring over Sauron; no great changes are made to the world by any character's acts, save in Gunn's *The Green Isle of the Great Deep*. Defeat and loss are primary. The self is seen as thin-walled, able to dissolve in a moment: it has doubles which assume part of its life, it can be dispelled in the unconscious (MacDonald), it hovers fraily on the borders of seen and unseen worlds (Oliphant), it is scarce differentiated from the world about it (Carlyle, James Meek); and it can die.

The imagery of Scottish fantasy is often bound up with that which is 'under' rather than 'over'. The fairies come from underground; Patrick Gordon's Penardo finds his Laissa in an underground labyrinth; Carlyle's Teufelsdröckh finds the truth beneath the clothes of the world; MacDonald's characters continually descend into the gulf of the mind; Stevenson's Hyde lives in the underworld. So too Mrs Oliphant takes us beneath the earth in 'The Land of Darkness' (1887); Lang's Randal goes underground with the fairies; Gunn's Green Isle is beneath the waters of Hazel Pool; the 'other' world of Gray's *Lanark* is reached by dropping oneself through a giant pair of open lips in a graveyard. There is a continual sense of undertow, of a greater gravitational force that will absorb the self (gravity is overtly an issue in fantasies by MacDonald, Lindsay, Gray and Meek).

This pull towards an underworld is part of the drive in Scottish fantasy towards the sub- or under-conscious mind. In part the institute beneath the mountain in Gray's *Lanark*, and the cities beyond it, express the dreaming side of the brain: they are in one sense Duncan Thaw's descent into himself in both night and death. In another way in Carlyle's *Sartor Resartus*, going beneath the clothes of the world involves going beneath the surface levels of consciousness into the imagination. And then we have the 'underselves' in Scottish fantasy – Hogg's Gil-Martin, MacDonald's Shadow, Stevenson's Hyde, Lindsay's Nightspore, Bridie's Mr Bolfry, Gray's Lanark, Iain Banks's Orr. Here we see how the impulses behind Scottish fantasy are of a piece. The isolation of the protagonists makes them more open to the processes of erosion that end in a journey downwards. Why this concern with the subconscious is so central is, however, something we have yet to answer.

But there is another side to such emphasis on underworlds, and that is the social one. Scottish fantasy admits the 'lower classes' as do few other national fantasies. Henryson's Cresseid is forced to join the under-people of the Greek town, Dunbar gives us a proletarian hell, MacDonald the goblins mining beneath the royal castle. Stevenson's Hyde, habitué of the dark places of London, in part represents London's underclasses just as Jekyll, living in his house in a well-to-do square represents their repressive opposite: and Jekyll's overthrow by Hyde is here as much social insurrection or revolution as it is the upwelling of the self. Naomi Mitchison's Erif Der learns more from the helots of Sparta than from the ruling classes, who are doomed despite all their social and political ideals. Part of Brown's *Magnus* is relayed to us through the vision of the peasant farmer Mans and a pair of tinkers. The socialism of Gray's *Lanark* is pervasive. Sometimes the underclasses are a threat, sometimes a source of health, but always their presence acts to undermine pride and wear down self-sufficiency. And as seen there are few conventional heroes in Scottish fantasy, where the heroic usually involves giving the self away, as do MacDonald's Anodos and Vane, Macleod's Torcall or Brown's Magnus the martyr.

How then are we to explain those features? It would be easy to link the uncertainties of identity, and the inclination towards the dream-like, to some tendency towards an inferiority complex in the Scottish character. But the real interest is in entering the unconscious: these features rather reflect a search for certainty than a confession of inadequacy. In work after work what is happening is a journey inwards, whereby the self is destroyed and possibly a new one created. The search is for a spiritual bedrock: it is in a sense a religious quest. This is even present by contraries in Hogg's Wringhim or Stevenson's Jekyll, where we have characters who refuse to look truly within, and pay for it. The process involves a continual moving away from all certainties, whether of self, or perception, or value, or knowledge, in a journey from which some further truth may arise. The wretched reduction of Henryson's Cresseid by the gods is one form of this; another is the search for Honour in Douglas's *The Palice of Honour*, the sight of which, enthroned as 'ane God omnipotent', strikes the pilgrim senseless; another is Fiona Macleod's continual quest for the 'deep elementals' through Celtic myth. The same process is found in the penetration to the world's mystery in Carlyle's *Sartor* or Brown's *Magnus*, and in the contrastive journeys inwards to the mysterious depths of the self in MacDonald and in Stevenson. It is seen too as much in the continual advocacy of despair and suicide in Thomson's *The City of*

Dreadful Night as in the final discovery of God beneath universal darkness in Gunn's *The Green Isle of the Great Deep*. It is present in desire, desire which is peculiarly intense in Scottish fantasy: desire for heaven or hell in Hogg, for 'contact' in Oliphant, for faërian glamour in Lang, for eternal childhood in Barrie, for the unutterable sublime in Lindsay; desire for renewed faith in Marshall, a Celtic paradise in Gunn, a loom of light in Brown, a giant mystery in Hayton; desire also in Gray simply to find a final death, or in Banks, a way off a seemingly endless bridge. This search for an absolute, this continual tearing away of life to find some final truth or supernatural mystery, is to be seen in writers from other countries, from Novalis to Kafka, or from Gautier to Gene Wolfe, but nowhere with such consistent emphasis as in the fantasy of Scotland.

Scottish fantasy is no static thing. In the time scale 1460–1995 covered by this anthology, the kinds of fantasy that are being written obviously shift. We move from dream allegory through Spenserian romance to the eighteenth-century sublime (*Ossian*); from Gothic fantasy to ghost story; and from science fantasy through dystopian novel to postmodernist and feminist fiction. Assumptions about 'reality' and the supernatural change. So far as 'reality' is concerned, we move from idealism to naturalism to relativism; and with the supernatural, broadly from a 'teleological' to an 'ontological' view of it, the first involving the numinous, the second another plane of reality (postmodernist fantasy). The moral element also alters: it does not disappear in the twentieth century as might be supposed, but simply comes up with other imperatives, from primitivism to ecology, and from socialism to feminism. There is a more political dimension to modern Scottish fantasy, from Mitchison's explorations of third-century BC civilisations, to Gunn's picture of dystopia or Gray's vision of macroeconomics. There is also a wider setting, whether a planet as in Lindsay or a historical turning point as in Hayton: indeed there is generally far more of a sense of time and space. Yet through all these changes, the primary character of Scottish fantasy remains the same.

Scottish fantasy as we have described it is a serious affair, reaching for the deepest levels of the spirit. While it is enormously energetic in character, full of wild flights of the imagination, it does not have the relaxed expansiveness of English fantasy, which fosters the growth of comic fantasy and fantasy for children. Both these and other sub-types are marked in English fantasy, which is diversified in character and harder to classify. But broadly, where English fantasy spreads, Scottish fantasy concentrates, penetrates. Scottish fantasies generally offer a serious view of the world, not a diversion or an escape from it. And this perhaps is why they are not commonly seen as fantasies at all.

ℱairy Tales

AN INTRODUCTION

Scotland is rich in fairy tales, and even now in the age of television oral tradition lingers among travelling people. Such tales are the oldest fantasies of any land, the values, hopes and fears of ordinary people turned to stories of magical events that transform human life. Only in the seventeenth century did they begin to be written down, in the bowdlerized forms that entered chapbooks. Among the best known Scottish fairy tales are 'Rashie Coat', 'Whuppity Stoorie', 'The Black Bull of Norroway', 'The Red Etin' and 'The Well at the World's End', three of which are presented here. Yet what makes these stories Scottish is not usually their narratives, which often derive from stories from other lands, but the idioms of their tellers, their local details, landscapes, characters and attitudes: the same narrative skeletons inhabit quite different bodies. 'Whuppity Stoorie' tells much the same basic story as the English 'Tom Tit Tot' or the German 'Rumpelstiltskin', but one glance at it here will show how soaked it is in the idiom and outlook of its teller. There are also a few stories in which the international analogues are faint enough for us to call them peculiarly Scottish: 'Thomas Rymer' and 'Tam Lin' together recall the Orpheus and Eurydice myth, but the peculiar fairy lore subdues any sense of influence.

The selection here is tiny. It omits the entire range of Gaelic folktales, as taken down by J. F. Campbell in his *Popular Tales of the West Highlands* (1860): but these tales are closer to Irish and Gaelic than to a peculiarly Scottish tradition. Further, each tale here represents only one telling: another speaker, and one might have a story of quite a different character. With the ballad tales it is different, since they are no longer oral: here it is a matter of choosing the best version from among the variants in F. J. Child's *The English and Scottish Popular Ballads* (1957). But the tales included here are intended to give some idea of their variety, from comic to tragic, moral to superstitious, bare to elaborate.

Is there anything identifiably Scottish that recurs in the country's fairy tales? Dangerous though it is to generalise, we do find a marked emphasis on the influence of women: England, by contrast, has its giant-killing Jacks, its Dick Whittingtons or Childe Rowlands. (This could reflect the fact that the tellers of Scottish (not Gaelic) fairy tales are almost always women – we find the same situation in the tales collected by the Grimms.) It is feminine wile that captures Thomas Rymer and feminine devotion that releases Tam Lin; and mothers and daughters are the prime movers in the best-known fairy tales that have taken root in Scotland, such as 'The Red Etin', 'Green Sleeves', 'Rashie Coat', 'Mally Whuppie' or 'Kate Crackernuts'. Scottish fairy tales show more interest in love and charity than English tales, which often involve heroism, cunning or self-seeking as their driving principles. There are comparatively few giants in Scottish fairy tales (though more in the Gaelic variety) apart from 'Mally Whuppie', which is a feminist version of 'Jack and the Beanstalk', and 'The Red Etin', the ogre story which Sir David Lyndsay is said to have told to the young James V.

₰Whuppity Stoorie

'I ken ye're fond o' clashes aboot fairies, bairns; and a story anent a fairy and the guidwife o' Kittlerumpit has joost come into my mind; but I canna very weel tell ye noo whereabouts Kittlerumpit lies. I think it's somewhere in amang the Debateable Grund; onygate I'se no pretend to mair than I ken, like a'body noo-a-days. I wuss they wad mind the ballant we used to lilt langsyne:

> "Mony ane sings the gerse, the gerse,
> And mony ane sings the corn;
> And mony ane clatters o' bold Robin Hood,
> Ne'er kent where he was born."

But hoosoever, about Kittlerumpit: the goodman was a vaguing sort o' a body; and he gaed to a fair ae day, and not only never came hame again, but never mair was heard o'. Some said he listed, and ither some that the wearifu' pressgang cleekit him up, though he was clothed wi' a wife and a wean forbye. Hechhow! that dulefu' pressgang! they gaed aboot the kintra like roaring lions, seeking whom they micht devoor. I mind weel, my auldest brither Sandy was a' but smoored in the meal ark hiding frae thae limmers. After they war gane, we pu'd him oot frae amang the meal, pechin' and greetin', and as white as ony corp. My mither had to pike the meal oot o' his mooth wi' the shank o' a horn spoon.

'Aweel, when the goodman o' Kittlerumpit was gane, the goodwife was left wi' a sma' fendin. Little gear had she, and a sookin' lad bairn. A'body said they war sorry for her; but naebody helpit her, whilk's a common case, sirs. Howsomever, the goodwife had a soo, and that was her only consolation; for the soo was soon to farra, and she hopit for a good bairn-time.

'But we a' weel ken hope's fallacious. Ae day the wife gaes to the sty to fill the soo's trough; and what does she find but the soo lying on her back, grunting and graning, and ready to gie up the ghost.

'I trow this was a new stoond to the goodwife's heart; sae she sat doon on the knockin'-stane, wi' her bairn on her knee, and grat sairer than ever she did for the loss o' her ain goodman.

'Noo, I premesse that the cot-hoose o' Kittlerumpit was biggit on a brae, wi' a muckle fir-wood behint it, o' whilk ye may hear mair or lang gae. So the goodwife, when she was dichtin' her een, chances to look down the brae, and what does she see but an auld woman, amaist like a leddy, coming slowly up the gaet. She was buskit in green, a' but a white short apron, and a black velvet hood, and a steeple-crowned beaver hat on her head. She had a lang walking-staff, as lang as hersel', in her hand – the sort of staff that auld men and auld women helpit themselves wi' lang syne; I see nae sic staffs noo, sirs.

'Aweel, when the goodwife saw the green gentlewoman near her, she rase and made a curchie; and "Madam," quo' she, greetin', 'I'm ane of the maist misfortunate women alive.'

'I dinna wish to hear pipers' news and fiddlers' tales, good-wife,' quo' the green woman. 'I ken ye've tint your goodman – we had waur losses at the Shirra Muir; and I ken that your soo's unco sick. Noo, what will ye gie me gin I cure her?'

'Onything your leddyship's madam likes,' quo' the witless goodwife, never guessin' what she had to deal wi'.

'Let's wat thooms on that bargain,' quo' the green woman: sae thooms war wat, I'se warrant ye; and into the sty madam marches.

'She looks at the soo wi' a lang glowr, and syne began to mutter to hersel' what the goodwife couldna weel understand; but she said it soundit like:

"Pitter patter,
Haly water."

'Syne she took oot o' her pouch a wee bottle, wi' something like oil in 't, and rubs the soo wi't abune the snoot, ahint the lugs, and on the tip o' the tail. "Get up, beast," quo' the green woman. Nae sooner said nor done – up bangs the soo wi' a grunt, and awa' to her trough for her breakfast.

'The goodwife o' Kittlerumpit was a joyfu' goodwife noo, and wad hae kissed the very hem o' the green madam's gown-tail, but she wadna let her. "I'm no sae fond o' fashions," quo' she; "but noo that I hae richtit your sick beast, let us end our sicker bargain. Ye'll no find me an unreasonable greedy body – I like aye to do a good turn for a sma' reward – a' I ask, and *wull* hae, is that lad bairn in your bosom."

'The goodwife o' Kittlerumpit, wha noo kent her customer, ga'e a skirl like a stickit gryse. The green woman was a fairy, nae doubt; sae she prays, and greets, and begs, and flytes; but a' wadna do. "Ye may spare your din," quo' the fairy, 'skirling as if I was as deaf as a door nail; but this I'll let ye to wut – I canna, by *the law we leeve on*, take your bairn till the third day after this day; and no then, if ye can tell me my right name.' Sae madam gaes awa' round the swine's-sty end, and the goodwife fa's doon in a swerf behint the knockin'-stane.

'Aweel, the goodwife o' Kittlerumpit could sleep nane that nicht for greetin', and a' the next day the same, cuddlin' her bairn till she near squeezed its breath out; but the second day she thinks o' taking a walk in the wood I tell't ye o'; and sae, wi' the bairn in her arms, she sets out, and gaes far in amang the trees, where was an old quarry-hole, grown owre wi' gerse, and a bonny spring well in the middle o't. Before she came very nigh, she hears the birring o' a lint-wheel, and a voice lilting a sang; sae the wife creeps quietly amang the bushes, and keeks owre the broo o' the quarry, and what does she see but the green fairy kemping at her wheel, and singing like ony precentor:

'Little kens our guid dame at hame
That Whuppity Stoorie is my name!'

'Ah, ha!' thinks the wife, 'I've gotten the mason's word at last; the deil gie them joy that tell't it!' Sae she gaed hame far lichter than she came out, as ye may weel guess, lauchin' like a madcap wi' the thought o' begunkin' the auld green fairy.

'Aweel, ye maun ken that this goodwife was a jokus woman, and aye merry when her heart wasna unco sair owreladen. Sae she thinks to hae some sport wi' the fairy; and at the appointit time she puts the bairn behint the knockin'-stane, and sits down on 't hersel'. Syne she pu's her mutch ajee owre her left lug, crooks her mou on the tither side, as gin she war greetin', and a filthy face she made, ye may be sure. She hadna lang to wait, for up the brae mounts the green fairy, nowther lame nor lazy; and lang or she gat near the knockin'-stane, she skirls out: 'Goodwife o' Kittlerumpit, ye weel ken what I come for – stand and deliver!' The wife pretends to greet sairer than before, and wrings her nieves, and fa's on her knees, wi': 'Och, sweet madam mistress, spare my only bairn, and take the weary soo!'

'The deil take the soo for my share,' quo' the fairy; 'I come na here for swine's flesh. Dinna be contramawcious, hizzie, but gie me the gett instantly!'

'Ochon, dear leddy mine,' quo' the greetin' goodwife; forbear my poor bairn, and take mysel'!'

'The deil's in the daft jad,' quo' the fairy, looking like the far-end o' a fiddle; 'I'll wad she's clean dementit. Wha in a' the earthly warld, wi' half an ee in their head, wad ever meddle wi' the likes o' thee?'

'I trow this set up the wife o' Kittlerumpit's birse; for though she had twa bleert een, and a lang red neb forbye, she thought hersel' as bonny as the best o' them. Sae she bangs aff her knees, sets up her mutch-croon, and wi' her twa hands faulded afore her, she maks a curchie down to the grund, and, 'In troth, fair madam,' quo' she, 'I might hae had the wit to ken that the likes o' me is na fit to tie the warst shoe-strings o' the heich and mighty princess, *Whuppity Stoorie!*' Gin a fluff o' gunpowder had come out o' the grund, it couldna hae gart the fairy loup heicher nor she did; syne down she came again, dump on her shoe-heels, and whurlin' round, she ran down the brae, scraichin' for rage, like a houlet chased wi' the witches.

'The goodwife o' Kittlerumpit leugh till she was like to ryve; syne she taks up her bairn, and gaes into her hoose, singin' till 't a' the gaet:

> 'A goo and a gitty, my bonny wee tyke,
> Ye'se noo hae your four-oories;
> Sin' we've gien Nick a bane to pyke,
> Wi' his wheels and his Whuppity Stoories.'''

THE BLACK BULL OF NORROWAY

In Norroway, langsyne, there lived a certain lady, and she had three dochters. The auldest o' them said to her mither: 'Mither, bake me a bannock, and roast me a collop, for I'm gaun awa' to spotch my fortune.' Her mither did sae; and the dochter gaed awa' to an auld witch washerwife and telled her purpose. The auld wife bade her stay that day, and gang and look out o' her back-door, and see what she could see. She saw nocht the first day. The second day she did the same, and saw nocht. On the third day she looked again, and saw a coach-and-six coming alang the road. She ran in and telled the auld wife what she saw. 'Aweel,' quo' the auld wife, 'yon 's for you.' Sae they took her into the coach, and galloped aff.

The second dochter next says to her mither: 'Mither, bake me a bannock, and roast me a collop, for I'm gaun awa' to spotch my fortune.' Her mither did sae; and awa she gaed to the auld wife, as her sister had dune. On the third day she looked out o' the back-door, and saw a coach-and-four coming alang the road. 'Aweel,' quo' the auld wife, 'yon's for you.' Sae they took her in, and aff they set.

The third dochter says to her mither: 'Mither, bake me a bannock, and roast me a collop, for I'm gaun awa' to spotch my fortune.' Her mither did sae; and awa' she gaed to the auld witch wife. She bade her look out o' her back-door, and see what she could see. She did sae; and when she came back, said she saw nocht. The second day she did the same, and saw nocht. The third day she looked again, and on coming back, said to the auld wife she saw nocht but a muckle Black Bull coming crooning alang the road. 'Aweel,' quo' the auld wife, 'yon's for you.' On hearing this she was next to distracted wi' grief and terror; but she was lifted up and set on his back, and awa' they went.

Aye they travelled, and on they travelled, till the lady grew faint wi' hunger. 'Eat out o' my right lug,' says the Black Bull, 'and drink out o' my left lug, and set by your leavings.' Sae she did as he said, and was wonderfully refreshed. And lang they gaed, and sair they rade, till they came in sight o' a very big and bonny castle. 'Yonder we maun be this night,' quo' the bull; 'for my auld brither lives yonder;' and presently they were at the place. They lifted her aff his back, and took her in, and sent him away to a park for the night. In the morning, when they brought the bull hame, they took the lady into a fine shining parlour, and gave her a beautiful apple, telling her no to break it till she was in the greatest strait ever mortal was in in the world, and that wad bring her out o't. Again she was lifted on the bull's back, and after she had ridden far, and farer than I can tell, they came in sight o' a far bonnier castle, and far farther awa' than the last. Says the bull till her: 'Yonder we maun be the night, for my second brither lives yonder;' and they were at the place directly. They lifted her down and took her in, and sent the bull to the field for the night. In the morning they took the lady into a fine and rich room, and gave her the finest pear she had ever seen, bidding her no to break it till she was in the greatest strait ever mortal could be in, and that wad get her out o't. Again she was lifted and set on his back, and awa' they went. And lang they rade, and sair they rade, till they came in sight o' the far biggest castle, and far farthest aff, they had yet seen. 'We maun be yonder the night,' says the bull, 'for my young brither lives yonder;' and they were there directly. They lifted her down, took her in, and sent the bull to the field for the night. In the morning they took her into a room, the finest of a', and gied her a plum, telling her no to break it till she was in the greatest strait mortal could be in, and that wad get her out o't. Presently they brought hame the bull, set the lady on his back, and awa' they went.

And aye they rade, and on they rade, till they came to a dark and ugsome glen, where they stopped, and the lady lighted down. Says the bull to her: 'Here ye maun stay till I gang and fight the deil. Ye maun seat yoursel' on that stane, and move neither hand nor fit till I come back, else I'll never find ye again. And if everything round about ye turns blue, I hae beaten the deil; but should a' things turn red, he'll hae conquered me.' She set hersel' down on the stane, and by-and-by a' round her turned blue. O'ercome wi' joy, she lifted the ae fit and crossed it owre the ither, sae glad was she that her companion was victorious. The bull returned and sought for, but never could find her.

Lang she sat, and aye she grat, till she wearied. At last she rase and gaed awa', she kendna whaur till. On she wandered, till she came to a great hill o' glass, that she tried a' she could to climb, but wasna able. Round the bottom o' the hill she gaed, sabbing and seeking a passage owre, till at last she came to a smith's house; and the smith promised, if she wad serve him seven years, he wad make her airn shoon, wherewi' she could climb owre the glassy hill. At seven years' end she got her airn shoon, clamb the glassy hill, and chanced to come to the auld washerwife's habitation. There she was telled of a gallant young knight that had given in some bluidy sarks to wash, and whaever washed thae sarks was to be his wife. The auld wife had washed till she was tired, and then she set to her dochter, and baith washed, and they washed, and they better washed, in hopes of getting the young knight; but a' they could do, they couldna bring out a stain. At length they set the stranger damosel to wark; and whenever she began, the stains came out pure and clean, and the auld wife made the knight believe it was her dochter had washed the sarks. So the knight and the eldest dochter were to be married, and the stranger damosel was distracted at the thought of it, for she was deeply in love wi' him. So she bethought her of her apple, and breaking it, found it filled with gold and precious jewellery, the richest she had ever seen. 'All these,' she said to the eldest dochter, 'I will give you, on condition that you put off your marriage for ae day, and allow me to go into his room alone at night.' So the lady consented; but meanwhile the auld wife had prepared a sleeping drink, and given it to the knight, wha drank it, and never wakened till next morning. The lee-lang night the damosel sabbed and sang:

> 'Seven lang years I served for thee,
> The glassy hill I clamb for thee,
> The bluidy shirt I wrang for thee;
> And wilt thou no wauken and turn to me?'

Next day she kentna what to do for grief. She then brak the pear, and fan't filled wi' jewellery far richer than the contents o' the apple. Wi' thae jewels she bargained for permission to be a second night in the young knight's chamber; but the auld wife gied him anither sleeping drink, and he again sleepit till morning. A' night she kept sighing and singing as before:

> 'Seven lang years I served for thee,' &c.

Still he sleepit, and she nearly lost hope a'thegither. But that day, when he was out at the hunting, somebody asked him what noise and moaning was yon they heard all last night in his bedchamber. He said he heardna ony noise. But they assured him there was sae; and he resolved to keep waking that night to try what he could hear. That being the third night, and the damosel being between hope and despair, she brak her plum, and it held far the richest jewellery of the three. She bargained as before; and the auld wife, as before, took in the sleeping drink to the young knight's chamber; but he telled her he couldna drink it that night without sweetening. And when she gaed awa' for some honey to sweeten it wi', he poured out the drink, and sae made the auld wife think he had drunk it. They a' went to bed again, and the damosel began, as before, singing:

'Seven lang years I served for thee,
The glassy hill I clamb for thee,
The bluidy shirt I wrang for thee;
And wilt thou no wauken and turn to me?'

He heard, and turned to her. And she telled him a' that had befa'en her, and he telled her a' that had happened to him. And he caused the auld washerwife and her dochter to be burnt. And they were married, and he and she are living happy till this day, for aught I ken.

❧

THE WAL AT THE WARLD'S END

❧

There was a king and a queen, and the king had a dochter, and the queen had a dochter. And the king's dochter was bonnie and guid-natured, and a'body liket her; and the queen's dochter was ugly and ill-natured, and naebody liket her. And the queen didna like the king's dochter, and she wanted her awa'. Sae she sent her to the wal at the warld's end, to get a bottle o' water, thinking she would never come back. Weel, she took her bottle, and she gaed and gaed or [ere] she cam to a pownie that was tethered, and the pownie said to her:

'Flit me, flit me, my bonnie May,
For I haena been flitted this seven year and a day.'

And the king's dochter said: 'Ay will I, my bonnie pownie, I'll flit ye.' Sae the pownie ga'e her a ride owre the muir o' heckle-pins.

Weel, she gaed far and far and farer nor I can tell, or she cam to the wal at the warld's end; and when she cam to the wal, it was awfu' deep, and she couldna get her bottle dippit. And as she was lookin' doon, thinkin' hoo to do, there lookit up to her three scaud men's heads, and they said to her:

'Wash me, wash me, my bonnie May,
And dry me wi' yer clean linen apron.'

And she said: 'Ay will I; I'll wash ye.' Sae she washed the three scaud men's heads, and dried them wi' her clean linen apron; and syne they took and dippit her bottle for her.

And the scaud men's heads said the tane to the tither:

'Weird, brother, weird, what'll ye weird?'

And the first ane said: 'I weird that if she was bonnie afore, she'll be ten times bonnier.' And the second ane said: 'I weird that ilka time she speaks, there'll a diamond and a ruby and a pearl drap oot o' her mouth. And the third ane said: 'I weird that ilka time she kaims her head, she'll get a peck o' gould and a peck o' siller oot o' it.'

Weel, she cam hame to the king's coort again, and if she was bonnie afore, she was ten times bonnier; and ilka time she opened her lips to speak, there was a diamond and a ruby and a pearl drappit oot o' her mouth; and ilka time she kaimed her head, she gat a peck o' gould and a peck o' silver oot o't. And the queen was that vext, she didna ken what to do, but she thocht she wad send her ain dochter to see if she could fa' in wi' the same luck. Sae she ga'e her a bottle, and tell't her to gang awa' to the wal at the warld's end, and get a bottle o' water.

Weel, the queen's dochter gaed and gaed or she cam to the pownie, an' the pownie said:

> 'Flit me, flit me, my bonnie May,
> For I haena been flitted this seven year and a day.'

And the queen's dochter said: 'Ou ye nasty beast, do ye think I'll flit ye? Do ye ken wha ye're speakin' till? I'm a queen's dochter.' Sae she wadna flit the pownie, and the pownie wadna gie her a ride owre the muir o' hecklepins. And she had to gang on her bare feet, and the hecklepins cuttit a' her feet, and she could hardly gang ava.

Weel, she gaed far and far and farer nor I can tell, or she cam to the wal at the warld's end. And the wal was deep, and she couldna get her bottle dippit; and as she was lookin' doon, thinkin' hoo to do, there lookit up to her three scaud men's heads, and they said till her:

> 'Wash me, wash me, my bonnie May,
> And dry me wi' yer clean linen apron.'

And she said: 'Ou ye nasty dirty beasts, div ye think I'm gaunie wash ye? Div ye ken wha ye're speakin' till? I'm a queen's dochter.' Sae she wadna wash them, and they wadna dip her bottle for her.

And the scaud men's heads said the tane to the tither:

> 'Weird, brother, weird, what'll ye weird?'

And the first ane said: 'I weird that if she was ugly afore, she'll be ten times uglier.' And the second said: 'I weird that ilka time she speaks, there'll a puddock and a taid loup oot o' her mouth.' And the third ane said: 'And I weird that ilka time she kaims her head, she'll get a peck o' lice and a peck o' flechs oot o't.' Sae she gaed awa hame again, and if she was ugly afore, she was ten times uglier; and ilka time (&c.). Sae they had to send her awa' fra the king's coort. And there was a bonnie young prince cam and married the king's dochter; and the queen's dochter had to put up wi' an auld cobbler, and he lickit her ilka day wi' a leather strap. – Sae ye see, bairns, &c.

Thomas Rymer

1 True Thomas lay on Huntlie bank,
  A ferlie he spied wi' his ee,
 And there he saw a lady bright,
  Come riding down by the Eildon Tree.

2 Her shirt was o the grass-green silk,
  Her mantle o the velvet fyne,
 At ilka tett of her horse's mane
  Hang fifty siller bells and nine.

3 True Thomas, he pulld aff his cap,
  And louted low down to his knee:
 'All hail, thou mighty Queen of Heaven!
  For thy peer on earth I never did see.'

4 'O no, O no, Thomas,' she said,
  'That name does not belang to me;
 I am but the queen of fair Elfland,
  That am hither come to visit thee.

5 'Harp and carp, Thomas,' she said,
  'Harp and carp along wi me,
 And if ye dare to kiss my lips,
  Sure of your bodie I will be.'

6 'Betide me weal, betide me woe,
  That weird shall never daunton me;'
 Syne he has kissed her rosy lips,
  All underneath the Eildon Tree.

7 'Now, ye maun go wi me,' she said,
  'True Thomas, ye maun go wi me,

And ye maun serve me seven years,
　　Thro weal or woe, as may chance to be.'

8　She mounted on her milk-white steed,
　　She's taen True Thomas up behind,
　　And aye wheneer her bridle rung,
　　The steed flew swifter than the wind.

9　O they rade on, and farther on –
　　The steed gaed swifter than the wind –
　　Untill they reached a desart wide,
　　And living land was left behind.

10　'Light down, light down, now, True Thomas,
　　And lean your head upon my knee;
　　Abide and rest a little space,
　　And I will shew you ferlies three.

11　'O see ye not yon narrow road,
　　So thick beset with thorns and briers?
　　That is the path of righteousness,
　　Tho after it but few enquires.

12　'And see not ye that braid braid road,
　　That lies across that lily leven?
　　That is the path of wickedness,
　　Tho some call it the road to heaven.

13　'And see not ye that bonny road,
　　That winds about the fernie brae?
　　That is the road to fair Elfland,
　　Where thou and I this night maun gae.

14　'But, Thomas, ye maun hold your tongue,
　　Whatever ye may hear or see,
　　For, if you speak word in Elflyn land,
　　Ye'll neer get back to your ain countrie.'

15　O they rade on, and farther on,
　　And they waded thro rivers aboon the knee,
　　And they saw neither sun nor moon,
　　But they heard the roaring of the sea.

16　It was mirk mirk night, and there was nae stern light,
　　And they waded thro red blude to the knee;

For a' the blude that's shed on earth
  Rins thro the springs o that countrie.

17 Syne they came on to a garden green,
  And she pu'd an apple frae a tree:
'Take this for thy wages, True Thomas,
  It will give the tongue that can never lie.'

18 'My tongue is mine ain,' True Thomas said;
  'A gudely gift ye wad gie to me!
I neither dought to buy nor sell,
  At fair or tryst where I may be.

19 'I dought neither speak to prince or peer,
  Nor ask of grace from fair ladye:'
'Now hold thy peace,' the lady said,
  'For as I say, so must it be.'

20 He has gotten a coat of the even cloth,
  And a pair of shoes of velvet green,
And till seven years were gane and past
  True Thomas on earth was never seen.

TAM LIN

1 O I forbid you, maidens a',
  That wear gowd on your hair,
To come or gae by Carterhaugh,
  For young Tam Lin is there.

2 There's nane that gaes by Carterhaugh
  But they leave him a wad,
Either their rings, or green mantles,
  Or else their maidenhead.

3 Janet has kilted her green kirtle
  A little aboon her knee,
And she has broded her yellow hair
  A little aboon her bree,

And she's awa to Carterhaugh,
    As fast as she can hie.

4   When she came to Carterhaugh
      Tam Lin was at the well,
    And there she fand his steed standing,
      But away was himsel.

5   She had na pu'd a double rose,
      A rose but only twa,
    Till up then started young Tam Lin,
      Says, Lady, thou's pu nae mae.

6   Why pu's thou the rose, Janet,
      And why breaks thou the wand?
    Or why comes thou to Carterhaugh
      Withoutten my command?

7   'Carterhaugh, it is my ain,
      My daddie gave it me;
    I'll come and gang by Carterhaugh,
      And ask nae leave at thee.'

8   Janet has kilted her green kirtle
      A little aboon her knee,
    And she has snooded her yellow hair
      A little aboon her bree,
    And she is to her father's ha,
      As fast as she can hie.

9   Four and twenty ladies fair
      Were playing at the ba,
    And out then cam the fair Janet,
      Ance the flower amang them a'.

10   Four and twenty ladies fair
      Were playing at the chess,
    And out then cam the fair Janet,
      As green as onie glass.

11   Out then spak an auld grey knight,
      Lay oer the castle wa,
    And says, Alas, fair Janet, for thee
      But we'll be blamed a'.

12 'Haud your tongue, ye auld fac'd knight,
    Some ill death may ye die!
Father my bairn on whom I will,
    I'll father nane on thee.'

13 Out then spak her father dear,
    And he spak meek and mild;
'And ever alas, sweet Janet,' he says,
    'I think thou gaes wi child.'

14 'If that I gae wi child, father,
    Mysel maun bear the blame;
There's neer a laird about your ha
    Shall get the bairn's name.

15 'If my love were an earthly knight,
    As he's an elfin grey,
I wad na gie my ain true-love
    For nae lord that ye hae.

16 'The steed that my true-love rides on
    Is lighter than the wind;
Wi siller he is shod before,
    Wi burning gowd behind.'

17 Janet has kilted her green kirtle
    A little aboon her knee,
And she has snooded her yellow hair
    A little aboon her bree,
And she's awa to Carterhaugh,
    As fast as she can hie.

18 When she cam to Carterhaugh,
    Tam Lin was at the well,
And there she fand his steed standing,
    But away was himsel.

19 She had na pu'd a double rose,
    A rose but only twa,
Till up then started young Tam Lin,
    Says Lady, thou pu's nae mae.

20 Why pu's thou the rose, Janet.
    Amang the groves sae green,

And a' to kill the bonie babe
    That we gat us between?

21 'O tell me, tell me, Tam Lin,' she says,
    'For's sake that died on tree,
If eer ye was in holy chapel,
    Or christendom did see?'

22 'Roxbrugh he was my grandfather,
    Took me with him to bide,
And ance it fell upon a day
    That wae did me betide.

23 'And ance it fell upon a day,
    A cauld day and a snell,
When we were frae the hunting come,
    That frae my horse I fell;
The Queen o Fairies she caught me,
    In yon green hill to dwell.

24 'And pleasant is the fairy land,
    But, an eerie tale to tell,
Ay at the end of seven years
    We pay a tiend to hell;
I am sae fair and fu o flesh,
    I'm feard it be mysel.

25 'But the night is Halloween, lady,
    The morn is Hallowday;
Then win me, win me, an ye will,
    For weel I wat ye may.

26 'Just at the mirk and midnight hour
    The fairy folk will ride,
And they that wad their true-love win,
    At Miles Cross they maun bide.'

27 'But how shall I thee ken, Tam Lin,
    Or how my true-love know,
Amang sae mony unco knights
    The like I never saw?'

28 'O first let pass the black, lady,
    And syne let pass the brown,

But quickly run to the milk-white steed,
    Pu ye his rider down.

29 'For I'll ride on the milk-white steed,
    And ay nearest the town;
Because I was an earthly knight
    They gie me that renown.

30 'My right hand will be glovd, lady,
    My left hand will be bare,
Cockt up shall my bonnet be,
    And kaimd down shall my hair,
And thae's the takens I gie thee,
    Nae doubt I will be there.

31 'They'll turn me in your arms, lady,
    Into an esk and adder;
But hold me fast, and fear me not,
    I am your bairn's father.

32 'They'll turn me to a bear sae grim,
    And then a lion bold;
But hold me fast, and fear me not,
    As ye shall love your child.

33 'Again they'll turn me in your arms
    To a red het gaud of airn;
But hold me fast, and fear me not,
    I'll do to you nae harm.

34 'And last they'll turn me in your arms
    Into the burning gleed;
Then throw me into well water,
    O throw me in wi speed.

35 'And then I'll be your ain true-love,
    I'll turn a naked knight;
Then cover me wi your green mantle,
    And cover me out o sight.'

36 Gloomy, gloomy was the night,
    And eerie was the way,
As fair Jenny in her green mantle
    To Miles Cross she did gae.

37 About the middle o the night
   She heard the bridles ring;
   This lady was as glad at that
   As any earthly thing.

38 First she let the black pass by,
   And syne she let the brown;
   But quickly she ran to the milk-white steed,
   And pu'd the rider down.

39 Sae weel she minded whae he did say,
   And young Tam Lin did win;
   Syne coverd him wi her green mantle,
   As blythe 's a bird in spring.

40 Out then spak the Queen o Fairies,
   Out of a bush o broom:
   'Them that has gotten young Tam Lin
   Has gotten a stately groom.'

41 Out then spak the Queen o Fairies,
   And an angry woman was she:
   'Shame betide her ill-far'd face,
   And an ill death may she die,
   For she 's taen awa the boniest knight
   In a' my companie.

42 'But had I kend, Tam Lin,' she says,
   'What now this night I see,
   I wad hae taen out thy twa grey een,
   And put in twa een o tree.'

The Testament of Cresseid

ROBERT HENRYSON

Of Robert Henryson's life (c. 1420–90) we know little, save that he was possibly a schoolmaster and notary public in the then cultural centre of Dunfermline, and that he may have been a teacher of law at Glasgow University: certainly the extract here shows an interest in legal process. Henryson was also the author of the satiric *Morall Fabillis* (c. 1475–90) based on Aesop, in which a short story of animal folly or vice leads to its just deserts, accompanied by a moral. Henryson's *The Testament of Cresseid* (c. 1460?) is an invented sequel to his admired Chaucer's *Troilus and Criseyde* (c. 1385): but it is much terser and more judgmental than its original, which takes thirteen times its length to describe the growth of the love-relation between the Trojan Troilus and the Greek Criseyde in Troy during the Trojan war, before Criseyde's transfer to the Greek camp and her betrayal of Troilus. Henryson's poem imagines a betrayal of Cresseid by her Greek lover Diomede and a subsequent moral decline into possible whoredom.

The extract here is from a comparatively expansive fantasy element at the centre of the poem, when Cresseid in despair goes one day into a secret oratory next to a temple to Venus and Cupid, managed by her father, and curses the gods for her misfortunes: she then falls into a swoon in which she beholds the seven planetary gods and Cupid descend in a pageant and proceed to judge her and make her a leper. (This judgment, presented as immediate supernatural intervention, is actually a vision of what would take much longer through natural process – indeed may have begun before this episode – but would still be divinely caused.) The gods represent the planetary influences on the human spirit, in which medieval society believed: Jupiter, for instance, is portrayed as both the cosmic source of generation and its operation in man. But because Cresseid has abused her generative nature through her wanton lust, Jupiter and the 'kinder' gods cannot speak for her. She has given herself to fickleness and to emotional cruelty, and therefore she is the lawful prey of the gods who represent these qualities. Their harsh sentence destroys her physical beauty and turns her to a leper: but the power of generation still remains to her in limited moral form, in her later realisation before her death that not the gods but she herself is to blame, 'Nane but my self as now I will accuse'.

The high style and the space given to the gods in the poem represents their majesty and force in the universe, beside which Cresseid's life is important as individual tragedy, but ultimately insignificant and subservient. Cresseid may have learned a little spiritually, but her learning goes into the grave with her: the narrator ends dimissively, 'Since scho is deid, I speik of hir no moir'.

🍂

THE TESTAMENT OF CRESSEID

🍂

'Lo', quod Cupide, 'quha will blaspheme the name
Of his awin god, outher in word or deid,
To all goddis he dois baith lak and schame,
And suld haue bitter panis to his meid.
I say this by ȝone wretchit Cresseid,
The quhilk throw me was sum tyme flour of lufe,
Me and my mother starklie can reprufe,

'Saying of hir greit infelicitie
I was the caus, and my mother Venus,
Ane blind goddes hir cald that micht not se,
With sclander and defame iniurious.
Thus hir leuing vnclene and lecherous
Scho wald retorte in me and my mother,
To quhome I schew my grace abone all vther.

'And sen ȝe ar all seuin deificait,
Participant of deuyne sapience,
This greit iniure done to our hie estait
Me think with pane we suld mak recompence;

Was neuer to goddes done sic violence:
Asweill for ȝow as for my self I say,
Thairfoir ga help to reuenge, I ȝow pray!'

Mercurius to Cupide gaue answeir
And said, 'Schir King, my counsall is that ȝe
Refer ȝow to the hiest planeit heir
And tak to him the lawest of degre,
The pane of Cresseid for to modifie:
As God Saturne, with him tak Cynthia.'
'I am content', quod he, 'to tak thay twa.'

Than thus proceidit Saturne and the Mone
Quhen thay the mater rypelie had degest:
For the dispyte to Cupide scho had done
And to Venus, oppin and manifest,
In all hir lyfe with pane to be opprest,
And torment sair with seiknes incurabill,
And to all louers be abhominabill.

This duleful sentence Saturne tuik on hand,
And passit doun quhair cairfull Cresseid lay,
And on hir heid he laid ane frostie wand;
Than lawfullie on this wyse can he say,
'Thy greit fairnes and all thy bewtie gay,
Thy wantoun blude, and eik thy goldin hair,
Heir I exclude fra the for euermair.

'I change thy mirth into melancholy,
Quhilk is the mother of all pensiuenes;
Thy moisture and thy heit in cald and dry;
Thyne insolence, thy play and wantones,
To greit diseis; thy pomp and thy riches
In mortall neid; and greit penuritie
Thow suffer sall, and as ane beggar die.'

O cruell Saturne, fraward and angrie,
Hard is thy dome and to malitious!
On fair Cresseid quhy hes thow na mercie,
Quhilk was sa sweit, gentill and amorous?
Withdraw thy sentence and be gracious –

As thow was neuer; sa schawis through thy deid,
Ane wraikfull sentence geuin on fair Cresseid.

Than Cynthia, quhen Saturne past away,
Out of hir sait discendit doun belyue,
And red ane bill on Cresseid quhair scho lay,
Contening this sentence diffinityue:
'Fra heit of bodie here I the depryue,
And to thy seiknes sall be na recure
Bot in dolour thy dayis to indure.

'Thy cristall ene mingit with blude I mak,
Thy voice sa cleir vnplesand hoir and hace,
Thy lustie lyre ouirspred with spottis blak,
And lumpis haw appeirand in thy face:
Quhair thow cummis, ilk man sall fle the place.
This sall thow go begging fra hous to hous
With cop and clapper lyke ane lazarous.'

This doolie dreame, this vglye visioun
Brocht to ane end, Cresseid fra it awoik,
And all that court and conuocatioun
Vanischit away: than rais scho vp and tuik
Ane poleist glas, and hir schaddow culd luik;
And quhen scho saw hir face sa deformait,
Gif scho in hart was wa aneuch, God wait!

Weiping full sair, 'Lo, quhat it is', quod sche,
'With fraward langage for to mufe and steir
Our craibit goddis; and sa is sene on me!
My blaspheming now haue I bocht full deir;
All eirdlie ioy and mirth I set areir.
Allace, this day; allace, this wofull tyde
Quhen I began with my goddis for to chyde!'

Be this was said, ane chyld come fra the hall
To warne Cresseid the supper was reddy;
First knokkit at the dure, and syne culd call,
'Madame, зour father biddis зow cum in hy:
He hes merwell sa lang on grouf зe ly,
And sayis зour beedes bene to lang sum deill;
The goddis wait all зour intent full weill.'

Quod scho, 'Fair chyld, ga to my father deir
And pray him cum to speik with me anone.'
And sa he did, and said, 'Douchter, quhat cheir?'
'Allace!' quod scho, 'Father, my mirth is gone!'
'How sa?' quod he, and scho can all expone,
As I haue tauld, the vengeance and the wraik
For hir trespas Cupide on hir culd tak.

He luikit on hir vglye lipper face,
The quhylk befor was quhite as lillie flour;
Wringand his handis, oftymes said allace
That he had leuit to se that wofull hour;
For he knew weill that thair was na succour
To hir seiknes, and that dowblit his pane;
Thus was thair cair aneuch betuix thame twane.

Quhen thay togidder murnit had full lang,
Quod Cresseid, 'Father, I wald not be kend;
Thairfoir in secreit wyse ʒe let me gang
To ʒone hospitall at the tounis end,
And thidder sum meit for cheritie me send
To leif vpon, for all mirth in this eird
Is fra me gane; sic is my wickit weird!'

Than in ane mantill and ane bawer hat,
With cop and clapper, wonder priuely,
He opnit ane secreit ʒet and out thair at
Conuoyit hir, that na man suld espy,
Wnto ane village half ane myle thairby;
Delyuerit hir in at the spittaill hous,
And daylie sent hir part of his almous.

Sum knew hir weill, and sum had na knawledge
Of hir becaus scho was sa deformait,
With bylis blak ouirspred in hir visage,
And hir fair colour faidit and alterait.
ʒit thay presumit, for hir hie regrait
And still murning, scho was of nobill kin;
With better will thairfoir they tuik hir in.

THE GOLDYN TARGE
&
THE DANCE OF THE SEVIN DEIDLY SYNNIS

WILLIAM DUNBAR

William Dunbar (c. 1460–1520) was court poet and diplomat to Scotland's 'Sun King' James IV, and favourite of his queen in the years before Flodden. Scotland's best-known medieval 'makar', Dunbar's facility in a range of tones and styles, from devotional to satiric, aureate to vernacular, and amorous to ribald, anticipates Donne or Burns. He is also often sharply original: his 'The Goldyn Targe' (c.1495) is both a dream vision in the tradition of Chaucer and the *Roman de la Rose* and a Renaissance pageant in the departure of the allegorical figures of the dream in a cannon-firing man-of-war. And while his vision 'The Dance of the Sevin Deidly Synnis' (c. 1506) is founded in a medieval commonplace, Dunbar is probably the first to portray it as a dance in hell with the devils for audience.

'The Goldyn Targe' is less directly a fantasy than an allegory, in which various personified aspects of feminine charm assail a man protected only by Reason and its shield; however, these attributes are accompanied by their divinised underwriters, from Nature and Venus to Minerva and Lucina. The poem is also fantastic*al*, in its bizarre insertion of a noisy fifteenth-century gunboat into a medieval garden ritual; the conceit here in bringing such disparate contexts together almost anticipates the style of the metaphysical poets – though they are united by a motif of warfare that runs throughout the poem. But the poem illustrates how ready the medieval poets were to present the qualities of this world through the refracting glass of a seemingly other reality. Arguably in this poem the relative inertia of the allegory and the lack of an amorous outcome shows the interests of the poet moving more towards the Renaissance concerns of nature and eloquence which, combined, produce the beautiful opening stanzas of the poem (lines 1–72): this is the Beauty which perhaps more truly overcomes him.

'The Dance of the Sevin Deidly Synnis' is the polar opposite of 'The Goldyn Targe': here we are with the ugly, the unnatural and the coarsely vernacular, with pain and antagonism rather than with union. The Dance is a vision of the possible hellish consequences of human evil: immediately it puts us in hell with the devil operating by his own diary ('Off Februar the fyiftene nycht') in a world next to our own. Because they are in their place of origin, the sins are here as real as they are allegorical, which makes them more menacing. The sins are free, the sinners are bound in an infernal circularity of pain; the very use of the dance and the particular day of its occurrence, suggest a variety in hell which heightens its eternal stasis and monotony.

THE GOLDYN TARGE

Ryght as the stern of day begouth to schyne
    Quhen gone to bed war Vesper and Lucyne
I raise and by a rosere did me rest;
Up sprang the goldyn candill matutyne
With clere depurit bemes cristallyne
    Glading the mery foulis in thair nest;
    Or Phebus was in purpur cape revest
Up raise the lark, the hevyns menstrale fyne,
    In May in till a morow myrthfullest.

Full angellike thir birdis sang thair houris
Within thair courtyns grene in to thair bouris
    Apparalit quhite and rede wyth blomes suete;
Anamalit was the felde wyth all colouris,
The perly droppis schake in silvir schouris,
    Quhill all in balme did branch and levis flete;
    To part fra Phebus did Aurora grete;
Hir cristall teris I saw hyng on the flouris
    Quhilk he for lufe all drank up wyth his hete.

For mirth of May wyth skippis and wyth happis
The birdis sang upon the tender croppis
    With curiouse note, as Venus chapell clerkis;
The rosis yong, new spreding of thair knopis,
War powdirit brycht with hevinly beriall droppis
    Throu bemes rede birnyng as ruby sperkis;
    The skyes rang for schoutyng of the larkis;
The purpur hevyn, ourscailit in silvir sloppis,
    Ourgilt the treis, branchis, lef and barkis.

Doune throu the ryce a ryvir ran wyth stremys
So lustily agayn thai lykand lemys
    That all the lake as lamp did leme of licht,
Quhilk schadowit all about wyth twynkling glemis
That bewis bathit war in secund bemys
    Throu the reflex of Phebus visage brycht:
    On every syde the hegies raise on hicht,
The bank was grene, the bruke was full of bremys,
    The stanneris clere as stern in frosty nycht.

The cristall air, the sapher firmament,
The ruby skyes of the orient
    Kest beriall bemes on emerant bewis grene;
The rosy garth depaynt and redolent
With purpur, azure, gold and goulis gent
    Arayed was by dame Flora the quene
    So nobily that joy was for to sene;
The roch agayn the rivir resplendent
    As low enlumynit all the leves schene.

Quhat throu the mery foulys armony
And throu the ryveris soune rycht ran me by
    On Florais mantill I slepit as I lay;
Quhare sone in to my dremes fantasy
I saw approch agayn the orient sky
    A saill als quhite as blossum upon spray,
    Wyth merse of gold brycht as the stern of day,
Quhilk tendit to the land full lustily
    Als falcoune swift desyrouse of hir pray:

And hard on burd unto the blomyt medis
Amang the grene rispis and the redis

Arrivit sche; quhar fro anone thare landis
Ane hundreth ladyes lusty in to wedis,
Als fresch as flouris that in May up spredis
    In kirtillis grene withoutyn kell or bandis;
    Thair brycht hairis hang gletering on the strandis
In tressis clere, wyppit wyth goldyn thredis;
    With pappis quhite and mydlis small as wandis.

Discrive I wald, bot quho coud wele endyte
How all the feldis wyth thai lilies quhite
    Depaynt war brycht, quhilk to the hevyn did glete?
Noucht thou, Omer, als fair as thou coud wryte,
For all thine ornate stilis so perfyte;
    Nor yit thou, Tullius, quhois lippis suete
    Off rethorike did in to termes flete:
Your aureate tongis both bene all to lyte
    For to compile that paradise complete.

Thare saw I Nature and Venus, quene and quene,
The fresh Aurora, and lady Flora schene,
    Juno Appollo, and Proserpyna,
Dyane the goddesse chaste of woddis grene,
My lady Cleo that help of makaris bene,
    Thetes, Pallas, and prudent Minerva,
    Fair feynit Fortune and lemand Lucina:
Thir mychti quenis in crounis mycht be sene
    With bemys blith, bricht as Lucifera.

Thare saw I May, of myrthfull monethis quene,
Betuix Aprile and June hir sistir schene
    Within the gardyng walking up and doune,
Quham of the foulis gladdith all bedene;
Scho was full tendir in hir yeris grene.
Thare saw I Nature present hir a goune
    Rich to behald and nobil of renoune,
Off eviry hew undir the hevin that bene
    Depaynt, and broud be gude proporcioun.

Full lustily thir ladyes all in fere
Enterit within this park of most plesere
    Quhare that I lay ourhelit wyth levis ronk;
The mery foulis blissfullest of chere

Salust Nature me thoucht on thair manere,
>And eviry blome on branch and eke on bonk
>Opnyt and spred thair balmy levis donk,
Full low enclynyng to thair quene so clere
>Quham of thair noble norising thay thonk.

Syne to dame Flora on the samyn wyse
Thay saluse and thay thank a thousand syse;
>And to dame Venus lufis mychti quene
Thay sang ballettis in lufe as was the gyse
With amourouse notis lusty to devise
>As thay that had lufe in thair hertis grene;
>Thair hony throtis opnyt fro the splene
With werblis suete did perse the hevinly skyes
>Quhill loud resownyt the firmament serene.

Ane othir court thare saw I consequent —
Cupide the king wyth bow in hand ybent
>And dredefull arowis grundyn scharp and square;
Thare saw I Mars the god armypotent,
Aufull and sterne, strong and corpolent;
>Thare saw I crabbit Saturn ald and haire,
>His luke was lyke for to perturb the aire;
Thare was Mercurius wise and eloquent,
>Of rethorike that fand the flouris faire;

Thare was the god of gardingis, Priapus;
Thare was the god of wildernes, Phanus,
>And Janus god of entree delytable;
Thare was the god of fludis, Neptunus;
Thare was the god of wyndis, Eolus,
>With variand luke rycht lyke a lord unstable;
>Thare was Bacus the gladder of the table;
Thare was Pluto the elrich incubus
>In cloke of grene — his court usit no sable.

And eviry one of thir in grene arayit
On harp or lute full merily thai playit
>And sang ballettis with michty notis clere;
Ladyes to dance full sobirly assayit,
Endlang the lusty ryvir so thai mayit
>Thair observance rycht hevynly was to here:

Than crap I throu the levis and drew nere
Quhare that I was rycht sudaynly affrayit,
   All throu a luke quhilk I have boucht full dere.

And schortly for to speke, be lufis quene
I was aspyit; scho bad hir archearis kene
   Go me arrest, and thay no tyme delayit.
Than ladyes fair lete fall thair mantillis grene;
With bowis big in tressit hairis schene
   All sudaynly thay had a felde arayit;
   And yit rycht gretly was I noucht affrayit.
The party was so plesand for to sene,
   A wonder lusty bikkir me assayit.

And first of all with bow in hand ybent
Come dame Beautee, rycht as scho wald me schent;
   Syne folowit all hir dameselis yfere
With mony diverse aufull instrument
Unto the pres; Fair Having wyth hir went,
   Fyne Portrature, Plesance, and Lusty Chere.
   Than come Resoun with schelde of gold so clere;
In plate and maille, as Mars armypotent,
   Defendit me that nobil chevallere.

Syne tender Youth come wyth hir virgyns ying,
Grene Innocence, and schamefull Abaising,
   And quaking Drede wyth humble Obedience:
The goldyn targe harmyt thay no thing;
Curage in thame was noucht begonne to spring;
   Full sore thay dred to done a violence.
   Suete Womanhede I saw cum in presence;
Of artilye a warld sche did in bring
   Servit wyth ladyes full of reverence.

Sche led wyth hir Nurture and Lawlynes,
Contenence, Pacience, Gude Fame and Stedfastnes,
   Discrecioun, Gentrise and Considerance,
Levefull Company and Honest Besynes,
Benigne Luke, Mylde Chere and Sobirnes.
   All thir bure ganyeis to do me grevance,
   Bot Resoun bure the targe wyth sik constance

Thair scharp assayes mycht do no dures
    To me, for all thair aufull ordynance.

Unto the pres persewit Hie Degree;
Hir folowit ay Estate and Dignitee,
    Comparisoun, Honour, and noble Array,
Will, Wantonnes, Renoun and Libertee,
Richesse, Fredome and eke Nobilitee.
    Wit ye thay did thair baner hye display;
    A cloud of arowis as hayle schour lousit thay,
And schot quhill wastit was thair artilye,
    Syne went abak reboytit of thair pray.

Quhen Venus had persavit this rebute
Dissymilance scho bad go mak persute
    At all powere to perse the goldyn targe;
And scho, that was of doubilnes the rute,
Askit hir choise of archeris in refute.
    Venus the best bad hir go wale at large;
    Scho tuke Presence (plicht ankers of the barge)
And Fair Callyng, that wele a flayn coud schute,
    And Cherising for to complete hir charge.

Dame Hamelynes scho tuke in company
That hardy was and hende in archery,
    And broucht dame Beautee to the felde agayn;
With all the choise of Venus chevalry
Thay come and bikkerit unabaisitly;
    The schour of arowis rappit on as rayn.
    Perilouse Presence that mony syre has slayn
The bataill broucht on bordour hard us by;
    The salt was all the sarar, suth to sayn.

Thik was the schote of grundyn dartis kene,
Bot Resoun with the scheld of gold so schene
    Warly defendit quho so evir assayit;
The aufull stoure he manly did sustene
Quhill Presence kest a pulder in his ene,
    And than as drunkyn man he all forvayit.
    Quhen he was blynd, the fule wyth hym they playit
And banyst hym amang the bewis grene;
    That sory sicht me sudaynly affrayit.

Than was I woundit to the deth wele nere,
And yoldyn as a wofull prisonnere
   To lady Beautee in a moment space;
Me thoucht scho semyt lustiar of chere
Efter that Resoun tynt had his eyne clere
   Than of before, and lufliare of face:
   Quhy was thou blyndit, Resoun? quhi, allace!
And gert ane hell my paradise appere,
   And mercy seme quhare that I fand no grace.

Dissymulance was besy me to sile,
And Fair Calling did oft apon me smyle,
   And Cherising me fed wyth wordis fair;
New Acquyntance enbracit me a quhile
And favouryt me, quhill men mycht go a myle,
   Syne tuke hir leve; I saw hir nevir mare.
   Than saw I Dangere toward me repair –
I could eschew hir presence be no wyle.
   On syde scho lukit wyth ane fremyt fare

And at the last departing coud hir dresse,
And me delyverit unto Hevynesse
   For to remayne; and scho in cure me tuke.
Be this the lord of wyndis, wyth wodenes,
God Eolus, his bugill blew I gesse,
   That with the blast the levis all to-schuke;
   And sudaynly in the space of a luke
All was hyne went; thare was bot wildernes,
   Thare was no more bot birdis, bank and bruke.

In twynklyng of ane eye to scip thai went
And swyth up saile unto the top thai stent
   And with swift course atour the flude thai frak;
Thai fyrit gunnis wyth powder violent
Till that the reke raise to the firmament;
   The rochis all resownyt wyth the rak,
   For rede it semyt that the raynbow brak.
Wyth spirit affrayde apon my fete I sprent
   Amang the clewis, so carefull was the crak.
And as I did awake of my sueving
The joyfull birdis merily did syng

For myrth of Phebus tendir bemes schene;
Suete war the vapouris, soft the morowing,
Hálesum the vale depaynt wyth flouris ying,
    The air attemperit, sobir and amene;
    In quhite and rede was all the felde besene
Throu Naturis nobil fresch anamalyng
    In mirthfull May, of eviry moneth quene.

O reverend Chaucere, rose of rethoris all,
As in oure tong ane flour imperiall
    That raise in Britane, evir quho redis rycht,
Thou beris of makaris the tryumph riall;
Thy fresch anamalit termes celicall
    This mater coud illumynit have full brycht:
    'Was thou noucht of oure Inglisch all the lycht,
Surmounting eviry tong terrestriall
    Alls fer as Mayes morow dois mydnycht?

O morall Gower and Ludgate laureate,
Your sugurit lippis and tongis aureate
    Bene to oure eris cause of grete delyte;
    Your angel mouthis most mellifluate
Oure rude langage has clere illumynate,
    And fair ourgilt oure spech that imperfyte
    Stude or your goldyn pennis schupe to write;
This ile before was bare and desolate
    Off rethorike, or lusty fresch endyte.

Thou lytill quair, be evir obedient,
Humble, subject, and symple of entent
    Before the face of eviry connyng wicht:
I knaw quhat thou of rethorike hes spent;
Off all hir lusty rosis redolent
    Is none in to thy gerland sett on hicht;
    Eschame thar of, and draw the out of sicht.
Rude is thy wede, disteynit, bare and rent;
    Wele aucht thou be aferit of the licht.

The Dance of the Sevin Deidly Synnis

Off Februar the fyiftene nycht
   Full lang befoir the dayis lycht
     I lay in till a trance;
And than I saw baith hevin and hell:
Me thocht amangis the feyndis fell
     Mahoun gart cry ane dance
Off schrewis that wer nevir schrevin
Aganis the feist of Fasternis evin
     To mak thair observance;
He bad gallandis ga graith a gyis
And kast up gamountis in the skyis
     That last came out of France.

Lat se, quod he, Now quha begynnis:
With that the fowll sevin deidly synnis
     Begowth to leip at anis.
And first of all in dance wes Pryd
With hair wyld bak and bonet on syd
     Lyk to mak waistie wanis,
And round abowt him as a quheill
Hang all in rumpillis to the heill
     His kethat for the nanis;
Mony prowd trumpour with him trippit –
Throw skaldand fyre ay as thay skippit
     Thay gyrnd with hiddous granis.

Heilie harlottis on hawtane wyis
Come in with money sindrie gyis,
     Bot ʒit luche nevir Mahoun
Quhill preistis come in with bair schevin nekkis –
Than all the feyndis lewche and maid gekkis,
     Blak Belly and Bawsy Broun.

Than Yre come in with sturt and stryfe;
His hand wes ay upoun his knyfe –

He brandeist lyk a beir:
Bostaris, braggaris and barganeris
Eftir him passit in to pairis
    All bodin in feir of weir;
In jakkis and stryppis and bonettis of steill,
Thair leggis wer chenʒeit to the heill,
    Frawart wes thair affeir;
Sum upoun uder with brandis beft,
Sum jaggit uthiris to the heft
    With knyvis that scherp cowd scheir.

Nixt followit in the dance Invy
Fild full of feid and fellony,
    Hid malyce and dispyte;
For pryvie hatrent that tratour trymlit:
Him followit mony freik dissymlit
    With fenʒeit wirdis quhyte,
And flattereris in to menis facis,
And bakbyttaris of sindry racis
    To ley that had delyte,
And rownaris of fals lesingis –
Allace, that courtis of noble kingis
    Of thame can nevir be quyte.

Nixt him in dans come Cuvatyce,
Rute of all evill and grund of vyce,
    That nevir cowd be content;
Catyvis, wrechis and ockeraris,
Hud pykis, hurdaris and gadderaris,
    All with that warlo went;
Out of thair throttis thay schot on udder
Hett moltin gold, me thocht a fudder,
    As fyreflawcht maist fervent;
Ay as thay tomit thame of schot
Feyndis fild thame new up to the thrott
    With gold of allkin prent.

Syne Sweirnes at the secound bidding
Come lyk a sow out of a midding –
    Full slepy wes his grunʒie;
Mony sweir bumbard belly huddroun,

Mony slute daw and slepy duddroun,
   Him servit ay with sounʒie:
He drew thame furth in till a chenʒie,
And Belliall with a brydill renʒie
   Evir lascht thame on the lunʒie.
In dance thay war so slaw of feit
Thay gaif thame in the fyre a heit
   And maid thame quicker of counʒie.

Than Lichery that lathly cors
Berand lyk a bagit hors —
   And Lythenes did him leid:
Thair wes with him ane ugly sort
And mony stynkand fowll tramort
   That had in syn bene deid.
Quhen thay wer entrit in the dance
Thay wer full strenge of countenance
   Lyk turkas birnand reid;
All led thay uthir by the tersis,
Suppois thay fycket with thair ersis
   It mycht be na remeid.

Than the fowll monstir Glutteny
Off wame unsasiable and gredy
   To dance he did him dres:
Him followit mony fowll drunckart
With can and collep, cop and quart,
   In surffet and exces;
Full mony a waistles wallydrag
With wamis unweildable did furth wag
   In creische that did incres:
Drynk! ay thay cryit, with mony a gaip —
The feyndis gaif thame hait leid to laip —
   Thair lovery wes na les.

Na menstrallis playit to thame but dowt
For glemen thair wer haldin owt
   Be day and eik by nycht —
Except a menstrall that slew a man;
Swa till his heretage he wan
   And entirt be breif of richt.

Than cryd Mahoun for a heleand padʒane:
Syne ran a feynd to feche Makfadʒane
    Far northwart in a nuke.
Be he the correnoch had done schout
Erschemen so gadderit him abowt
    In hell grit rowme thay tuke.
Thae tarmegantis with tag and tatter
Full lowd in Ersche begowth to clatter
    And rowp lyk revin and ruke.
The Devill sa devit wes with thair ʒell
That in the depest pot of hell
    He smorit thame with smuke.

THE PALICE OF HONOUR

GAVIN DOUGLAS

The Palice of Honour by Gavin Douglas (c. 1474–1522) is the early poetic triumph of a young nobleman who during his life was also scholar, bishop (of Dunkeld), courtier, ambassador and intriguer with his family faction at the courts of James IV and James V. In it Douglas partly follows the pattern of dream allegory as seen in Chaucer's *The House of Fames*, in which the poet is described visiting Venus's temple and then being flown to the House of Fame in the claws of a loquacious golden eagle: Douglas displays a similar love of fantastic landscapes and journeys, of which the extract here is an example.

   Douglas's interest in honour is one peculiar to the Renaissance with its Roman-inspired stress on civic virtue, though his poem also allows for a reading of honour in Christian and mystical terms. Here too we find medieval love allegory shifting into a cultural quest for poetic worth, as the poet leaves Venus and sets out with the nymph of Calliope, the muse of epic, towards Honour. Douglas is famed for his later *Eneados* (1513), the first major translation of the whole of that great Roman epic portraying the search for a more collective cultural rebirth, Virgil's *Aeneid*. To these humanist strains we should add Douglas's evident love of eloquence, which he shared with Dunbar; this is seen both in his deployment of a rich range of language from Latinate to broad Scots and in his poetic subject.

   But while the poem has these affinities, it is also the work of a young writer eagerly trying his hand in as many forms as he can. The poem has the air of continual shifts of subject and context, from Fortune to such figures as Minerva, Diana, Venus, Calliope and then Honour; and its language is often so crammed with impressions that it bristles like a thicket. And if a core of allegory can be detected running through the poem, we are a little less inclined to look for it if there is no great sense of direction and the quest for the Palace of Honour is first proposed only halfway through the poem. There is a grain of truth in C. S. Lewis's comment in his *The Allegory of Love*, 'Unless the *significacio* throughout has escaped me, the poem as a whole illustrates the furthest point yet reached in the liberation of fantasy from its allegorical justification'.

The extract here is from the beginning of the poem. In the prologue, the poet-lover has entered a beautiful garden of love, lamented the state of wretchedness that does not let him fit in with it, and been cast into a swoon, out of which he wakes to find himself in a desert near a river. Dream has changed to nightmare. Now he is in a brutish landscape that matches his present mind: it is a picture of his unnatural and chaotic inner world, at the mercy of fortune and wild passion. Across it, at first threatening, then magnificent, passes the goddess of wisdom Minerva – a wisdom that among other virtues the pilgrim is later to meet in the ordered and part-heavenly context of the Palace of Honour.

The Palice of Honour: The First Part

Thow barrant wit ouirset with fantasyis,
Schaw now the craft that in thy memor lyis,
Schaw now thy schame, schaw now thy badnystie,
Schaw thy endite reprufe of rethoryis,
Schaw now thy beggit termis mair than thryis,
Schaw now thy rymis, and thine harlotrie,
Schaw now thy dull exhaust inanitie,
Schaw furth thy cure and write thir frenesyis
Quhilks of thy sempill cunning nakit the.

My rauist spreit in that desert terribill,
Approchit neir that vglie flude horribill,
Like till Cochyte the riuer infernall,
With vile water quhilk maid a hiddious trubil,
Rinnand ouirheid, blude reid, and impossibill
That it had been a riuer naturall;
With brayis bair, raif rochis like to fall.

Quhairon na gers nor herbis wer visibill,
Bot swappis brint with blastis boriall.

This laithlie flude rumland as thonder routit,
In quhome the fisch ʒelland as eluis schoutit,
Thair ʒelpis wilde my heiring all fordeifit,
Thay grym monstures my spreits abhorrit and doutit.
Not throw the soyl bot muskane treis sproutit,
Combust, barrant, vnblomit and vnleifit,
Auld rottin runtis quhairin na sap was leifit,
Moch, all waist, widderit with granis moutit,
A ganand den, quhair murtherars men reifit.

Quhairfoir my seluin was richt sair agast,
This wildernes abhominabill and waist,
(In quhome nathing was nature comfortand)
Was dark as rock, the quhilk the sey vpcast.
The quhissilling wind blew mony bitter blast,
Runtis rattillit and vneith micht I stand.
Out throw the wod I crap on fute and hand,
The riuer stank, the treis clatterit fast.
The soyl was nocht bot marres, slike, and sand.

And not but caus my spreitis wer abaisit.
All solitair in that desert arraisit,
Allace, I said, is nane vther remeid,
Cruell fortoun quhy hes thow me betraisit?
Quhy hes thow thus my fatall end compassit?
Allace, allace, sall I thus sone be deid
In this desert, and wait nane vther reid,
Bot be deuoirit with sum beist rauenous.
I weip, I waill, I plene, I cry, I pleid,
Inconstant warld and quheill contrarious.

Thy transitorie plesance quhat auaillis?
Now thair, now heir, now hie and now deuaillis,
Now to, now fra, now law, now magnifyis,
Now hait, now cauld, now lauchis, now beuaillis,
Now seik, now haill, now werie, now not aillis,
Now gude, now euill, now weitis, and now dryis,
Now thow promittis, and richt now thow denyis,
Now wo, now weill, now firme, now friuolous,

Now gam, now gram, now lowis, now defyis,
Inconstant warld and quheill contrarious.

Ha, quha suld haue affyance in thy blis?
Ha, quha suld haue firme esperance in this
Quhilk is allace sa freuch and variant?
Certes nane; sum hes no wicht? surelie ʒis.
Than has my self bene gyltie? ʒe, I wis.
Thairfoir allace sall danger thus me dant?
Quhidder is become sa sone this duillie hant?
And ver translait in winter furious?
Thus I beuaill my faitis repugnant,
Inconstant warld and quheill contrarious.

Bydand the deid thus in my extasie,
Ane dyn I hard approching fast me by,
Quhilk mouit fra the plague Septentrionall,
As heird of beistis stamping with loud cry.
Bot than, God wait, how affrayit was I!
Traistand to be stranglit with bestiall.
Amid a stock richt priuelie I stall,
Quhair luikand out anone I did espy
Ane lustie rout of beistis rationall.

Of ladyis fair and gudlie men arrayit
In constant weid, that weill my spreitis payit,
With degest mind, quharin all wit aboundit.
Full soberlie thair haiknayis thay assayit
Efter the faitis auld, and not forwayit.
Thair hie prudence schew furth and naithing roundit
With gude effeir quhairat the wod resoundit.
In steidfast ordour, to vesie vnaffrayit
Thay ryding furth with stabilnes ygroundit.

Amiddis quhome borne in ane goldin chair,
Ouirfret with perle and stanis maist preclair,
That drawin was by haiknayis all milk quhite,
Was set a Quene, as lyllie sweit of swair,
In purpour rob hemmit with gold ilk gair,
Quhilk gemmit claspis closit all perfite.
A diademe maist plesandlie polite

Set on the tressis of her giltin hair,
And in hir hand a scepter of delite.

Sine nixt hir raid in granit violate
Twelf damisellis, ilk ane in thair estait,
Quhilks semit of her counsell maist secre,
And nixt thame was a lustie rout, God wait,
Lords, ladyis, and mony fair prelait,
Baith borne of hie estait and law degre,
Furth with thair Quene, thay all by passit me
Ane esie pais, thay ryding furth the gait,
And I abaid alone within the tre.

PENARDO AND LAISSA

PATRICK GORDON

From about 1530 to 1760 there is very little Scottish fantasy, or indeed fiction. The anti-fictive attitude of the increasingly dominant Scottish Calvinism, the loss of a sense of Scottish cultural identity with the departure of the crown southwards in 1603, and the growing empirical and anti-supernaturalist outlook of the period 1620 to 1750 – all these may have been factors. England, with Spenser, Shakespeare, Milton, Bunyan and even Pope and Swift, was not so bereft.

A bright exception is Patrick Gordon's* romance *The First Booke of the Famous Historye of Penardo and Laissa* (Dort, 1615). This is a story of war and love, of knights and ladies, in the tradition of Ariosto, Tasso and Spenser, with magic in the form of enchantments, giants and dragons that have to be overcome. The beautiful Princess Laissa has been shut by the wizard Mansay in a vat of boiling blood in a dark labyrinth, from which she is eventually released by Prince Penardo, whom for several cantos we have seen engaged in wars consequent upon the deaths of two princes who fought over Laissa. But finding her apparently dead after her rescue, Penardo leaves her, and is then caught up in a series of amorous entanglements. Laissa, later recovered, rescues him from the last of these: but the pair no sooner meet and begin to fall in love than a passing damsel in apparent distress requires Penardo's assistance and he obligingly rides after her ... That is all the story, for as with his *Famous Historie of ... Robert surnamed the Bruce* (also Dort, 1615), Gordon did not proceed beyond *The First Booke*.

* Probably Patrick Gordon of Ruthven (1580–1650)

The poem is virtually unknown, there being only three library copies in the world, but its oblivion is undeserved. Unfinished, often pallid from its derivativeness, maimed by its frequent artistic ineptitudes and the Dutch printer's carelessness alike, Gordon's poem yet controls a complex narrative and theme, and often rises to scenes of inspired imagination and of psychological insight. The eleventh canto here shows a poet who can create a sense of dread and confusion, a Gothic darkness riven by flames and violence, in which what is seen has a surreal force. Penardo is here traversing love's unconscious, the landscape of tormented desire which Gordon is later to label morally as Lechery. The theme of the poem is (and here it is indebted to Book III of Spenser's *The Faerie Queene, 1590*), education in love. For Gordon, as for Spenser, magic and enchantment are functions of evil and distorted human passion. Penardo, who has so far followed Mars and warfare rather than love, here sufficiently represents the chastity required to release Laissa from her own excess involvement in love (symbolised in her fiery torture on the altar and in her daily immersion in the blood of her erstwhile lovers). But Penardo's chastity is less a virtue than an absence, and after this he is continually preyed upon by women of unsteady and violent passion and cheated by frauds: he himself must follow the educational path he ended for Laissa, and the pair presumably cannot have a lasting meeting till this is complete.

❧

PENARDO AND LAISSA

❧

[In this extract I have retained occasional oddities of idiom to fit with the rhyme; and have also added punctuation to help clarify the sense.]

Canto XI
Argument

The burning altar's keeper, of
His life Penardo spoils;
He sees the daily funeral,
In blood the virgin boils.
He that by love could not be wooed,
The taper does obtain;

About the Queen of love he sees
All those that Love had slain.

1   O now you Muses matchless and divine,
      Help by your sacred skill my gross defects,
      Make sharp my wit and pregnant my ingyne,
      That by your friendly aid in all respects
      My pen supplied may boldly breathe his name,
      Enrolled above the stars by endless fame.

2   Whose mind the seat of royal virtue's birth,
      And who all goodness knew, but knew no ill,
      Admired of all the world for his rare worth,
      Which caused Envy for rage her self to kill,
      Even he without all fear or care did enter,
      And through this cave like grisly hell did venture.

3   At last a thirling light he did espy,
      Which from a door did glancing forth appear,
      Wherto whenas the gallant Prince drew nigh,
      He saw a flame, most pure, most bright, most clear,
      Upon an altar burn; and in the same,
      Burnt, scorched, tormented, lay a virgin dame.

4   While on this piteous spectacle he gazed,
      From out a corner dark he might perceive
      A monster huge that made him much amazed,
      Whose greatness seemed to fill that empty cave:
      He breathed forth clouds of smoke which dimmed the flame,
      And darkened all the place about the same.

5   So thundering tempests dim the golden sun,
      And darken all the crystal heavens so high;
      The reeking clouds like smoke down molten run,
      By force of fire that thunders through the sky;
      At last such roars he thunders in his ear,
      It seemed the cave shook, trembled, quaked for fear.

6   This monster fiercely did assail the Prince,
      Who nimble, quick, sharp, ready, light, avoiding
      His mighty blows, so brave was his defence,
      Oft him he harmed, himself unharmed abiding,

So that the monster roared for grief and pain,
Forth casting floods of poisoned gore amain.

7   Thus each pursuing other to the death,
With strength, with rage, with fury, hate and ire,
That neither gave the other leave to breathe;
The monster still threw forth bright flames of fire,
Whose scales bore from the Prince his furious dint,
Like tempered steel, hard diamond, or flint.

8   Wherefore a stranger kind of fight he chooses:
Quitting his sword he draws a dagger fine,
His skill, his sleight, his might and strength he uses
To rid this devilish monster out of pain:
Who lifting up his armed crest with ire,
Smoke from his mouth, his eyes forth sparkling fire,

9   Did fiercely forward to the Prince forth pace,
Enfolds, enrolls in links, with gaping jaws;
But he with foresight, weighing well the case,
His scaly gorge in his strong arm he thrawes,
And through his burning eye with fatal knife,
Brought forth his brains and with his brains his life.

10   Glad was he to be rid of such a foe.
Yet pity, care and sorrow, chased delight,
To see so fair a maid tormented so;
His eyes with child of tears, his heart still sighed,
Tears from his eyes springs, rivers, floods forth sent,
Sighs from his heart like blustering winds upwent.

11   When nearer to the altar he was come,
Of sorrow he might hear the saddest sound,
There grievous groans were intermixed with some
Weak breathing words, that did sad death resound:
The words were sweet and pitiful to hear,
The accent soft, the voice was sharp and clear.

12   Those were the woeful words he pitied most:
Ah, Pluto, Pluto, *end this sacrifice*,
Hell, Hell, devour my soul's tormented ghost.
Ah, cruel Heav'n, that glories to tyrannize,

Ah, pain, pain, pain, let endless pain remove;
Curse death, curse Hell, curse earth, curse Heavens above.

13   While thus she spoke, Penardo heard a noise,
And suddenly appeared a greater light,
A hundred torches borne by little boys,
All clad in mourning weed, a woeful sight.
Softly the Prince conveys himself aside,
To see of these events what would betide.

14   After these torches were two horses led,
Whose trappings were of purple silk and gold;
Such curious work, so rich embroidered,
Was admirable rare for to behold;
For griffon-like they pacing seemed to fly
With golden plumed wings right curiously.

15   These horses were kept by lackeys two who had
Two shields which seemed of sundry knights to hold;
And after them two pages richly clad
Two mighty lances bore with heads of gold;
Next after them four gallant coursers drew
A crimson coach that seemed of bloody hew.

16   Within this coach two knights were sadly placed
In glistening armour that was finely framed;
The armour's shining lustre was defaced
With purple blood that from their bodies streamed.
Sad were their minds where sorrow did remain,
Great were their wounds but greater far their pain.

17   The one still sighed and groaned but spoke no word,
For in his breast a bloody dagger stood.
The other through his body had a sword
From whose steel point ran streams of crimson blood.
Death over them long since had spread her wings,
Yet life by art, pain, grief and sorrow brings.

18   Behind the altar stood a brazen porch,
Which opened wide for to receive this train,
Where enter all the boys with every torch,
The horse, and all the rest that did remain:

But while the coach near to the altar drew,
The woeful dame her sorrows did renew.

19 *Ah, Heavens, alas, come, come, I gladly go,*
    Let death give end to Hell's tormenting flame,
    Blood, blood, glut up both soul and body, lo,
    Stop now my breath and suffocate the same:
    Let these two live and then impose on me
    Ten thousand deaths so I may once but die.

20 No sooner did she end her plaints, whenas
    Two old and aged hags came in their sights,
    Who bore an huge great vessel made of brass
    That kept the blood of those tormented knights.
    Long gazed the Prince on their hid mysteries,
    While pain on pain, and grief on grief he sees.

21 The virgin from the fire began to move her;
    The vessel near, she threw her in the same;
    While as the blood began to boil above her,
    And otherwhiles above the blood she came:
    So bubbling streams of brooks from high that fell
    Raise up the pebbles pure, white, clear and small.

22 They gone, the Prince did with himself devise
    To spill the blood, but now he hears a sound:
    It seemed a high and blustering wind did rise,
    And looking where the vessel to have found,
    He saw a pillar raised up whose end
    Reached from the ground almost unto the pend.

23 Then did he hear a murmur and a noise,
    A doleful mourning and a woeful sound:
    So from a hollow pit resounds a voice
    Of one that lies tormented underground,
    Or like the ghostly and the dreadful din
    That roaring bulls make hollow caves within.

24 The pillar seemed to be of marble stone,
    In form of a pyramid as it stood,
    Within the which the virgin was alone,
    Tormented still within the boiling blood.

Penardo knew but help of human hand,
That it was framed his fury to withstand.

25   But nearer to the pillar when he drew,
Some golden lettered lines he might espy,
Whose meaning was as after doth ensue:
Be not too bold this adventure to try,
Lest Fates who made thee most admired of all
Should make thee most infamous for thy fall.

26   But careless who had thus menaced him so,
Which served but to affray a fainting heart,
Now round about the pillar does he go,
While as he finds some other lines insert,
Whereby he knew the former feigned denial
Was but to stay him from a further trial.

27   *Whate'er thou be that proves to end the pains*
Of this tormented maid that here remains,
And would undo the great and wondrous frame
Which Mansay's art has builded for the same:
The taper from the burning altar take,
And drench it in the fearful thundering lake;
But first from burning lust seek some relief
For these two Princes wrapped in all mischief.

28   Not half so fast the tiger swift forth goes
Through desert ways for to redeem her brood,
As does the Prince when these glad news he knows:
Unto the altar where the taper stood
He hopes, yet doubts some ill might him befall
To mar his hope, hap, will, desire, and all.

29   Cassandra's armour was not now for nought,
Else of that dame enamoured had he been:
For the effect of this enchantment wrought
On every one before that had her seen;
And being once entangled by her love,
To torch they could not steer, nor touch, nor move.

30   Yea surely if his armour's virtue strong
Had not resisted the enchantment's force,
Within the cave he should have stayed so long,

While he had died for love without remorse.
Her beauty was of force, strength, power to move,
Yea, massacre a world of hearts with love.

31 But he who in his armour does retain
The rare and precious stone of chastity
(Whose virtue is the owner to restrain
From love, or lust, or Venus' fantasy),
Could not be moved to love, so none but he
Could end the fair Laissa's misery.

32 And entering now within the brazen porch,
The which he thinks to be the only way
Even with the light of this his little torch
He saw some lines engraved (which made him stay),
Upon the brazen gate he did behold
Indented all with curious works of gold.
If ought thou lose that thou hast bravely win
Thou dearly shalt repent thy coming in.

33 Now he began to gaze upon the ground,
And calling presently unto his mind
The dying knight whom he before had found
Within the cave, and of his counsel kind,
He knew it was the taper to defend,
Or else her sorrow should with death have end.

34 And by this time within a goodly hall
He entered was; when viewing well this sight,
The rare proportion was majestical,
To every art there was a gallant light,
And glad thereof, joy cheered his countenance,
So Phoebus' flower spreads when her lord does glance.

35 Long stayed he not, when looking here and there
On his left hand a door he might espy
Within the which he saw a gall'ry fair
Where pleasure did invite a gazing eye.
While through this pleasant gall'ry he was walking,
He thought he heard some people softly talking.

36 Whose murmuring sound had drawn him now in sight
Of a fair chamber that was richly hung

Where, sporting at their dallying delight,
Were knights and ladies, lying all along
Upon the pavement wrought of crystal rock,
Whose glances bright the Prince's sight did shock.

37 But his delight did him thereafter lead
Unto another chamber much more fair,
For there the crystal pavement all was spread
With crimson velvet, costly, rich and rare;
And in the midst a pillar stood upright,
Of gold that shined, flamed, glanced, with sparkling light.

38 Adjoined unto the pillar rose a throne
Of beaten gold, of lustre clear unstained;
The beautifullest queen did sit thereon
That crystal heaven or solid earth contained;
And round about her stood a comely train
Of kings, queens, lords, knights, dames, that love had slain.

39 There was the Queen of Carthage, Dido fair,
Who for Aeneas' love had lost her breath;
And for Antonius' love with vipers there
Sad Cleopatra stinged herself to death;
There Ariadne that her self had slain
For proud unthankful Theseus' disdain,

40 Whose life decreed to Minotaurus' rage
She freed, and from the labyrinth him gained;
There was Medea by whose counsel sage
Jason the golden fleece obtained;
There Phyllis who did many passions prove,
Chasing sad death for sweet Demophon's love;

41 There Julia the wife of great Pompey,
Who died because she feared her husband's death;
There Portia for Brutus' love did stay,
Who with hot burning coals had choked her breath;
There Pisca with her lover loved to be,
Who threw themselves both headlong in the sea;

42 There might Pandorus' loving dame be seen,
That chosed for to be buried quick in grave
Rather than be the Persian monarch's queen,

Because he did her lover's life bereave;
The Grecian dame fair Camma there did move,
Who slew herself and him that slew her love.

43   These women with their lovers did enjoy
A pleasant life about this princely Queen.
And men that did for love themselves destroy:
Menon, that hanged himself, might there be seen,
For to the proud Assyrian king alone
His best beloved Semiramis had gone;

44   And there Tiberius Gracchus did remain,
That found two serpents on his chamber floor,
And knowing if the female first were slain
His life should longer nor his wife's endure,
The male he slew, so well he loved his wife,
And made his death the ransom of her life;

45   And Marcus Lepidus did there abide,
That slew himself even for his love's disdain;
And Platius Numidius by his side
That for his dear love's death himself had slain;
There old Sylvanus that himself had hanged
Because proud Nero would his love have wranged;

46   There Pollio grave and sad, a German born,
A famous knight, though fortune wrought his fall;
This was the knight that in the cave beforn
Had told the Prince what there should him befall;
There many more that died without remorse,
For Laissa's love by the enchantment's force.

47   All these and many thousand there remain
Who to that court do momently resort;
The winged boy delights in all their pains,
And of their greatest grief he makes a sport.
But lo, that glorious Queen bred all their joys,
Their love, their fancy and their amorous toys.

48   For to enthrall the heart that Queen well knew,
The sovereign mistress of that art she was:
Her wanton shining looks and heavenly hue
With sweet allurements secretly would pass,

For still the glancing of her wanton eye
Would make her train sad, joyful, live, or die.

49   Her wanton eyes betrayed her inward mind,
Her countenance declared her heart's desire:
To burning lust she seemed to be inclined,
Consuming still with never-quenching fire,
Dissembling all with such a crafty mind,
That any save Adonis would be kind.

50   Her modest blush would divers times betray
That which (it seemed) she shamed for to unfold;
With amours quaint her wanton eyes would play,
And from her heart in sport their message told;
Her lowering looks or cheerful smiles doth move
To laugh, to weep, to smile, to sigh forth love.

51   Amongst the rest Penardo might espy
Phelarnon brave and Tropolance the bold,
Whom by their woeful looks he did descry
To be even far against their will withheld;
Phelarnon's breast betrayed his ceaseless pain,
Wherein a bloody dagger did remain.

52   And Tropolance's woeful heart was rent
With bloody sword, tormented still he goes;
Yea these two princes only did lament
While as the rest did seem for to rejoice.
But now sad shadows of the dankish night
Began to drive away the cheerful light.

Ossian

JAMES MACPHERSON

When James Macpherson (1736–90) published his *Fragments of Ancient Poetry* in 1760, he was not prepared for the storm of enthusiasm it produced. Fascinated by the Celtic mythology of the north-west of Scotland, he had decided to publish translations of some of the stories he had found. But now he set about recovering for Scotland from the scattered remnants of bardic tradition a national epic to rival Homer. The result was *Fingal* (1761) and *Temora* (1763), published together as *The Works of Ossian* in 1765: both actually involve Irish rather than Scottish mythology, but the geography is non-specific. They are ostensibly the recovered epics of the third-century bard Ossian, son of the warrior-king Fingal.

Ossian immediately became a cult, and a conundrum. Macpherson quickened the contemporary tide of fascination for romantic landscape, desperate passion, hidden myth and national identity, as against the previous cultural values of order, reason, urbanity and universal truth. What Gray had attempted to do with Wales in his bardic *Odes* (1757), Macpherson had certainly achieved for Scotland: he had mythologised its land and people, and Scotland soon became a touchstone of the wildly Romantic and the sublime throughout Europe, particularly in Germany. (Napoleon took a copy of *Ossian* on all his campaigns, though it is doubtful if the book contributed to his military successes.) As for Scotland itself, one of the attractions of Macpherson's work after the 1745 rebellion must have lain in its picture of ultimate victory over invaders and its implicit reassertion of Highland identity in the time of its suppression.

But Macpherson's book also raised a storm of debate as to

whether he actually had found a northern mythology or had invented it. Eventually it became clear from research that Macpherson had worked from some Gaelic manuscripts, but in a highly creative mode, and that there was no connected myth and no Ossianic original. Ambiguous or not, Macpherson's fame was long assured: and certainly even as an inventor he had genius. Forgotten now for almost a century, his work has recently seen a revival of interest.

The extract here is Book II of *Fingal*. Macpherson's evident use of the supernatural is confined to the occasional admonitory or lamenting ghost as here; but his picture of living warriors is also semi-supernatural in the way that they are continually merged with nature, with rocks, waves, fire, or huge beasts. In *Fingal* the conflict with the invading Swaran is in part one between land and sea. The narrative moves in a mist, one event slipping into another, ghosts, men, the past and present, battle and rest, sky and earth and sea, all losing boundaries. The story becomes like a dream, a series of swirling images from the unconscious. In this it is Romantic: but it also displays the character of Scottish fantasy.

The story to this point is that Swaran King of Lochlin (Denmark) has invaded Ireland and has been met in a so far inconclusive battle by Cuthullin, general of the young King Cormac of Ireland's forces. Cuthullin has sent for help from Fingal, King of the Caledonians in north west Scotland. Connal is an Irish sub-king and friend to Cuthullin.

&

OSSIAN

&

FINGAL BOOK II

ARGUMENT TO BOOK II

The ghost of Crugal, one of the Irish heroes who was killed in battle, appearing to Connal, foretels the defeat of Cuchullin in the next battle; and earnestly advises him to make peace with Swaran. Connal communicates the vision; but Cuchullin is inflexible; from a principle of honour he would not be the first to sue for peace, and he resolved to continue the war. Morning comes; Swaran proposes dishonourable terms to Cuchullin, which are rejected. The battle begins, and is obstinately fought for some time, until, upon the flight of Grumal, the whole Irish army gave way. Cuchullin and Connal cover their retreat: Carril leads them to a neighbouring hill, whither they are soon followed by Cuchullin himself, who descries the fleet of Fingal making towards the coast; but, night coming on, he lost sight of it again. Cuchullin, dejected after his defeat, attributes his ill success to the death of Ferda his friend, whom he had killed some time before. Carril, to shew that ill success did not always attend those who innocently killed their friends, introduces the episode of Comal and Galvina.

Connal lay by the sound of the mountain stream, beneath the aged tree. A stone, with its moss, supported his head. Shrill thro' the heath of Lena, he heard the voice of night. At distance from the heroes he lay, for the son of the sword feared no foe.

My hero saw in his rest a dark-red stream of fire coming down from the hill. Crugal sat upon the beam, a chief that lately fell. He fell by the hand of Swaran, striving in the battle of heroes. His face is like the beam of the setting moon; his robes are of the clouds of the hill: his eyes are like two decaying flames. Dark is the wound of his breast.

Crugal, said the mighty Connal, son of Dedgal famed on the hill of deer. Why so pale and sad, thou breaker of the shields? Thou hast never been pale for fear. – What disturbs the son of the hill?

Dim, and in tears, he stood and stretched his pale hand over the hero. – Faintly he raised his feeble voice, like the gale of the reedy Lego.

My ghost, O Connal, is on my native hills; but my corse is on the sands of Ullin. Thou shalt never talk with Crugal, or find his lone steps in the heath. I am light as the blast of Cromla, and I move like the shadow of mist. Connal, son of Colgar, I see the dark cloud of death: it hovers over the plains of Lena. The sons of green Erin shall fall. Remove from the field of ghosts. – Like the darkened moon he retired, in the midst of the whistling blast.

Stay, said the mighty Connal, stay my dark-red friend. Lay by that beam of heaven, son of the windy Cromla. What cave of the hill is thy lonely house? What green-headed hill is the place of thy rest? Shall we not hear thee in the storm? In the noise of the mountain-stream? When the feeble sons of the wind come forth, and ride on the blast of the desart.

The soft-voiced Connal rose in the midst of his sounding arms. He struck his shield above Cuchullin. The son of battle waked.

Why, said the ruler of the car, comes Connal through the night? My spear might turn against the sound; and Cuchullin mourn the death of his friend. Speak, Connal, son of Colgar, speak, thy counsel is like the son of heaven.

Son of Semo, replied the chief, the ghost of Crugal came from the cave of his hill. – The stars dim-twinkled through his form; and his voice was like the sound of a distant stream. – He is a messenger of death. – He speaks of the dark and narrow house. Sue for peace, O chief of Dunscaich; or fly over the heath of Lena.

He spoke to Connal, replied the hero, though stars dim-twinkled through his form. Son of Colgar, it was the wind that murmured in the caves of Lena. – Or if it was the form of Crugal, why didst thou not force him to my sight. Hast thou enquired where is his cave? The house of the son of the wind? My sword might find that voice, and force his knowledge from him. And small is his knowledge, Connal, for he was here to day. He could not have gone beyond our hills, and who could tell him there of our death?

Ghosts fly on clouds and ride on winds, said Connal's voice of wisdom. They rest together in their caves, and talk of mortal men.

Then let them talk of mortal men; of every man but Erin's chief. Let me be forgot in their cave; for I will not fly from Swaran. – If I must fall, my tomb shall rise amidst the fame of future times. The hunter shall shed a tear on my stone; and sorrow dwell round the high-bosomed Bragéla. I fear not death, but I fear to fly, for Fingal saw me often victorious. Thou dim phantom of the hill, shew thyself to me! come on thy beam of heaven, and shew me my death in thine hand; yet will I not fly, thou feeble son of the wind. Go, son of Colgar, strike the shield of Caithbat, it hangs between the spears. Let my heroes rise to the sound in the midst of the battles of Erin. Though Fingal delays his coming with the race of the stormy hills; we shall fight, O Colgar's son, and die in the battle of heroes.

The sound spreads wide; the heroes rise, like the breaking of a blue-rolling wave. They stood on the heath, like oaks with all their branches round them; when they eccho to the stream of frost, and their withered leaves rustle to the wind.

High Cromla's head of clouds is gray; the morning trembles on the half-enlightened ocean. The blue, gray mist swims slowly by, and hides the sons of Innis-fail.

Rise ye, said the king of the dark-brown shields, ye that came from Lochlin's waves. The sons of Erin have fled from our arms – pursue them over the plains of Lena. – And, Morla, go to Cormac's hall and bid them yield to Swaran; before the people shall fall into the tomb; and the hills of Ullin be silent. – They rose like a flock of sea-fowl when the waves expel them from the shore. Their sound was like a thousand streams that meet in Cona's vale, when after a stormy night, they turn their dark eddies beneath the pale light of the morning.

As the dark shades of autumn fly over the hills of grass; so gloomy, dark, successive came the chiefs of Lochlin's echoing woods. Tall as the stag of

Morven moved on the king of groves. His shining shield is on his side like a flame on the heath at night, when the world is silent and dark, and the traveller sees some ghost sporting in the beam.

A blast from the troubled ocean removed the settled mist. The sons of Innis-fail appear like a ridge of rocks on the shore.

Go, Morla, go, said Lochlin's king, and offer peace to these. Offer the terms we give to kings when nations bow before us. When the valiant are dead in war, and the virgins weeping on the field.

Great Morla came, the son of Swart, and stately strode the king of shields. He spoke to Erin's blue-eyed son, among the lesser heroes.

Take Swaran's peace, the warrior spoke, the peace he gives to kings, when the nations bow before him. Leave Ullin's lovely plains to us, and give thy spouse and dog. Thy spouse high-bosom'd heaving fair. Thy dog that overtakes the wind. Give these to prove the weakness of thine arm, and live beneath our power.

Tell Swaran, tell that heart of pride, that Cuchullin never yields. – I give him the dark-blue rolling of ocean, or I give his people graves in Erin! Never shall a stranger have the lovely sun-beam of Dunscaich; nor ever deer fly on Lochlin's hills before the nimble-footed Luäth.

Vain ruler of the car, said Morla, wilt thou fight the king; that king whose ships of many groves could carry off thine Isle? So little is thy green-hilled Ullin to the king of stormy waves.

In words I yield to many, Morla; but this sword shall yield to none. Erin shall own the sway of Cormac, while Connal and Cuchullin live. O Connal, first of mighty men, thou hast heard the words of Morla; shall thy thoughts then be of peace, thou breaker of the shields? Spirit of fallen Crugal! why didst thou threaten us with death? The narrow house shall receive me in the midst of the light of renown. – Exalt, ye sons of Innis-fail, exalt the spear and bend the bow; rush on the foe in darkness, as the spirits of stormy nights.

Then dismal, roaring, fierce, and deep the gloom of battle rolled along; as mist that is poured on the valley, when storms invade the silent sunshine of heaven. The chief moves before in arms, like an angry ghost before a cloud; when meteors inclose him with fire; and the dark winds are in his hand. – Carril, far on the heath, bids the horn of battle sound. He raises the voice of the song, and pours his soul into the minds of heroes.

Where, said the mouth of the song, where is the fallen Crugal? He lies forgot on earth, and the hall of shells is silent. – Sad is the spouse of Crugal, for she is a stranger in the hall of her sorrow. But who is she, that, like a sun-beam, flies before the ranks of the foe? It is Degrena, lovely fair, the spouse of fallen Crugal. Her hair is on the wind behind. Her eye is red;

her voice is shrill. Green, empty is thy Crugal now, his form is in the cave of the hill. He comes to the ear of rest, and raises his feeble voice; like the humming of the mountain-bee, or collected flies of evening. But Degrena falls like a cloud of the morn; the sword of Lochlin is in her side. Cairbar, she is fallen, the rising thought of thy youth. She is fallen, O Cairbar, the thought of thy youthful hours.

Fierce Cairbar heard the mournful sound, and rushed on like ocean's whale; he saw the death of his daughter; and roared in the midst of thousands. His spear met a son of Lochlin, and battle spread from wing to wing. As a hundred winds in Lochlin's groves, as fire in the firs of a hundred hills; so loud, so ruinous and vast the ranks of men are hewn down. – Cuchullin cut off heroes like thistles, and Swaran wasted Erin. Curach fell by his hand, and Cairbar of the bossy shield. Morglan lies in lasting rest; and Ca-olt quivers as he dies. His white breast is stained with his blood; and his yellow hair stretched in the dust of his native land. He often had spread the feast where he fell; and often raised the voice of the harp: when his dogs leapt around for joy; and the youths of the chace prepared the bow.

Still Swaran advanced, as a stream that bursts from the desert. The little hills are rolled in its course; and the rocks half-sunk by its side. But Cuchullin stood before him like a hill, that catches the clouds of heaven. – The winds contend on its head of pines; and the hail rattles on its rocks. But, firm in its strength, it stands and shades the silent vale of Cona.

So Cuchullin shaded the sons of Erin, and stood in the midst of thousands. Blood rises like the fount of a rock, from panting heroes around him. But Erin falls on either wing like snow in the day of the sun.

O sons of Innis-fail, said Grumal, Lochlin conquers on the field. Why strive we as reeds against the wind? Fly to the hill of dark-brown hinds. He fled like the stag of Morven, and his spear is a trembling beam of light behind him. Few fled with Grumal, the chief of the little soul: they fell in the battle of heroes on Lena's echoing heath.

High on his car, of many gems, the chief of Erin stood; he slew a mighty son of Lochlin, and spoke, in haste, to Connal. O Connal, first of mortal men, thou hast taught this arm of death! Though Erin's sons have fled, shall we not fight the foe? O Carril, son of other times, carry my living friends to that bushy hill. – Here, Connal, let us stand like rocks, and save our flying friends.

Connal mounts the car of light. They stretch their shields like the darkened moon, the daughter of the starry skies, when she moves, a dun circle, through heaven. Sithfadda panted up the hill, and Dusronnal haughty steed. Like waves behind a whale behind them rushed the foe.

Now on the rising side of Cromla stood Erin's few sad sons; like a grove through which the flame had rushed hurried on by the winds of the stormy night. – Cuchullin stood beside an oak. He rolled his red eye in silence, and heard the wind in his bushy hair; when the scout of ocean came, Moran the son of Fithil. – The ships, he cried, the ships of the lonely isle! There Fingal comes, the first of men, the breaker of the shields. The waves foam before his black prows. His masts with sails are like groves in clouds.

Blow, said Cuchullin, all ye winds that rush over my isle of lovely mist. Come to the death of thousands, O chief of the hills of hinds. Thy sails, my friend, are to me like the clouds of the morning; and thy ships like the light of heaven; and thou thyself like a pillar of fire that giveth light in the night. O Connal, first of men, how pleasant are our friends! But the night is gathering around; where now are the ships of Fingal? Here let us pass the hours of darkness, and wish for the moon of heaven.

The winds came down on the woods. The torrents rushed from the rocks. Rain gathered round the head of Cromla. And the red stars trembled between the flying clouds. Sad, by the side of a stream whose sound was echoed by a tree, sad by the side of a stream the chief of Erin sat. Connal son of Colgar was there, and Carril of other times.

Unhappy is the hand of Cuchullin, said the son of Semo, unhappy is the hand of Cuchullin since he slew his friend. – Ferda, thou son of Damman, I loved thee as myself.

How, Cuchullin, son of Semo, fell the breaker of the shields? Well I remember, said Connal, the noble son of Damman. Tall and fair he was like the rain-bow of the hill.

Ferda from Albion came, the chief of a hundred hills. In Muri's hall he learned the sword, and won the friendship of Cuchullin. We moved to the chace together; and one was our bed in the heath.

Deugala was the spouse of Cairbar, chief of the plains of Ullin. She was covered with the light of beauty, but her heart was the house of pride. She loved that sun-beam of youth, the noble son of Damman. Cairbar, said the white-armed woman, give me half of the herd. No more I will remain in your halls. Divide the herd, dark Cairbar.

Let Cuchullin, said Cairbar, divide my herd on the hill. His breast is the seat of justice. Depart, thou light of beauty. – I went and divided the herd. One snow-white bull remained. I gave that bull to Cairbar. The wrath of Deugala rose.

Son of Damman, begun the fair, Cuchullin pains my soul. I must hear of his death, or Lubar's stream shall roll over me. My pale ghost shall wander near thee, and mourn the wound of my pride. Pour out the blood of Cuchullin or pierce this heaving breast.

Deugala, said the fair-haired youth, how shall I slay the son of Semo? He is the friend of my secret thoughts, and shall I lift the sword? She wept three days before him, on the fourth he consented to fight.

I will fight my friend, Deugala! but may I fall by his sword. Could I wander on the hill and behold the grave of Cuchullin? We fought on the hills of Muri. Our swords avoid a wound. They slide on the helmets of steel; and sound on the slippery shields. Deugala was near with a smile, and said to the son of Damman, thine arm is feeble, thou sun-beam of youth. Thy years are not strong for steel. – Yield to the son of Semo. He is like the rock of Malmor.

The tear is in the eye of youth. He faultering said to me, Cuchullin, raise thy bossy shield. Defend thee from the hand of thy friend. My soul is laden with grief: for I must slay the chief of men.

I sighed as the wind in the chink of a rock. I lifted high the edge of my steel. The sun-beam of the battle fell; the first of Cuchullin's friends. –

Unhappy is the hand of Cuchullin since the hero fell.

Mournful is thy tale, son of the car, said Carril of other times. It sends my soul back to the ages of old, and to the days of other years. – Often have I heard of Comal who slew the friend he loved; yet victory attended his steel; and the battle was consumed in his presence.

Comal was a son of Albion; the chief of an hundred hills. His deer drunk of a thousand streams. A thousand rocks replied to the voice of his dogs. His face was the mildness of youth. His hand the death of heroes. One was his love, and fair was she! the daughter of mighty Conloch. She appeared like a sun-beam among women. And her hair was like the wing of the raven. Her dogs were taught to the chace. Her bow-string sounded on the winds of the forest. Her soul was fixed on Comal. Often met their eyes of love. Their course in the chace was one, and happy were their words in secret. – But Grumal loved the maid, the dark chief of the gloomy Ardven. He watched her lone steps in the heath; the foe of unhappy Comal.

One day, tired of the chace, when the mist had concealed their friends, Comal and the daughter of Conloch met in the cave of Ronan. It was the wonted haunt of Comal. Its sides were hung with his arms. A hundred shields of thongs were there; a hundred helms of sounding steel.

Rest here, he said, my love Galvina; thou light of the cave of Ronan. A deer appears on Mora's brow. I go; but I will soon return. I fear, she said, dark Grumal my foe; he haunts the cave of Ronan. I will rest among the arms; but soon return, my love.

He went to the deer of Mora. The daughter of Conloch would try his love. She cloathed her white sides with his armour, and strode from the cave of Ronan. He thought it was his foe. His heart beat high. His colour changed, and darkness dimmed his eyes. He drew the bow. The arrow flew. Galvina fell in blood. He run with wildness in his steps and called the daughter of Conloch. No answer in the lonely rock. Where art thou, O my love! He saw, at length, her heaving heart beating around the feathered dart. O Conloch's daughter, is it thou? He sunk upon her breast.

The hunters found the hapless pair; he afterwards walked the hill. But many and silent were his steps round the dark dwelling of his love. The fleet of the ocean came. He fought; the strangers fled. He searched for his death over the field. But who could kill the mighty Comal! He threw away his dark-brown shield. An arrow found his manly breast. He sleeps with his loved Galvina at the noise of the sounding surge. Their green tombs are seen by the mariner, when he bounds on the waves of the north.

Tam o' Shanter

ROBERT BURNS

With *Tam o' Shanter* (1791), the only truly narrative poem by Robert Burns (1759–96), we are back with the 'elrich fantasyis' of Dunbar, that mixture of infernal horror and wild mirth that occasionally surfaces in Scottish fantasy; but the more contemporary context of the poem is the Gothic novel, then at its height, and the Romantic delight in the imagination. Most immediately the poem springs from the local legend of an Ayrshire farmer's experiences while travelling home from Ayr via Alloway Kirk. Burns's mother's maid used to tell him fairy tales when he was a child, and these, he said, 'had so strong an effect on my imagination, that to this hour, in my nocturnal rambles, I sometimes keep a sharp lookout in suspicious places'. But Burns, who never settled to any one view, also derided the credulity of such tales as 'trumpery': and *Tam o' Shanter*, while giving us a terrifying enough picture of the hellish ceilidh in Kirk-Alloway, leaves us ample scope, unlike its source, to suppose that the entire fantasy may also be the product of the mind of a drunken and superstitious farmer.

The poem is a medley of feelings and styles in which extremes of fantasy and realism somehow coexist. Burns takes an ironic stance of varying pressure to his material: obvious when recounting Tam's insouciance in the bar before his dark journey, fainter when describing Gothic horrors – though even here he can let the weight tip over into potential bathos, as in 'Where Mungo's mither hang'd hersel', 'The grey hairs yet stuck to the heft'. He loves counterpoint – the conviviality of the inn and the social glee of the witches, the warm indoors world and the cold chaotic one without, the roaring darkness and the cold light of the corpse-held tapers. The story moves Tam past three contrastive women, the landlady of the pub, Nanny the witch, and Kate his wife at home, 'Nursing her wrath to keep it warm'. There is continual oscillation between scenes of fear and of comfort or safety, and the narrator shifts distance from Tam between near and far, sometimes mock-moralising, sometimes sympathising, sometimes abandoning him to his fate. As for the style, it shifts throughout between broad Scots and eighteenth-century English poetic diction, and among Augustan, Gothic and folk-tale modes. The core of the poem is musical: it is a series of variations on a theme. It is also social: the narrator rarely mentions one thing without going on to three – 'A blethering, blustering, drunken blellum', 'His ancient, trusty, drouthy crony', 'favours secret, sweet, and precious'; his similes use multiple terms; even his horrors come in lists and crowds. And yet all the yelling mob of witches is abruptly stilled at the end as we are left with the absurd and dreadful singularity of the lost tail; and beyond that the differently dreadful singularity of the waiting wife.

So far as the 'meaning' of the poem is concerned, the morality concerning Tam's excesses is present only to be mocked. The midnight deeds in the Kirk may symbolise the dark undercurrents of human nature, but given the earlier riotous scene in the pub, we can hardly call this a picture of repressed Scots character breaking loose. What is more present, however, is the world of the unconscious, where all is fluid chaos – and this is of course a central feature of Scottish fantasy. That chaos is at once the dark world outside the warmth of society, and the no less darkened world well within it, that of the inebriated psyche of Tam o' Shanter.

TAM O' SHANTER

When chapman billies leave the street,
And drouthy neebors neebors meet;
As market-days are wearing late,
An' folk begin to tak the gate;
While we sit bousing at the nappy,
An' getting fou and unco happy,
We think na on the lang Scots miles,
The mosses, waters, slaps, and styles,
That lie between us and our hame,

Whare sits our sulky, sullen dame,
Gathering her brows like gathering storm,
Nursing her wrath to keep it warm.

This truth fand honest Tam o' Shanter,
As he frae Ayr ae night did canter:
(Auld Ayr, wham ne'er a town surpasses,
For honest men and bonie lasses.)

O Tam, had'st thou but been sae wise,
As taen thy ain wife Kate's advice!
She tauld thee weel thou was a skellum,
A blethering, blustering, drunken blellum;
That frae November till October,
Ae market-day thou was nae sober;
That ilka melder wi' the miller,
Thou sat as lang as thou had siller;
That ev'ry naig was ca'd a shoe on,
The smith and thee gat roaring fou on;
That at the Lord's house, even on Sunday,
Thou drank wi' Kirkton Jean till Monday,
She prophesied, that, late or soon,
Thou would be found deep drown'd in Doon,
Or catch'd wi' warlocks in the mirk
By Alloway's auld, haunted Kirk.

Ah! gentle dames, it gars me greet,
To think how monie counsels sweet,
How monie lengthen'd, sage advices
The husband frae the wife despises!

But to our tale: Ae market-night,
Tam had got planted unco right,
Fast by an ingle, bleezing finely,
Wi' reaming swats, that drank divinely;
And at his elbow, Souter Johnie,
His ancient, trusty, drouthy cronie:
Tam lo'ed him like a very brither;
They had been fou for weeks thegither.
The night drave on wi' sangs and clatter;
And ay the ale was growing better:
The landlady and Tam grew gracious

Wi' secret favours, sweet and precious:
The Souter tauld his queerest stories;
The landlord's laugh was ready chorus:
The storm without might rair and rustle,
Tam did na mind the storm a whistle.

Care, mad to see a man sae happy,
E'en drown'd himsel amang the nappy.
As bees flee hame wi' lades o' treasure,
The minutes wing'd their way wi' pleasure:
Kings may be blest but Tam was glorious,
O'er a' the ills o' life victorious!

But pleasures are like poppies spread:
You seize the flow'r, its bloom is shed;
Or like the snow falls in the river,
A moment white – then melts for ever;
Or like the Borealis race,
That flit ere you can point their place;
Or like the rainbow's lovely form
Evanishing amid the storm.
Nae man can tether time or tide;
The hour approaches Tam maun ride:
That hour, o' night's black arch the key-stane,
That dreary hour Tam mounts his beast in;
And sic a night he taks the road in,
As ne'er poor sinner was abroad in.

The wind blew as 'twad blawn its last;
The rattling showers rose on the blast;
The speedy gleams the darkness swallow'd;
Loud, deep, and lang the thunder bellow'd:
That night, a child might understand,
The Deil had business on his hand.

Weel mounted on his gray mare Meg,
A better never lifted leg,
Tam skelpit on thro' dub and mire,
Despising wind, and rain, and fire;
Whiles holding fast his guid blue bonnet,
Whiles crooning o'er some auld Scots sonnet,
Whiles glow'ring round wi' prudent cares,

Lest bogles catch him unawares:
Kirk-Alloway was drawing nigh,
Whare ghaists and houlets nightly cry.

By this time he was cross the ford,
Whare in the snaw the chapman smoor'd;
And past the birks and meikle stane,
Whare drunken Charlie brak's neck-bane;
And thro' the whins, and by the cairn,
Whare hunters fand the murder'd bairn;
And near the thorn, aboon the well,
Whare Mungo's mither hang'd hersel.
Before him Doon pours all his floods;
The doubling storm roars thro' the woods;
The lightnings flash from pole to pole;
Near and more near the thunders roll:
When, glimmering thro' the groaning trees,
Kirk-Alloway seemed in a bleeze,
Thro' ilka bore the beams were glancing,
And loud resounded mirth and dancing.

Inspiring bold John Barleycorn!
What dangers thou canst make us scorn!
Wi' tippenny, we fear nae evil;
Wi' usquabae, we'll face the Devil!
The swats sae ream'd in Tammie's noddle,
Fair play, he car'd na deils a boddle.
But Maggie stood, right sair astonish'd,
Till, by the heel and hand admonish'd,
She ventur'd forward on the light;
And, wow! Tam saw an unco sight!
Warlocks and witches in a dance:
Nae cotillion, brent new frae France,
But hornpipes, jigs, strathspeys, and reels,
Put life and mettle in their heels.
A winnock-bunker in the east,
There sat Auld Nick, in shape o' beast;
A tousie tyke, black, grim, and large,
To gie them music was his charge:
He screw'd the pipes and gart them skirl,
Till roof and rafters a' did dirl.

Coffins stood round, like open presses,
That shaw'd the dead in their last dresses;
And, by some devilish cantraip sleight,
Each in its cauld hand held a light:
By which heroic Tam was able
To note upon the haly table,
A murderer's banes, in gibbet-airns;
Twa span-lang, wee, unchristen'd bairns;
A thief new-cutted frae a rape –
Wi' his last gasp his gab did gape;
Five tomahawks wi' bluid red-rusted;
Five scymitars wi' murder crusted;
A garter which a babe had strangled;
A knife a father's throat had mangled –
Whom his ain son o' life bereft –
The grey hairs yet stack to the heft;
Wi' mair of horrible and awefu',
Which even to name wad be unlawfu'.

As Tammie glowr'd, amaz'd, and curious,
The mirth and fun grew fast and furious;
The piper loud and louder blew,
The dancers quick and quicker flew,
They reel'd, they set, they cross'd, they cleekit,
Till ilka carlin swat and reekit,
And coost her duddies to the wark,
And linket at it in her sark!

Now Tam, O Tam, had thae been queans,
A' plump and strapping in their teens!
Their sarks, instead o' creeshie flannen,
Been snaw-white seventeen hunder linen!
Thir breeks o' mine, my only pair,
That ance were plush, o' guid blue hair,
I wad hae gi'en them off my hurdies
For ae blink o' the bonie burdies!

But wither'd beldams, auld and droll,
Rigwoodie hags wad spean a foal,
Louping and flinging on a crummock,
I wonder didna turn thy stomach!

But Tam kend what was what fu' brawlie:
There was ae winsome wench and wawlie,
That night enlisted in the core,
Lang after kend on Carrick shore
(For monie a beast to dead she shot,
An' perish'd monie a bonie boat,
And shook baith meikle corn and bear,
And kept the country-side in fear.)
Her cutty sark, o' Paisley harn,
That while a lassie she had worn,
In longitude tho' sorely scanty,
It was her best, and she was vauntie.
Ah! little kend thy reverend grannie,
That sark she coft for her wee Nannie,
Wi' twa pund Scots ('twas a' her riches,)
Wad ever grac'd a dance of witches!

But here my Muse her wing maun cour,
Sic flights as far beyond her power:
To sing how Nannie lap and flang
(A souple jad she was and strang;)
And how Tam stood like ane bewitch'd,
And thought his very een enrich'd;
Even Satan glowr'd, and fidg'd fu' fain,
And hotch'd and blew wi' might and main;
Till first ae caper, syne anither,
Tam tint his reason a' thegither,
And roars out: 'Weel done, Cutty-sark!'
And in an instant all was dark;
And scarcely had he Maggie rallied,
When out the hellish legion sallied.

As bees bizz out wi' angry fyke,
When plundering herds assail their byke;
As open pussie's mortal foes,
When, pop! she starts before their nose;
As eager runs the market-crowd,
When 'Catch the thief!' resounds aloud;
So Maggie runs, the witches follow,
Wi' mony an eldritch skreech and hollow.

Ah, Tam! Ah, Tam! thou'll get thy fairin!
In hell they'll roast thee like a herrin!
In vain thy Kate awaits thy comin!
Kate soon will be a woefu' woman!
Now, do thy speedy utmost, Meg,
And win the key-stane of the brig;
There, at them thou thy tail may toss,
A running stream they dare na cross!
But ere the key-stane she could make,
The fient a tail she had to shake:
For Nannie, far before the rest,
Hard upon noble Maggie prest,
And flew at Tam wi' furious ettle;
But little wist she Maggie's mettle!
Ae spring brought off her master hale,
But left behind her ain grey tail:
The carlin claught her by the rump,
And left poor Maggie scarce a stump.

Now, wha this tale o' truth shall read,
Ilk man, and mother's son, take heed:
Whene'er to drink you are inclin'd,
Or cutty sarks run in your mind,
Think! ye may buy the joys o'er dear:
Remember Tam o' Shanter's mare.

Kilmeny,
The Three Perils of Man
&
Confessions of a Justified Sinner

JAMES HOGG

'Be it mine to cherish the visions that have been, as well as the hope of visions yet in reserve, far in the ocean of eternity, beyond the stars and the sun. For, after all, what is the soul of man without these? What but a cold phlegmatic influence, so inclosed within the walls of modern scepticism, as scarcely to be envied by the spirits of the beasts that perish?' If Hogg's fantasy has any 'message', it is that the universe is far more various and mysterious than our reasonable minds suppose. His own work is unclassifiable. In 'Kilmeny' (1813) and *The Pilgrims of the Sun* (1815) he writes mystic poems envisioning heaven; in 'The Witch of Fife' (1813) he creates a comic ballad of a frisky wife's magical excursions; his long prose romance *The Three Perils of Man* (1822) shifts between English-Scottish battles on the Borders and fantastic happenings in a wizard's castle; the celebrated *Confessions of a Justified Sinner* (1824) describes a murder which may or may not have been at the devil's instigation; and a whole range of short stories from 1818 to 1831 explores possible interventions of supernatural evil in human affairs. In his later works Hogg allows a varyingly possible way out from having to accept the supernatural. But if not magic, then the no less mysterious delusions of the mind are being portrayed: everywhere Hogg is pushing beyond the rational into the subconscious or the numinous. He is the first Scottish writer to put the fantastic at the centre of his vision.

Hogg's life (1770–1835) is equally various. An Ettrick shepherd, he was as happy living in a cave as pursuing the literary life in Edinburgh or being lionised in London. Raised on a diet of fairy tales by his mother, he was just as ready to use complex German romances in his fantasy, and to enter the minds of characters far removed from the folk. He is omnivorous, he enters every area of life and art with an explorer's zest.

The extracts here can only hint at Hogg's range. That from 'Kilmeny' shows the mystic, that from *The Three Perils* the eldritch comedian, that from the *Confessions* the speculative demonologist, with contrasting styles. 'Kilmeny' lures us in with widening possibilities until we arrive at heaven; the extract from *The Three Perils* depends on vivid contrasts, between menace and mockery, terror and bravado and the supernatural and the domestic; while in the *Confessions* passage we have a nightmare of alienation, despair and entrapment. But all are pictures of frail humanity surrounded by forces and depths of which it has small knowledge.

The lines from 'Kilmeny' come from the opening of the poem. The passage from *The Three Perils* is from chapter 21, where the disguised devil is overhearing the plots of those who would rescue the band he has imprisoned in the castle of Aikwood. The extract from the *Confessions* comes from near the end of the novel, when the sinner is in flight from the law for murder, assailed continually by demons who are supposedly kept from him only by the now dreaded agency of his erstwhile confederate Gil-Martin.

KILMENY

Bonny Kilmeny gaed up the glen;
But it wasna to meet Duneira's men,
Nor the rosy monk of the isle to see,
For Kilmeny was pure as pure could be.
It was only to hear the yorlin sing,
And pu' the cress-flower round the spring;
The scarlet hypp and the hindberrye,
And the nut that hang frae the hazel tree;
For Kilmeny was pure as pure could be.
But lang may her minny look o'er the wa',
And lang may she seek i' the green-wood shaw;
Lang the laird of Duneira blame,
And lang, lang greet or Kilmeny come hame!

When many a day had come and fled,
When grief grew calm, and hope was dead,
When mess for Kilmeny's soul had been sung,

When the bedes-man had prayed, and the dead-bell rung,
Late, late in a gloamin, when all was still,
When the fringe was red on the westlin hill,
The wood was sere, the moon i' the wane,
The reek o' the cot hung over the plain,
Like a little wee cloud in the world its lane;
When the ingle lowed with an eiry leme,
Late, late in the gloaming Kilmeny came hame!

'Kilmeny, Kilmeny, where have you been?
Lang hae we sought baith holt and den;
By linn, by ford, and green-wood tree,
Yet you are halesome and fair to see.
Where gat you that joup o' the lilly scheen?
That bonny snood of the birk sae green?
And these roses, the fairest that ever were seen?
Kilmeny, Kilmeny, where have you been?' ——

Kilmeny looked up with a lovely grace,
But nae smile was seen on Kilmeny's face;
As still was her look, and as still was her ee,
As the stillness that lay on the emerant lea,
Or the mist that sleeps on a waveless sea.
For Kilmeny had been she knew not where,
And Kilmeny had seen what she could not declare;
Kilmeny had been where the cock never crew,
Where the rain never fell, and the wind never blew.
But it seemed as the harp of the sky had rung,
And the airs of heaven played round her tongue,
When she spake of the lovely forms she had seen,
And a land where sin had never been;
A land of love, and a land of light,
Withouten sun, or moon, or night:
Where the river swa'd a living stream,
And the light a pure celestial beam:
The land of vision it would seem,
A still, an everlasting dream.

In yon green-wood there is a waik,
And in that waik there is a wene,
    And in that wene there is a maike,

That neither has flesh, blood, nor bane;
   And down in yon green-wood he walks his lane.

In that green wene Kilmeny lay,
Her bosom happed wi' the flowerits gay;
But the air was soft and the silence deep,
And bonny Kilmeny fell sound asleep.
She kend nae mair, nor opened her ee,
Till waked by the hymns of a far countrye.

She 'wakened on couch of the silk sae slim,
All striped wi' the bars of the rainbow's rim;
And lovely beings round were rife,
Who erst had travelled mortal life;
And aye they smiled, and 'gan to speer,
'What spirit has brought this mortal here?' ——

❦

THE THREE PERILS OF MAN:
WAR, WOMEN AND WITCHCRAFT

❧

As the imps concluded their song, our prisoners on the top of the castle perceived a large rough watch-dog jogging out at the gate of the castle, and following in the direction of the fugitives. When the brute saw that he was perceived he turned round, set up his snout toward the battlements, and uttered a loud bow-wow-wow, which, when the great Master heard, he started to his feet, and, with wild staring looks. and his hair standing on end, took shelter behind the friar.

'Behold thou, and see with thine eyes, that it is only a watch-dog come from the camp of our captain,' said the friar. 'Lo, thy very nature is changed since first I saw thee.'

'Then would to the gods that I had never seen thee, or that I had seen thee sooner,' said the Master; and strode away to discourage any farther reply. The dog followed the fugitives, and bent his course toward the mill.

That being the next inhabited house to the eastward, Dan Chisholm and his yeomen landed all there; and in full assembly he related, to their terror and astonishment, how he had seen the devil himself and several of his monstrous agents, who had chased him from the castle, spuing fire and brimstone on him like a cataract. The rest said, that though they had not seen the devil, they had seen and heard enough to put any rational being out of his senses, and as much as to teach them never to go there again. Dan swore that they were not to be taught any such thing; for, said he, 'Our captain's friends, and our own brethren in arms, are most unwarrantably, and I must also say unaccountably, confined there, – and we will either free them or perish in the attempt. I can find plenty of holy men that, with book and candle, can withstand the devil, and shall make him flee from his stronghold like fire from the flint. If I had the gospel friar on the one side of him, and Father Brand, or Capuchin Cairnabie, on the other, I shall gar him skip.' While Dan was in the middle of this speech, in comes the great rough watchdog; who, after fawning on some of the warriors as on old acquaintances, took his station in a dark corner of the miller's thronged hall, and began a licking his feet, but at the same time taking good heed to all that passed. It was finally agreed that Dan and a companion should ride straight to Melrose, and represent their case to the holy abbot there, who was devoted to the interests of their captain, and who, it was not doubted, would devise means of expelling the old demon from his guardship, and letting free their friends, who were all baptised men and good Christians. As they formed these sapient devices, many hard things were said of the devil; and our warriors seemed rather inclined to make a laughing-stock of him, till the miller's maid interrupted them with the following question:

'Wha o' you trooper chaps does this maskis dog belang to?'

'To nane o' us,' was answered by several at the same time.

'I wish ye wad tent him, then,' said she, 'for, this wee while bygane, his een hae been glentin like twa blue burnin candles. I wish he be nae a mad ane.'

'Sneck doors, and out swords,' cried the miller: 'We'll hae him proven.'

The doors were shut, and the yeomen surrounded the dog with their drawn weapons. The poor beast lay as harmlesslike as a lamb, with his head upon his fore feet so as to hide them, turning up his eyes from below his shaggy brows in a beseeching manner, and wagging his tail till it played thump, thump, on the floor. But this did not hinder the miller from reconnoitring, though it gave him rather a favourable opinion of his shaggy guest. 'Poor fellow,' said the miller, 'wha's dog may ye be?' The dog forgot himself; he lifted up his head in a kind acknowledging manner to the miller, who, looking narrowly at him, cried out: 'A marvel!, a marvel! saw ever ony mortal man the like o' this? Here's a tyke wi' cloven cloots like a gait, fairney cloots and a' thegither. The Holy Virgin be wi' us! I believe we hae gotten the ——'

Here the miller was interrupted, without getting the sentence concluded.

The dog sprung to his feet, appearing twice as big as when he entered. 'Bow-wow-wow!' roared he in the miller's face with the voice of an enraged lion; 'Bow-wow-wow!' And as he bayed from side to side on the warrior circle, they all retreated backward till the wall stopped them. Well might they, – for they perceived, by his open mouth, the same appearance that Dan had before witnessed, namely, a stomach and chest of burning flame. 'Bow-wow-wow!' reiterated he: 'Youph, youph, youph.' All fled back aghast: but the attack was of short duration. The miller had a huge fire of seeds, above a burning log of wood, which he had heaped on for the comfort of his guests. When the dog reached that, he broke into it, appearing to bury himself in the coil of fiery dust. It flashed upwards in millions of burning atoms, and in the midst of them up flew the dog out at the top of the lum, with a tremendous 'Bow-wow-wow!'

All was silence for a few seconds, while our yeomen stood in a circle, with their weapons drawn, and their backs at the wall, gaping with affright, and staring on one another. 'By Saint Thomas, we are haunted!' cried Dan, breaking silence; 'That is the same chap I forgathered wi' afore in the staircase of the castle, I ken him by his lowin lungs, though he has changed his shape.' He was interrupted by a loud laugh on the top of the house, and a voice that said, in a jeering tone, 'Ha, ha, ha! Andrew Chisholm is that you? I have found out a' your plans, – and ride you to Melrose, or ride you to Dryburgh, I'll be there afore you to lend you a lift. Ay, and I'll keep Aikwood castle in spite o' you and a' your master's men.'

Dan could not contain his indignation on hearing this brag. He ran forward to the brace, put his neck under it, and turning his nose up the lum (or rustic chimney) answered, 'Deil o' that ye're fit to do, auld tyke. Ye're but a liar at best and the father o' liars. Gang and toast heathen bacon in your ain het hame. What seek ye here amang leel men?'

'Weel answered, and like yoursel, Dan!' said one of the yeomen, and slapped him on the shoulder, which rousing his spirit still farther, he added, 'Confound you Robin's Geordie o' Feindhope-haugh, what for didna ye strike when the foul thief set up his gousty gab at your nose wi' his impudent bow-wow-wow; I see nae right ony o' God's creatures hae to be hurlbarrowed out o' their standing wi' him.'

As he finished the remark, there was something came to the door, and gave two or three rude impatient scratches, exactly in the same manner that a strong dog does that wants to be in. This instantly changed the cheer of our sturdy group, that with one involuntary movement closed round the hearth, as the point the most distant from the door.

'That's him again,' said the miller's lass.

'The Lord forbid,' said the miller: 'I wonder what multure he wants frae me. Though I live on the lands of a Master of Arts, I had nae inkling that I was thirl to hell. Brave lads, can nane of you rhame a mass, a credo, or a paternoster? He is but a coward at best; I hae kend a monk, wi' his crosier and his cowl, chace him like a rabbit.'

'I fear we'll prove but lame hands at that,' said Dan, 'and think we had better sally out on him sword in hand, and see what he can either say or do for himself. But, Chryste, I needna say that, considering that I ken sae weel what his lining's made of.'

'I hae a cross and chain in the house,' said the miller, 'that was consecrated at the shrine of St Bothan; whoever will be our leader shall bear that before him, and we'll bang the auld thief away frae our bigging.'

The scratching was renewed with redoubled fury. Our yeomen crowded closer around the fire, till all at once their ears were saluted by a furious 'bow-wow-wow' down the lum, which, in spite of their utmost resolution, scattered them like a covey of heath-fowl over which the hawk is hovering, when every one endeavours to shift for itself, and hide in its own heather bush.

Their faces were by this time flushed with shame as well as fear, that they should be thus cuffed about by 'the auld thief,' as they styled him. Resolved, therefore, to make one great and strenuous effort, the miller brought out his consecrated cross, some tied sticks, and others horn spoons across, till all were armed with the same irresistible symbol, and then they marshalled up before the fire, uncovered their heads, and with the ensigns reared before them, waited for a moment the word of command to march out to the grand attack. The arch fiend, not choosing to wait the issue, raised such a horse laugh on the top of the lum that their ears were deafened with the noise; and clapping his paws that sounded like the strokes of battering ram's horns, he laughed till the upper and nether millstones chattered against each other, and away he bounded through the clouds of the night, apparently in an agony of laughter.

'Aha! there he goes!' said Dan: 'There's nae guidance to be had o' him, and as little mense in meddling wi' him.'

'Ay, let him e'en gang,' said the miller; 'he's the warst mouse o' the mill. Ane had better tine the blind bitch's litter than hae the mill singed wi' brimstone. I lurd rather deal wi' the thankless maltster, that neither gi'es coup, neivefu', nor lippie, than wi' him. I have no part of the breviary but a glorious preamble; kneel till I repeat it.'

The troopers kneeled round the miller, who, lifting up his hands, said, with great fervour, 'O semper timidum scelus! Obstupui, steteruntque comae et vox faucibus haesit. O Deus; nusquam tuta fides! Amen.' 'Amen!' repeated all the group, and arose greatly strengthened and encouraged by the miller's *preamble*.

They spent that night around the miller's hearth, and had a cog of good brose to their supper. The next morning Dan and two associates rode off for Melrose, to lay their case before the friendly abbot, and to beg assistance; which, notwithstanding the devil's brag, they were not afraid of obtaining.

THE PRIVATE MEMOIRS AND CONFESSIONS OF A JUSTIFIED SINNER

After crossing the Tweed, I saw no more of my persecutor that day, and had hopes that he had left me for a season; but, alas, what hope was there of my relief after the declaration I had so lately heard! I took up my lodgings that night in a small miserable inn in the village of Ancrum, of which the people seemed alike poor and ignorant. Before going to bed, I asked if it was customary with them to have family worship of evenings? The man answered, that they were so hard set with the world, they often could not get time, but if I would be so kind as officiate they would be much obliged to me. I accepted the invitation, being afraid to go to rest lest the commotions of the foregoing night might be renewed, and continued the worship as long as in decency I could. The poor people thanked me, hoped my prayers would be heard both on their account and my own, seemed much taken with my abilities, and wondered how a man of my powerful eloquence chanced to be wandering about in a condition so forlorn. I said I was a poor student of theology, on my way to Oxford. They stared at one another with expressions of wonder, disappointment, and fear. I afterwards came to learn, that the term *theology* was by them quite misunderstood, and that they had some crude conceptions that nothing was taught at Oxford but the *black arts*, which ridiculous idea prevailed over all the south of Scotland. For the present I could not understand what the people meant, and less so, when the man asked me, with deep concern, 'If I was serious in my intentions of going to Oxford? He hoped not, and that I would be better guided.'

I said my education wanted finishing; – but he remarked, that the Oxford arts were a bad finish for a religious man's education. – Finally, I requested him to sleep with me, or in my room all the night, as I wanted some serious and religious conversation with him, and likewise to convince him that the study of the fine arts, though not absolutely necessary, were not incompatible with the character of a Christian divine. He shook his head, and wondered how I could call them *fine arts* – hoped I did not mean to convince him by any ocular demonstration, and at length reluctantly condescended to sleep with me, and let the lass and wife sleep together for one night. I believe he would have declined it, had it not been some hints from his wife, stating, that it was a good arrangement, by which I understood there were only two beds in the house, and that when I was preferred to the lass's bed, she had one to shift for.

The landlord and I accordingly retired to our homely bed, and conversed for some time about indifferent matters, till he fell sound asleep. Not so with me: I had that within which would not suffer me to close my eyes; and about the dead of night, I again heard the same noises and contention begin outside the house, as I had heard the night before; and again I heard it was about a sovereign and peculiar right in me. At one time the noise was on the top of the house, straight above our bed, as if the one party were breaking through the roof, and the other forcibly preventing it; at another time it was at the door, and at a third time at the window; but still mine host lay sound by my side, and did not waken. I was seized with terrors indefinable, and prayed fervently, but did not attempt rousing my sleeping companion until I saw if no better could be done. The women, however, were alarmed, and, rushing into our apartment, exclaimed that all the devils in hell were besieging the house. Then, indeed, the landlord awoke, and it was time for him, for the tumult had increased to such a degree, that it shook the house to its foundations; being louder and more furious than I could have conceived the heat of battle to be when the volleys of artillery are mixed with groans, shouts, and blasphemous cursing. It thundered and lightened; and there were screams, groans, laughter, and execrations, all intermingled.

I lay trembling and bathed in a cold perspiration, but was soon obliged to bestir myself, the inmates attacking me one after the other.

'O, Tam Douglas! Tam Douglas! haste ye an' rise out fra-yont that incarnal devil!' cried the wife: 'Ye are in ayont the auld ane himsel, for our lass Tibbie saw his cloven cloots last night.'

'Lord forbid!' roared Tam Douglas, and darted over the bed like a flying fish. Then, hearing the unearthly tumult with which he was surrounded, he returned to the side of the bed, and addressed me thus, with long and fearful intervals:

'If ye be the deil, rise up, an' depart in peace out o' this house – afore the bedstrae take kindling about ye, an' than it'll maybe be the waur for ye – Get up – an' gang awa out amang your cronies, like a good – lad – There's nae body here wishes you ony ill – D'ye hear me?'

'Friend,' said I, 'no Christian would turn out a fellow creature on such a night as this, and in the midst of such a commotion of the villagers.'

'Na, if ye be a mortal man,' said he, 'which I rather think, from the use you made of the holy book – Nane o' your practical jokes on strangers an' honest foks. These are some o' your Oxford tricks, an' I'll thank you to be ower wi' them. – Gracious heaven, they are brikkin through the house at a' the four corners at the same time!'

The lass Tibby, seeing the innkeeper was not going to prevail with me to rise, flew toward the bed in desperation, and seizing me by the waist, soon landed me on the floor, saying: 'Be ye deil, be ye chiel, ye's no lie there till baith the house an' us be swallowed up!'

Her master and mistress applauding the deed, I was obliged to attempt dressing myself, a task to which my powers were quite inadequate in the state I was in, but I was readily assisted by every one of the three; and as soon as they got my clothes thrust on in a loose way, they shut their eyes lest they should see what might drive them distracted, and thrust me out to the street, cursing me, and calling on the fiends to take their prey and begone.

The scene that ensued is neither to be described, nor believed, if it were. I was momently surrounded by a number of hideous fiends, who gnashed on me with their teeth, and clenched their crimson paws in my face; and at the same instant I was seized by the collar of my coat behind, by my dreaded and devoted friend, who pushed me on, and, with his gilded rapier waving and brandishing around me, defended me against all their united attacks. Horrible as my assailants were in appearance, (and they had all monstrous shapes,) I felt that I would rather have fallen into their hands, than be thus led away captive by my defender at his will and pleasure, without having the right or power to say my life, or any part of my will, was my own. I could not even thank him for his potent guardian-ship, but hung down my head, and moved on I knew not whither, like a criminal led to execution, and still the infernal combat continued, till about the dawning, at which time I looked up, and all the fiends were expelled but one, who kept at a distance; and still my persecutor and defender pushed me by the neck before him.

❧ SARTOR RESARTUS ❧

THOMAS CARLYLE

Sartor Resartus ('the tailor re-patched'), the first major work by Carlyle (1795–1881), was written in 1830–1 while he was living in literary isolation and relative poverty at Craigenputtock in Dumfriesshire: the book's tale of despair overcome reflects both this and Carlyle's much earlier struggles. The work shows the influence of the often mystic vision of the German Romantics, particularly Goethe, Jean Paul Richter (of *Titan*) and E. T. A. Hoffmann, several of whose works Carlyle had just translated in his *Specimens of German Romance* (1828); but in its subject of clothes and its chaotic style and biography it owes much, respectively, to Swift's *A Tale of a Tub* (1709) and to Sterne's *Tristram Shandy* (1759–67). The work appears absurd, the irritated musings of an English editor at the confused ramblings he has been sent of a ludicrous German professor called Devil's Dung (Teufelsdröckh), but under these bizarre clothes its body constitutes a devastating critique of nineteenth-century utilitarianism and materialism. It is a fantasy in its insistence on the super-natural and divinely-based wonder of life when rightly seen: this is the subject of the extract here. The book is no preachment, but moves us vitally, through a sense of excitement, personality, the interplay of opposites, and the force of its language-tearing style: in this way it attempts to imitate both the chaos of the universe and its naked energy.

The chapter here is the climax of the book. Its target is the mental habits that hide or clothe the wonder of the universe. 'Laws of nature' and names may have their uses, and it may comfort us to ignore the miracle of any event merely because it is recurrent, but the world goes far beyond our little capturings of it. Worst, it seems, are our categories of time and space, by which we give reality only to what is now and here: in God, Carlyle's professor argues, all is eternally co-present. Carlyle moves further from secular to sacred argument, from mocking scepticism to amazed faith, in his picture of us all as immortal ghosts momentarily dressed in the clothes of the material world until we return once more naked to the divine sea from which we came. To the miracle of the material universe succeeds the greater miracle of the universe of continually embodied souls; derision at man's mental cagings of immensity changes to admiration at the spirit designed by the Almighty to do such things. Carlyle was to be a storehouse of arguments for Victorian Christians striving to maintain their faith: but here we see him working as much by clashing as by harmonising his arguments; he will not have us slip into the very complacencies he is attacking. In just the same way he leaves us often uncertain of his tone, suspended between gravity and laughter: for one thing, is it not absurd that these wonders should be conveyed to us via the confused outpourings of a fantastical German professor? By these and other means Carlyle seeks to wear away our own mental certainties, so that we can freely enter the unconscious that is the universe.

Sartor Resartus: Natural Supernaturalism

It is in his stupendous Section, headed *Natural Supernaturalism*, that the Professor first becomes a Seer; and, after long effort, such as we have witnessed, finally subdues under his feet this refractory Clothes-Philosophy, and takes victorious possession thereof. Phantasms enough he has had to struggle with; 'Cloth-webs and Cob-webs,' of Imperial Mantles, Superannuated Symbols, and what not: yet still did he courageously pierce through. Nay, worst of all, two quite mysterious, world-embracing Phantasms, TIME and SPACE, have ever hovered round him, perplexing and bewildering: but with these also he now resolutely grapples, these also he victoriously rends asunder. In a word, he has looked fixedly on Existence, till one after the other, its earthly hulls and garnitures, have all melted away; and now to his rapt vision the interior, celestial Holy of Holies, lies disclosed.

Here therefore properly it is that the Philosophy of Clothes attains to Transcendentalism; this last leap, can we but clear it, takes us safe into the promised land, where *Palingenesia*, in all senses, may be considered as beginning. 'Courage, then!' may our Diogenes exclaim, with better right than Diogenes the First once did. This stupendous Section we, after long, painful meditation, have found not to be unintelligible; but on the contrary to grow clear, nay radiant, and all-illuminating. Let the reader, turning on it what utmost force of speculative intellect is in him, do his part; as we, by judicious selection and adjustment, shall study to do ours:

'Deep has been, and is, the significance of Miracles,' thus quietly begins the Professor; 'far deeper perhaps than we imagine. Meanwhile, the question of questions were: What specially is a Miracle? To that Dutch King of Siam, an icicle had been a miracle; whoso had carried with him an air-pump, and phial of vitriolic ether, might have worked a miracle. To my Horse again, who unhappily is still more unscientific, do not I work a miracle, and magical *'open sesame!'* every time I please to pay twopence, and open for him an impassable *Schlagbaum*, or shut Turnpike?

'"But is not a real Miracle simply a violation of the Laws of Nature?" ask several. Whom I answer by this new question: What are the Laws of Nature? To me perhaps the rising of one from the dead were no violation of these Laws, but a confirmation; were some far deeper Law, now first penetrated into, and by Spiritual Force, even as the rest have all been, brought to bear on us with its Material Force.

'Here too may some inquire, not without astonishment: On what ground shall one, that can make Iron swim, come and declare that therefore he can teach Religion? To us, truly, of the Nineteenth Century, such declaration were inept enough; which nevertheless to our fathers, of the First Century, was full of meaning.

'"But is it not the deepest Law of Nature that she be constant?" cries an illuminated class: "Is not the Machine of the Universe fixed to move by unalterable rules?" Probable enough, good friends: nay, I too must believe that the God, whom ancient, inspired men assert to be 'without variableness or shadow of turning,' does indeed never change; that Nature, that the Universe, which no one whom it so pleases can be prevented from calling a Machine, does move by the most unalterable rules. And now of you too I make the old inquiry: What those same unalterable rules, forming the complete Statute-Book of Nature, may possibly be?

'They stand written in our Works of Science, say you; in the accumulated records of man's Experience? – Was man with his Experience present at the Creation, then, to see how it all went on? Have any deepest scientific individuals yet dived down to the foundations of the Universe, and gauged every thing there? Did the Maker take them into His counsel; that they read His ground-plan of the incomprehensible All; and can say, This stands marked therein, and no more than this? Alas, not in anywise! These scientific individuals have been nowhere but where we also are; have seen some handbreadths deeper than we see into the Deep that is infinite, without bottom as without shore.

'Laplace's Book on the Stars, wherein he exhibits that certain Planets, with their Satellites, gyrate round our worthy Sun, at a rate and in a course, which, by greatest good fortune, he and the like of him have succeeded in detecting, – is to me as precious as to another. But is this what thou namest "Mechanism of the Heavens," and "System of the World;" this, wherein Sirius and the Pleiades, and all Herschel's Fifteen thousand Suns per minute, being left out, some paltry handful of Moons, and inert Balls, had been – looked at, nicknamed, and marked in the Zodiacal Waybill; so that we can now prate of their Whereabout; their How, their Why, their What, being hid from us as in the signless Inane?

'System of Nature! To the wisest man, wide as is his vision, Nature remains of quite *infinite* depth, of quite infinite expansion; and all Experience thereof limits itself to some few computed centuries, and measured square-miles. The course of Nature's phases, on this our little fraction of a Planet, is partially known to us; but who knows what deeper courses these depend on; what infinitely larger Cycle (of causes) our little Epicycle revolves on? To the Minnow every cranny and pebble, and quality and accident, of its little native Creek may have become familiar: but does the Minnow understand the Ocean Tides and periodic Currents, the Trade-winds, and Monsoons, and Moon's Eclipses; by all which the condition of its little Creek is regulated, and may, from time to time (*un*miraculously enough), be quite overset and reversed? Such a minnow is man; his Creek this Planet Earth; his Ocean the immeasurable All; his Monsoons and periodic Currents the mysterious Course of Providence through Aeons of Aeons.

'We speak of the Volume of Nature: and truly a Volume it is, – whose Author and Writer is God. To read it! Dost thou, does man, so much as well know the Alphabet thereof? With its Words, Sentences, and grand descriptive Pages, poetical and philosophical, spread out through Solar Systems, and Thousands of Years, we shall not try thee. It is a Volume written in celestial hieroglyphs, in the true Sacred-writing; of which even Prophets are happy that they can read here a line and there a line. As for your Institutes, and Academies of Science, they strive bravely; and, from amid the thick-crowded, inextricably intertwisted hieroglyphic writing, pick out, by dextrous combination, some Letters in the vulgar Character, and therefrom put together this and the other economic Recipe, of high avail in Practice. That Nature is more than some boundless Volume of such Recipes, or huge, well-nigh inexhaustible Domestic-Cookery Book, of which the whole secret will, in this wise, one day, evolve itself, the fewest dream.

'Custom,' continues the Professor, 'doth make dotards of us all. Consider well, thou wilt find that Custom is the greatest of Weavers; and weaves air-raiment for all the Spirits of the Universe; whereby indeed these dwell with us visibly, as ministering servants, in our houses and workshops; but their spiritual nature becomes, to the most, for ever hidden. Philosophy complains that Custom has hoodwinked us, from the first; that we do every thing by Custom, ever Believe by it; that our very Axioms, let us boast of Free-thinking as we may, are oftenest simply such Beliefs as we have never heard questioned. Nay, what is Philosophy throughout but a continual battle against Custom; an ever-renewed effort to *transcend* the sphere of blind Custom, and so become Transcendental?

'Innumerable are the illusions and legerdemain tricks of Custom: but of all these perhaps the cleverest is her knack of persuading us that the Miraculous, by simple repetition, ceases to be Miraculous. True, it is by this means we live; for man must work as well as wonder: and herein is Custom so far a kind nurse, guiding him to his true benefit. But she is a fond foolish nurse, or rather we are false foolish nurselings, when, in our resting and reflecting hours, we prolong the same deception. Am I to view the Stupendous with stupid indifference, because I have seen it twice, or two hundred, or two million times? There is no reason in Nature or in Art why I should: unless, indeed, I am a mere Work-Machine, for whom the divine gift of Thought were no other than the terrestrial gift of Steam is to the Steam-engine; a power whereby Cotton might be spun, and money and money's worth realised.

'Notable enough too, here as elsewhere, wilt thou find the potency of Names; which indeed are but one kind of such Custom-woven, wonder-hiding garments. Witchcraft, and all manner of Spectre-work, and Demonology, we have now named Madness, and Diseases of the Nerves. Seldom reflecting that still the new question comes upon us: What is Madness, what are Nerves? Ever, as before, does Madness remain a mysterious-terrific, altogether *infernal* boiling up of the Nether Chaotic Deep, through this fair-painted Vision of Creation, which swims thereon, which we name the Real. Was Luther's Picture of the Devil less a Reality, whether it were formed within the bodily eye, or without it? In every the wisest Soul, lies a whole world of internal Madness, an authentic Demon-

Empire; out of which, indeed, his world of Wisdom has been creatively built together, and now rests there, as on its dark foundations does a habitable flowery Earth-rind.

'But deepest of all illusory Appearances, for hiding Wonder, as for many other ends, are your two grand fundamental world-enveloping Appearances, SPACE and TIME. These, as spun and woven for us from before Birth itself, to clothe our celestial ME for dwelling here, and yet to blind it, – lie all-embracing, as the universal canvass, or warp and woof, whereby all minor Illusions, in this Phantasm Existence, weave and paint themselves. In vain, while here on Earth, shall you endeavour to strip them off; you can, at best, but rend them asunder for moments, and look through.

'Fortunatus had a wishing Hat, which when he put it on, and wished himself Anywhere, behold he was There. By this means had Fortunatus triumphed over Space, he had annihilated Space; for him there was no Where, but all was Here. Were a Hatter to establish himself, in the Wahngasse of Weissnichtwo, and make felts of this sort for all mankind, what a world we should have of it! Still stranger, should, on the opposite side of the street, another Hatter establish himself; and, as his fellow-craftsman made Space-annihilating Hats, make Time-annihilating! Of both would I purchase, were it with my last groschen; but chiefly of this latter. To clap on your felt, and, simply by wishing that you were Any*where*, straightway to be *There!* Next to clap on your other felt, and, simply by wishing that you were Any*when*, straightway to be *Then!* This were indeed the grander: shooting at will from the Fire-Creation of the World to its Fire-Consummation; here historically present in the First Century, conversing face to face with Paul and Seneca; there prophetically in the Thirty-first, versing also face to face with other Pauls and Senecas, who as yet stand hidden in the depth of that late Time!

'Or thinkest thou, it were impossible, unimaginable? Is the Past annihilated, then, or only past; is the Future non-extant, or only future? Those mystic faculties of thine, Memory and Hope, already answer: already through those mystic avenues, thou the Earth-blinded summonest both Past and Future, and communest with them, though as yet darkly, and with mute beckonings. The curtains of Yesterday drop down, the curtains of To-morrow roll up; but Yesterday and To-morrow both *are*. Pierce through the Time-Element, glance into the Eternal. Believe what thou findest written in the sanctuaries of Man's Soul, even as all Thinkers, in all ages, have devoutly read it there; that Time and Space are not God, but creations of God; that with God as it is a universal HERE, so is it an Everlasting Now.

'And seest thou therein any glimpse of IMMORTALITY? – O heaven! Is the white Tomb of our Loved One, who died from our arms, and must be left behind us there, which rises in the distance, like a pale, mournfully receding Milestone, to tell how many toilsome uncheered miles we have journeyed on alone, – but a pale spectral Illusion! Is the lost Friend still mysteriously Here, even as we are Here mysteriously, with God! – Know of a truth that only the Time-shadows have perished, or are perishable; that the real Being of whatever was, and whatever is, and whatever will be, *is* even now and for ever. This, should it unhappily seem new, thou mayst ponder, at thy leisure; for the next twenty years, or the next twenty centuries: believe it thou must; understand it thou canst not.

'That the Thought-forms, Space and Time, wherein, once for all, we are sent into this Earth to live, should condition and determine our whole Practical reasonings, conceptions, and imagings (not imaginings), – seems altogether fit, just, and unavoidable. But that they should, farthermore, usurp such sway over pure spiritual Meditation, and blind us to the wonder every where lying close on us, seems nowise so. Admit Space and Time to their due rank as Forms of Thought; nay, even, if thou wilt, to their quite undue rank of Realities: and consider, then, with thyself how their thin disguises hide from us the brightest God-effulgences! Thus, were it not miraculous, could I stretch forth my hand, and clutch the Sun? Yet thou seest me daily stretch forth my hand, and therewith clutch many a thing, and swing it hither and thither. Art thou a grown Baby, then, to fancy that the Miracle lies in miles of distance, or in pounds avoirdupois of weight; and not to see that the true inexplicable God-revealing Miracle lies in this, that I can stretch forth my hand at all; that I have free Force to clutch aught therewith? Innumerable other of this sort are the deceptions, and wonder-hiding stupefactions, which Space practises on us.

'Still worse is it with regard to Time. Your grand antimagician, and universal wonder-hider, is this same lying Time. Had we but the Time-annihilating Hat, to put on for once only, we should see ourselves in a World of Miracles, wherein all fabled or authentic Thaumaturgy, and feats of Magic, were outdone. But unhappily we have not such a Hat; and man, poor fool that he is, can seldom and scantily help himself without one.

'Were it not wonderful, for instance, had Orpheus built the walls of Thebes by the mere sound of his Lyre? Yet tell me, who built these walls of Weissnichtwo; summoning out all the sandstone rocks, to dance along from the *Steinbruch* (now a huge Troglodyte Chasm, with frightful green-mantled pools); and shape themselves into Doric and Ionic pillars, squared ashlar houses, and noble streets? Was it not the still higher Orpheus, or Orpheuses, who, in past centuries, by the divine Music of Wisdom, succeeded in civilising Man? Our highest Orpheus walked in Judea, eighteen hundred years ago: his sphere-melody, flowing in wild native tones, took captive the ravished souls of men; and, being of a truth sphere-melody, still flows and sounds, though now with thousandfold Accompaniments, and rich symphonies, through all our hearts; and modulates, and divinely leads them. Is that a wonder, which happens in two hours; and does it cease to be wonderful if happening in two million? Not only was Thebes built by the Music of an Orpheus; but without the music of some inspired Orpheus was no city ever built, no work that man glories in ever done.

'Sweep away the Illusion of Time: glance, if thou have eyes, from the near moving-cause to its far distant Mover: The stroke that came transmitted through a whole galaxy of elastic balls, was it less a stroke than if the last ball only had been struck, and sent flying? Oh, could I (with the Time-annihilating Hat) transport thee direct from the Beginnings to the Endings, how were thy eyesight unsealed, and thy heart set flaming in the Light-sea of celestial wonder! Then sawest thou that this fair Universe, were it in the meanest province thereof, is in very deed the star-domed City of God; that through every star, through every grass-blade, and most through every Living Soul, the glory of a present God still beams. But Nature, which is the Time-vesture of God, and reveals Him to the wise, hides Him from the foolish.

'Again, could any thing be more miraculous than an actual authentic Ghost? The English Johnson longed, all his life, to see one; but could not, though he went to Cock Lane, and thence to the church-vaults, and tapped on coffins. Foolish Doctor! Did he never, with the mind's eye as well as with the body's, look round him into that full tide of human Life he so loved; did he never so much as look into Himself? The good Doctor was a Ghost, as actual and authentic as heart could wish; well nigh a million of Ghosts were travelling the streets by his side. Once more I say, sweep away the illusion of Time; compress the three-score years into three minutes: what else was he, what else are we? Are we not Spirits, shaped into a body, into an Appearance; and that fade away again into air, and Invisibility? This is no metaphor, it is a simple scientific *fact*: we start out of Nothingness, take figure, and are Apparitions; round us, as round the veriest spectre, is Eternity; and to Eternity minutes are as years and aeons. Come there not tones of Love and Faith, as from celestial harp-strings, like the Song of beatified Souls? And again, do we not squeak and gibber (in our discordant, screech-owlish debatings and recriminatings); and glide bodeful, and feeble, and fearful; or uproar (*poltern*), and revel in our mad Dance of the Dead, – till the scent of the morning-air summons us to our still Home; and dreamy Night becomes awake and Day? Where now is Alexander of Macedon: does the steel Host, that yelled in fierce battle-shouts at Issus and Arbela, remain behind him; or have they all vanished utterly, even as perturbed Goblins must? Napoleon too, and his Moscow Retreats and Austerlitz Campaigns! Was it all other than the veriest Spectre-Hunt; which has now, with its howling tumult that made Night hideous, flitted away? – Ghosts! There are nigh a thousand million walking the earth openly at noontide; some half-hundred have vanished from it, some half-hundred have arisen in it, ere thy watch ticks once.

'O Heaven, it is mysterious, it is awful to consider that we not only carry each a future Ghost within him; but are, in very deed, Ghosts! These Limbs, whence had we them; this stormy Force; this life-blood with its burning Passion? They are dust and shadow; a Shadow-system gathered round our M E ; wherein, through some moments or years, the Divine Essence is to be revealed in the Flesh. That warrior on his strong war-horse, fire flashes through his eyes; Force dwells in his arm and heart: but warrior and war-horse are a vision; a revealed Force, nothing more. Stately they tread the Earth, as if it were a firm substance: fool! the Earth is but a film; it cracks in twain, and warrior and war-horse sink beyond plummet's sounding. Plummet's? Fantasy herself will not follow them. A little while ago they were not; a little while and they are not, their very ashes are not.

'So has it been from the beginning, so will it be to the end. Generation after generation takes to itself the Form of a Body; and forth-issuing from Cimmerian Night, on Heaven's mission, A P P E A R S . What Force and Fire is in each he expends: one grinding in the mill of Industry; one hunter-like climbing the giddy Alpine heights of Science; one madly dashed in pieces on the rocks of Strife, in war with his fellow: – and then the Heaven-sent is recalled; his earthly Vesture falls away, and soon even to Sense becomes a vanished Shadow. Thus, like some wild-flaming, wild-thundering train of Heaven's Artillery, does this mysterious M A N K I N D thunder and flame, in long-drawn, quick-succeeding grandeur, through the unknown Deep. Thus, like a God-created, fire-breathing Spirit-host, we emerge from the Inane; haste stormfully across the astonished Earth; then plunge again into the Inane. Earth's mountains are levelled, and her seas filled up, in our passage: can the Earth, which is but dead and a vision, resist Spirits which have reality and are alive? On the hardest adamant some foot-print of us is stamped in; the last Rear of the host will read traces of the earliest Van. But whence? – O Heaven, whither? Sense knows not; Faith knows not; only that it is through Mystery to Mystery, from God and to God.

> We *are such stuff*
> As Dreams are made of, and our little Life
> Is rounded with a sleep!

ᝈPHANTASTES
&
ᝈTHE ᝈPRINCESS AND THE ᝈGOBLIN

GEORGE MACDONALD

Born and raised at Huntly in Aberdeenshire, George MacDonald (1824–1905) graduated in chemistry and physics at Aberdeen University before turning to the Congregational Church. He studied theology in London and received his first ministry at Arundel in Sussex in 1850; but in 1853 he was forced to resign for his 'heretical' views, particularly that animals and even heathens might be among the saved. He was unable to find another church and turned to writing to express his faith and earn a living. He began with poetry and moved to fantasy with *Phantastes* (1858), which had poor sales and reviews, being condemned by the *Athenaeum* as 'a confusedly furnished second-hand symbol shop'. But on being told by his publisher George Smith that '"Nothing but fiction pays"', MacDonald turned to the 'realistic' novel, writing some thirty examples of it between 1863 and 1897; though he also wrote several children's fantasies. In his last major work, *Lilith* (1895), he returned to fantasy and the style of *Phantastes*.

'Our life is no dream, but it should and will perhaps become one.' This view is behind much of MacDonald's fantasy. *Phantastes* is a journey into the unconscious where mystic truth is to be found; the more overtly Christian *Lilith* shows universal redemption through vision-filled sleep in a giant underground chamber of death. MacDonald thought with Wordsworth that children were uniquely attuned to such unconscious seeing, and he portrays this in his children's fairy tales and fantasies, 'The Golden Key' (1867), *At the Back of the North Wind* (1870), *The Princess and the Goblin* (1872) and *The Princess and Curdie* (1883). MacDonald's literary debts are due most to the more mystical and extreme German and British Romantic writers, Novalis, E. T. A. Hoffmann, Blake and Shelley, all of whom exalt imagination and vision above reason and 'sense-making'.

In the two opening chapters of *Phantastes* here, we see the world slipping away from the grasp of the conscious mind. Anodos (Greek meaning 'directionless') no sooner tells us that he wakes up than he shifts us back to a scene which took place the day before. The fairy he finds in the dark room has nothing to do with his search in the bureau; she undermines his notions of possibility, size, time, relation and significance. Nor does she give any reason for what she is going to do with Anodos. In the next chapter we return abruptly to the time that began the first, and see the solidity of Anodos's bedroom slip into a faërian landscape. The rigid and manufactured world of the rational mind has dissolved into the flowing and natural one of a dream, a world of the unconscious in which all his subsequent adventures are to take place.

The Princess and the Goblin is the story of a young princess, Irene, who is the unwitting object of a goblin plot in the caverns and mines beneath the castle in which she lives. Twice she has met a mysterious lady in a room at the top of the castle who says she is her "'great-great-grandmother'". The extract here is from Chapter 15, when Irene has come late to her third meeting, having been diverted by a goblin creature which chased her. Irene here comes to see much more of the magic power of her grandmother, and this is because she now sees more with her imagination and with faith rather than with mere physical sight. In one sense she has entered, like Anodos in *Phantastes*, the boundlessness of her own unconscious world. In another she has penetrated to a real supernatural world beyond sense. The passage works by symbolising the spiritual in the physical. The dirt on Irene's clothes is her fallen lack of faith, which the rose of Christ's blood can wash away; yet this does not remove the sense of it being a diverting magic trick for a child. The chapter suspends itself gracefully between the happy talk of an excited little girl with an old lady and the mystic conversation of a soul and its source.

❦

ℙHANTASTES

❧

I awoke one morning with the usual perplexity of mind which accompanies the return of consciousness. As I lay and looked through the eastern window of my room, a faint streak of peach-colour, dividing a cloud that just rose above the low swell of the horizon, announced the approach of the sun. As my thoughts, which a deep and apparently dreamless sleep had dissolved, began again to assume crystalline forms, the strange events of the foregoing night presented themselves anew to my wondering consciousness. The day before had been my one-and-twentieth birthday. Among other ceremonies investing me with my legal rights, the keys of an old secretary, in which my father had kept his private papers, had been delivered up to me. As soon as I was left alone, I ordered lights in the chamber where the secretary stood, the first lights that had been there for many a year; for, since my father's death, the room had been left undisturbed. But, as if the darkness had been too long an inmate to be easily expelled, and had dyed with blackness the walls to which, bat-like, it had clung, these tapers served but ill to light up the gloomy hangings, and seemed to throw yet darker shadows into the hollows of the deep-wrought cornice. All the further portions of the room lay shrouded in a mystery whose deepest folds were gathered around the dark oak cabinet which I now approached with a strange mingling of reverence and curiosity. Perhaps, like a geologist, I was about to turn up to the light some of the buried strata of the human world, with its fossil remains charred by passion and petrified by tears. Perhaps I was to learn how my father, whose personal history was unknown to me, had woven his web of story; how he had found the world, and how the world had left him. Perhaps I was to find only the records of lands and moneys, how gotten and how secured; coming down from strange men, and through troublous times, to me, who knew little or nothing of them all.

To solve my speculations, and to dispel the awe which was fast gathering around me as if the dead were drawing near, I approached the secretary; and having found the key that fitted the upper portion, I opened it with some difficulty, drew near it a heavy high-backed chair, and sat down before a multitude of little drawers and slides and pigeon-holes. But the door of a little cupboard in the centre especially attracted my interest, as if there lay the secret of this long-hidden world. Its key I found. One of the rusty hinges cracked and broke as I opened the door: it revealed a number of small pigeon-holes. These, however, being but shallow compared with the depth of those around the little cupboard, the outer ones reaching to the back of the desk, I concluded that there must be some accessible space behind; and found, indeed, that they were formed in a separate framework, which admitted of the whole being pulled out in one piece. Behind, I found a sort of flexible portcullis of small bars of wood laid close together horizontally. After long search, and trying many ways to move it, I discovered at last a scarcely projecting point of steel on one side. I pressed this repeatedly and hard with the point of an old tool that was lying near, till at length it yielded inwards; and the little slide, flying up suddenly, disclosed a chamber – empty, except that in one corner lay a little heap of withered rose-leaves, whose long-lived scent had long since departed; and, in another, a small packet of papers, tied with a bit of ribbon, whose colour had gone with the rose-scent. Almost fearing to touch them, they witnessed so mutely to the law of oblivion, I leaned back in my chair, and regarded them for a moment; when suddenly there stood on the threshold of the little chamber, as though she had just emerged from its depth, a tiny woman-form, as perfect in shape as if she had been a small Greek statuette roused to life and motion. Her dress was of a kind that could never grow old-fashioned, because it was simply natural: a robe plaited in a band around the neck, and confined by a belt about the waist, descended to her feet. It was only afterwards, however, that I took notice of her dress, although my surprise was by no means of so overpowering a degree as such an apparition might naturally be expected to excite. Seeing, however, as I suppose, some astonishment in my countenance, she came forward within a yard of me, and said, in a voice that strangely recalled a sensation of twilight, and reedy river banks, and a low wind, even in this deathly room:

'Anodos, you never saw such a little creature before, did you?'

'No,' said I; 'and indeed I hardly believe I do now.'

'Ah! that is always the way with you men; you believe nothing the first time; and it is foolish enough to let mere repetition convince you of what you consider in itself unbelievable. I am not going to argue with you, however, but to grant you a wish.'

Here I could not help interrupting her with the foolish speech, of which, however, I had no cause to repent ——

'How can such a very little creature as you grant or refuse anything?'

'Is that all the philosophy you have gained in one-and-twenty years?' she said. 'Form is much, but size is nothing. It is a mere matter of relation. I suppose your six-foot lordship does not feel altogether insignificant, though to others you do look small beside your old Uncle Ralph, who rises above you a great half-foot at least. But size is of so little consequence with me, that I may as well accommodate myself to your foolish prejudices.'

So saying, she leapt from the desk upon the floor, where she stood a tall, gracious lady, with pale face and large blue eyes. Her dark hair flowed behind, wavy but uncurled, down to her waist, and against it her form stood clear in its robe of white.

'Now,' said she, 'you will believe me.'

Overcome with the presence of a beauty which I could now perceive, and drawn towards her by an attraction irresistible as incomprehensible, I suppose I stretched out my arms towards her, for she drew back a step or two, and said ——

'Foolish boy, if you could touch me, I should hurt you. Besides, I was two hundred and thirty-seven years old, last Midsummer eve; and a man must not fall in love with his grandmother, you know.'

'But you are not my grandmother,' said I.

'How do you know that?' she retorted. 'I dare say you know something of your great-grandfathers a good deal further back than that; but you know very little about your great-grandmothers on either side. Now, to the point. Your little sister was reading a fairytale to you last night.'

'She was.'

'When she had finished, she said, as she closed the book, "Is there a fairy-country, brother?" You replied with a sigh, "I suppose there is, if one could find the way into it."'

'I did; but I meant something quite different from what you seem to think.'

'Never mind what I seem to think. You shall find the way into Fairy Land to-morrow. Now look in my eyes.'

Eagerly I did so. They filled me with an unknown longing. I remembered somehow that my mother died when I was a baby. I looked deeper and deeper, till they spread around me like seas, and I sank in their waters. I forgot all the rest, till I found myself at the window, whose gloomy curtains were withdrawn, and where I stood gazing on a whole heaven of stars, small and sparkling in the moonlight. Below lay a sea, still as death and hoary in the moon, sweeping into bays and around capes and islands, away, away, I knew not whither. Alas! it was no sea, but a low fog burnished by the moon. 'Surely there is such a sea somewhere!' said I to myself. A low sweet voice beside me replied ——

'In Fairy Land, Anodos.'

I turned, but saw no one. I closed the secretary, and went to my own room, and to bed.

All this I recalled as I lay with half-closed eyes. I was soon to find the truth of the lady's promise, that this day I should discover the road into Fairy Land.

Chapter II

*"'Wo ist der Strom?" rief er mit Thränen. "Siehst du nicht seine blauen Wellen
über uns?" Er sah hinauf, und der blaue Strom floss leise über ihrem Haupte.'* –
NOVALIS, *Heinrich von Ofterdingen.*

*"'Where is the stream?" cried he, with tears. "Seest thou not its blue waves above
us?" He looked up, and lo! the blue stream was flowing gently over their heads.'*

While these strange events were passing through my mind, I suddenly, as
one awakes to the consciousness that the sea has been moaning by him for
hours, or that the storm has been howling about his window all night,
became aware of the sound of running water near me; and, looking out of
bed, I saw that a large green marble basin, in which I was wont to wash, and
which stood on a low pedestal of the same material in a corner of my room,
was overflowing like a spring; and that a stream of clear water was running
over the carpet, all the length of the room, finding its outlet I knew not
where. And, stranger still, where this carpet, which I had myself designed
to imitate a field of grass and daisies, bordered the course of the little stream,
the grass-blades and daisies seemed to wave in a tiny breeze that followed the
water's flow; while under the rivulet they bent and swayed with every
motion of the changeful current, as if they were about to dissolve with it,
and, forsaking their fixed form, become fluent as the waters.

My dressing-table was an old-fashioned piece of furniture of black oak,
with drawers all down the front. These were elaborately carved in foliage, of
which ivy formed the chief part. The nearer end of this table remained just as
it had been, but on the further end a singular change had commenced. I
happened to fix my eye on a little cluster of ivy-leaves. The first of these
was evidently the work of the carver; the next looked curious; the third
was unmistakable ivy; and just beyond it a tendril of clematis had twined
itself about the gilt handle of one of the drawers. Hearing next a slight
motion above me, I looked up, and saw that the branches and leaves
designed upon the curtains of my bed were slightly in motion. Not
knowing what change might follow next, I thought it high time to get up;
and, springing from the bed, my bare feet alighted upon a cool green sward;
and although I dressed in all haste, I found myself completing my toilet
under the boughs of a great tree, whose top waved in the golden stream of
the sunrise with many interchanging lights, and with shadows of leaf and
branch gliding over leaf and branch, as the cool morning wind swung it to
and fro, like a sinking sea-wave.

After washing as well as I could in the clear stream, I rose and looked around me. The tree under which I seemed to have lain all night was one of the advanced guard of a dense forest, towards which the rivulet ran. Faint traces of a footpath, much overgrown with grass and moss, and with here and there a pimpernel even, were discernible along the right bank. 'This,' thought I, 'must surely be the path into Fairy Land, which the lady of last night promised I should so soon find.' I crossed the rivulet, and accompanied it, keeping the footpath on its right bank, until it led me, as I expected, into the wood. Here I left it, without any good reason: and with a vague feeling that I ought to have followed its course, I took a more southerly direction.

The Princess and the Goblin: Woven and Then Spun

'Come in, Irene,' said the silvery voice of her grandmother.

The princess opened the door, and peeped in. But the room was quite dark, and there was no sound of the spinning-wheel. She grew frightened once more, thinking that, although the room was there, the old lady might be a dream after all. Every little girl knows how dreadful it is to find a room empty where she thought somebody was; but Irene had to fancy for a moment that the person she came to find was nowhere at all. She remembered however that at night she spun only in the moonlight, and concluded that must be why there was no sweet, bee-like humming: the old lady might be somewhere in the darkness. Before she had time to think another thought, she heard her voice again, saying as before ———

'Come in, Irene.'

From the sound, she understood at once that she was not in the room beside her. Perhaps she was in her bedroom. She turned across the passage, feeling her way to the other door. When her hand fell on the lock, again the old lady spoke ———

'Shut the other door behind you, Irene. I always close the door of my workroom when I go to my chamber.'

Irene wondered to hear her voice so plainly through the door: having shut the other, she opened it and went in. Oh, what a lovely haven to reach from the darkness and fear through which she had come! The soft light made her feel as if she were going into the heart of the milkiest pearl; while the blue walls and their silver stars for a moment perplexed her with the fancy that they were in reality the sky which she had left outside a minute ago covered with rainclouds.

'I've lighted a fire for you, Irene: you're cold and wet,' said her grandmother.

Then Irene looked again, and saw that what she had taken for a huge bouquet of red roses on a low stand against the wall, was in fact a fire which burned in the shapes of the loveliest and reddest roses, glowing gorgeously between the heads and wings of two cherubs of shining silver. And when she came nearer, she found that the smell of roses with which the room was filled, came from the fire-roses on the hearth. Her grandmother was dressed in the loveliest pale-blue velvet, over which her hair, no longer white, but of a rich golden colour, streamed like a cataract, here falling in dull gathered heaps, there rushing away in smooth shining falls. And ever as she looked, the hair seemed pouring down from her head, and vanishing in a golden mist ere it reached the floor. It flowed from under the edge of a circle of shining silver, set with alternated pearls and opals. On her dress was no ornament whatever, neither was there a ring on her hand, or a necklace or carcanet about her neck. But her slippers glimmered with the light of the milky way, for they were covered with seed-pearls and opals in one mass. Her face was that of a woman of three-and-twenty.

The princess was so bewildered with astonishment and admiration that she could hardly thank her, and drew nigh with timidity, feeling dirty and uncomfortable. The lady was seated on a low chair by the side of the fire, with hands outstretched to take her, but the princess hung back with a troubled smile.

'Why, what's the matter? asked her grandmother. 'You haven't been doing anything wrong – I know that by your face, though it *is* rather miserable. What's the matter, my dear?'

And she still held out her arms.

'Dear grandmother,' said Irene, 'I'm not so sure that I haven't done something wrong. I ought to have run up to you at once when the long-legged cat came in at the window, instead of running out on the mountain, and making myself such a fright.'

'You were taken by surprise, my child, and are not so likely to do it again. It is when people do wrong things wilfully that they are the more likely to do them again. Come.'

And still she held out her arms.

'But, grandmother, you're so beautiful and grand with your crown on! and I am so dirty with mud and rain! – I should quite spoil your beautiful blue dress.'

With a merry little laugh, the lady sprung from her chair, more lightly far than Irene herself could, caught the child to her bosom, and kissing the tear-stained face over and over, sat down with her in her lap.

'Oh, grandmother! you'll make yourself such a mess!' cried Irene, clinging to her.

'You darling! do you think I care more for my dress than for my little girl? Besides – look here.'

As she spoke she set her down, and Irene saw to her dismay that the lovely dress was covered with the mud of her fall on the mountain road. But the lady stooped to the fire, and taking from it, by the stalk in her fingers, one of the burning roses, passed it once and again and a third time over the front of her dress; and when Irene looked, not a single stain was to be discovered.

'There!' said her grandmother, 'you won't mind coming to me now?'

But Irene again hung back, eyeing the flaming rose which the lady held in her hand.

'You're not afraid of the rose – are you?' she said, about to throw it on the hearth again.

'Oh! don't, please!' cried Irene. 'Won't you hold it to my frock and my hands and my face? And I'm afraid my feet and my knees want it too!'

'No,' answered her grandmother, smiling a little sadly, as she threw the rose from her; 'it is too hot for you yet. It would set *your* frock in a flame. Besides, I don't want to make you clean tonight. I want your nurse and the rest of the people to see you as you are, for you will have to tell them how you ran away for fear of the long-legged cat. I should like to wash you, but they would not believe you then. Do you see that bath behind you?'

The princess looked, and saw a large oval tub of silver, shining brilliantly in the light of the wonderful lamp.

'Go and look into it,' said the lady.

Irene went, and came back very silent, with her eyes shining.

'What did you see?' asked her grandmother.

'The sky and the moon and the stars,' she answered. 'It looked as if there was no bottom to it.'

The lady smiled a pleased satisfied smile, and was silent also for a few moments. Then she said ——

'Any time you want a bath, come to me. I know you have a bath every morning, but sometimes you want one at night too.'

'Thank you, grandmother; I will – I will indeed,' answered Irene, and was again silent for some moments thinking. Then she said, 'How was it, grandmother, that I saw your beautiful lamp – not the light of it only – but the great round silvery lamp itself, hanging alone in the great open air high up? It was your lamp I saw – wasn't it?'

'Yes, my child; it was my lamp.'

'Then how was it? I don't see a window all round.'

'When I please, I can make the lamp shine through the walls – shine so strong that it melts them away from before the sight, and shows itself as you saw it. But, as I told you, it is not everybody can see it.'

'How is it that I can then? I'm sure I don't know.'

'It is a gift born with you. And one day I hope everybody will have it.'

'But how do you make it shine through the walls?'

'Ah! that you would not understand if I were to try ever so much to make you – not yet – not yet. But,' added the lady rising, 'you must sit in my chair while I get you the present I have been preparing for you. I told you my spinning was for you. It is finished now, and I am going to fetch it. I have been keeping it warm under one of my brooding pigeons.'

Irene sat down in the low chair, and her grandmother left her, shutting the door behind her. The child sat gazing, now at the rose-fire, now at the starry walls, now at the silvery light; and a great quietness grew in her heart. If all the long-legged cats in the world had come rushing at her then, she would not have been afraid of them for a moment. How this was she could not tell – she only knew there was no fear in her, and everything was so right and safe that it could not get in.

She had been gazing at the lovely lamp for some minutes fixedly: turning her eyes, she found the wall had vanished, for she was looking out on the dark cloudy night. But though she heard the wind blowing, none of it blew upon her. In a moment more, the clouds themselves parted, or rather vanished like the wall, and she looked straight into the starry herds, flashing gloriously in the dark blue. It was but for a moment. The clouds gathered again and shut out the stars; the wall gathered again and shut out the clouds; and there stood the lady beside her with the loveliest smile on her face, and a shimmering ball in her hand, about the size of a pigeon's egg.

'There, Irene; there is my work for you!' she said, holding out the ball to the princess.

She took it in her hand, and looked at it all over. It sparkled a little, and shone here and shone there, but not much. It was of a sort of grey whiteness, something like spun-glass.

'Is this *all* your spinning, grandmother?' she asked.

'All since you came to the house. There is more there than you think.'

'How pretty it is! What am I to do with it, please?'

'That I will now explain to you,' answered the lady, turning from her, and going to her cabinet.

The City of Dreadful Night

JAMES THOMSON

Thomson's fantasy is the product of nightmare. His *The City of Dreadful Night* (1874) seems to offer another world, but is in large part a horrific Dantean picture of this one. Fantasy for Thomson is not escape, but rather a closer embrace of the hideous actual; the only true escape is death. Even in his fantasy journey 'A Walk Abroad' (1866), where he travels the solar system, he finds nothing but poverty, disease and depravity. The tension between putative escape and inevitable entrapment is also seen in his Swiftian 'Proposals for the Speedy Extinction of Evil and Misery' (1868), in which he argues that the best way forward for mankind is universal suicide.

We can readily trace Thomson's gloom to his unhappy life (1834–82), one marked by family poverty, the early death of his parents, a London orphanage, the sudden and shattering death of his fiancée (1853), his harsh expulsion from his job as an army schoolmaster (1862) and the increasing alcoholism which eventually killed him. But Thomson was also a constitutional melancholic. The dark realms he describes are his spiritual home, even while he would fly them. His best energies, his inspiration, and even a mordant wit are awakened by them. *The City of Dreadful Night* succeeds because its gloomy vision is countered by the surreal vividness of the imagery and the lively intelligence of a habitué.

Thomson's object in the poem is to show that God is dead and nothing has value or meaning, so that our best friend is death. This counsel of despair he followed only crabwise himself. The poem is an inversion of Tennyson's *In Memoriam* (1842), which found faith out of personal loss; it has something of the air of Browning's 'Childe Rowland' (1855), of Poe, and of the Gothic novel. But most strikingly it continually uses Christian imagery to deny faith: with fierce zest Thomson is turning Victorian values to dust. It is ironic that Margaret Oliphant should have used some of the imagery of this poem to Christian effect in her picture of an urban Hell in her 'The Land of Darkness' (1887); more apposite that the modernist T. S. Eliot should be indebted to the poem in his *The Waste Land* (1922). In his time, however, Thomson wrote for the few; and few read him.

The passage here is from Sections I and II of the poem. The landscape it describes is of the unconscious mind; the poem slips from stanza to stanza like a dream, yet each stanza's end is like a little death. Thomson evokes interest out of monotony, and can give his bald statements as much vitality as his mysterious images.

THE CITY OF DREADFUL NIGHT

The City is of Night; perchance of Death,
   But certainly of Night; for never there
Can come the lucid morning's fragrant breath
   After the dewy dawning's cold grey air;
The moon and stars may shine with scorn or pity;
The sun has never visited that city,
   For it dissolveth in the daylight fair.

Dissolveth like a dream of night away;
   Though present in distempered gloom of thought
And deadly weariness of heart all day.
   But when a dream night after night is brought
Throughout a week, and such weeks few or many
Recur each year for several years, can any
   Discern that dream from real life in aught?

For life is but a dream whose shapes return,
   Some frequently, some seldom, some by night
And some by day, some night and day: we learn,
   The while all change and many vanish quite,
In their recurrence with recurrent changes
A certain seeming order; where this ranges
   We count things real; such is memory's might.

A river girds the city west and south,
   The main north channel of a broad lagoon,
Regurging with the salt tides from the mouth;
   Waste marshes shine and glister to the moon
For leagues, then moorland black, then stony ridges;
Great piers and causeways, many noble bridges,
   Connect the town and islet suburbs strewn.

Upon an easy slope it lies at large,
   And scarcely overlaps the long curved crest
Which swells out two leagues from the river marge.
   A trackless wilderness rolls north and west,
Savannahs, savage woods, enormous mountains,
Bleak uplands, black ravines with torrent fountains;
   And eastward rolls the shipless sea's unrest.

The city is not ruinous, although
   Great ruins of an unremembered past,
With others of a few short years ago
   More sad, are found within its precincts vast.
The street-lamps always burn; but scarce a casement
In house or palace front from roof to basement
   Doth glow or gleam athwart the mirk air cast.

The street-lamps burn amidst the baleful glooms,
   Amidst the soundless solitudes immense
Of rangèd mansions dark and still as tombs.
   The silence which benumbs or strains the sense
Fulfils with awe the soul's despair unweeping:
Myriads of habitants are ever sleeping,
   Or dead, or fled from nameless pestilence!

Yet as in some necropolis you find
   Perchance one mourner to a thousand dead,
So there; worn faces that look deaf and blind
   Like tragic masks of stone. With weary tread,
Each wrapt in his own doom, they wander, wander,
Or sit foredone and desolately ponder
   Through sleepless hours with heavy drooping head.

Mature men chiefly, few in age or youth,
   A woman rarely, now and then a child:
A child! If here the heart turns sick with ruth

To see a little one from birth defiled,
Or lame or blind, as preordained to languish
Through youthless life, think how it bleeds with anguish
    To meet one erring in that homeless wild.

They often murmur to themselves, they speak
    To one another seldom, for their woe
Broods maddening inwardly and scorns to wreak
    Itself abroad; and if at whiles it grow
To frenzy which must rave, none heeds the clamour,
Unless there waits some victim of like glamour,
    To rave in turn, who lends attentive show.

The City is of Night, but not of Sleep;
    There sweet sleep is not for the weary brain;
The pitiless hours like years and ages creep,
    A night seems termless hell. This dreadful strain
Of thought and consciousness which never ceases,
Or which some moments' stupor but increases,
    This, worse than woe, makes wretches there insane.

They leave all hope behind who enter there:
    One certitude while sane they cannot leave,
One anodyne for torture and despair;
    The certitude of Death, which no reprieve
Can put off long; and which, divinely tender,
But waits the outstretched hand to promptly render
    That draught whose slumber nothing can bereave.

II

Because he seemed to walk with an intent
    I followed him; who, shadowlike and frail,
Unswervingly though slowly onward went,
    Regardless, wrapt in thought as in a veil:
Thus step for step with lonely sounding feet
We travelled many a long dim silent street.

At length he paused: a black mass in the gloom,
    A tower that merged into the heavy sky;
Around, the huddled stones of grave and tomb:
    Some old God's-acre now corruption's sty:

He murmured to himself with dull despair,
Here Faith died, poisoned by this charnel air.

Then turning to the right went on once more,
    And travelled weary roads without suspense;
And reached at last a low wall's open door,
    Whose villa gleamed beyond the foliage dense:
He gazed, and muttered with a hard despair,
Here Love died, stabbed by its own worshipped pair.

Then turning to the right resumed his march,
    And travelled streets and lanes with wondrous strength,
Until on stooping through a narrow arch
    We stood before a squalid house at length:
He gazed, and whispered with a cold despair,
Here Hope died, starved out in its utmost lair.

When he had spoken thus, before he stirred,
    I spoke, perplexed by something in the signs
Of desolation I had seen and heard
    In this drear pilgrimage to ruined shrines:
When Faith and Love and Hope are dead indeed,
Can Life still live? By what doth it proceed?

As whom his one intense thought overpowers,
    He answered coldly, Take a watch, erase
The signs and figures of the circling hours,
    Detach the hands, remove the dial-face;
The works proceed until run down; although
Bereft of purpose, void of use, still go.

Then turning to the right paced on again,
    And traversed squares and travelled streets whose glooms
Seemed more and more familiar to my ken;
    And reached that sullen temple of the tombs;
And paused to murmur with the old despair,
Here Faith died, poisoned by this charnel air.

I ceased to follow, for the knot of doubt
    Was severed sharply with a cruel knife:
He circled thus for ever tracing out
    The series of the fraction left of Life;
Perpetual recurrence in the scope
Of but three terms, dead Faith, dead Love, dead Hope.

❦

A BELEAGUERED CITY
OLD LADY MARY
&
THE LAND OF DARKNESS
❧

MARGARET OLIPHANT

Margaret Oliphant (1828–97), friend of George MacDonald and
devotee of his work, was a novelist of almost Dickensian industry
who wrote to support her family and relatives after the death of her
husband in 1859. A life punctuated by the deaths of children and
other loved ones, produced in her, as in other late Victorians faced
by weakened religious certainty, a heightened longing for the
reality of a spiritual world. This is in part expressed in the stories
of the supernatural for which she became remembered. Some of
these, picturing life in heaven, purgatory and hell beyond the
grave, are interlinked – *A Little Pilgrim in the Unseen* (1882) and
The Land of Darkness (1888): the first, describing a female soul's
arrival in a Home Counties heaven, was particularly popular. In
other tales Mrs Oliphant portrays spirits either visiting or
inhabiting the earth. These are her famed 'ghost stories', for
which fiction there was an increasing vogue in her day. Here she is
more concerned with whether the two worlds of the seen and the
unseen can make contact below: the others give that assurance, but
only under overtly Christian aegis and elsewhere after we are dead.
Here she becomes an artist of the 'so near and so far', the poignantly
tenuous and the indefinite. Did Jeanie in 'The Library Window'
(1896) really see the figure writing by a window painted on the
stone wall of the library opposite? Will Edmund in 'Earthbound'
(1880) be able to come together with the spirit lady he has fallen in
love with? In her negotiations between the seen and the unseen
Margaret Oliphant captures and part-assuages the growing sense
of a split between the material and the spiritual worlds that
agonized her contemporaries.

In 'A Beleaguered City' (1879) a supernatural host temporarily enters the French town of Semur and its human inhabitants leave, with the exception of one Paul Lecamus, a mystic and visionary; from whose later account to the mayor of what he saw, the extract here is taken. As often in her stories, Mrs Oliphant leaves a measure of ambiguity to heighten desire. 'Old Lady Mary' (1885), from which the second extract comes, describes a vain old lady of means returned to earthly purgatory; in the passage here we see her trying to put right her careless concealment of her will leaving all to her deserving god-daughter. The passage from 'The Land of Darkness' is a picture of hell's torments in terms of Victorian materialism and utilitarianism – with one terrible difference, that this is prescribed under God's love.

❦

A Beleaguered City

❦

I awakened as out of a dream. What roused me was the pealing of the Cathedral bells. I was made to pause and stand still, and return to myself. Then I perceived, but dimly, that the thing which had happened to me was that which I had desired all my life. I leave this explanation of my failure in public duty to the charity of M. le Maire.

The bells of the Cathedral brought me back to myself – to that which we call reality in our language; but of all that was around me when I regained consciousness, it now appeared to me that I only was a dream. I was in the midst of a world where all was in movement. What the current was which flowed around me I know not; if it was thought which becomes sensible among spirits, if it was action, I cannot tell. But the energy, the force, the living that was in them, that could no one misunderstand. I stood in the streets, lagging and feeble, scarcely able to wish, much less to think. They pushed against me, put me aside, took no note of me. In the unseen world described by a poet whom M. le Maire has probably heard of, the man who traverses Purgatory (to speak of no other place) is seen by all, and is a wonder to all he meets – his shadow, his breath separate him from those around him. But whether the unseen life has changed, or if it is I who am not worthy their attention, this I know that I stood in our city like a ghost, and no one took any heed of me. When there came back upon me slowly my old desire to inquire, to understand, I was met with this difficulty at the first – that no one heeded me. I went through and through the streets, sometimes I paused to look round, to implore that which swept by me to make itself known. But the stream went along like soft air, like the flowing of a river, setting me aside from time to time, as the air will displace a straw, or the water a stone, but no more. There was neither languor nor lingering. I was the only passive thing, the being without occupation. Would you have paused in your labours to tell an idle traveller the meaning of our lives, before the day when you left Semur? Nor would they: I was driven hither and thither by the current of that life, but no one stepped forth out of the unseen to hear my questions or to answer me how this might be.

You have been made to believe that all was darkness in Semur. M. le Maire, it was not so. The darkness wrapped the walls in a winding sheet; but within, soon after you were gone, there arose a sweet and wonderful light – a light that was neither of the sun nor of the moon; and presently, after the ringing of the bells, the silence departed as the darkness had departed. I began to hear, first a murmur, then the sound of the going which I had felt without hearing it – then a faint tinkle of voices – and at the last, as my mind grew attuned to these wonders, the very words they said. If they spoke in our language or in another, I cannot tell; but I understood. How long it was before the sensation of their presence was aided by the happiness of hearing I know not, nor do I know how the time has passed, or how long it is, whether years or days, that I have been in Semur with those who are now there; for the light did not vary – there was no night or day. All I know is that suddenly, on awakening from a sleep (for the wonder was that I could sleep, sometimes sitting on the Cathedral steps, sometimes in my own house; where sometimes also I lingered and searched about for the crusts that Leocadie had left), I found the whole world full of sound. They sang going in bands about the streets; they talked to each other as they went along every way. From the houses, all open, where everyone could go who would, there came the soft chiming of those voices. And at first every sound was full of gladness and hope. The song they sang first was like this: 'Send us, send us to our father's house. Many are our brethren, many and dear. They have forgotten, forgotten, forgotten! But when we speak, then will they hear.' And the others answered: 'We have come, we have come to the house of our fathers. Sweet are the homes, the homes we were born in. As we remember, so will they remember. When we speak, when we speak, they will hear.' Do not think that these were the words they sang; but it was like this. And as they sang there was joy and expectation everywhere. It was more beautiful than any of our music, for it was full of desire and longing, yet hope and gladness; whereas among us, where there is longing, it is always sad. Later a great singer, I know not who he was, one going past as on a majestic soft wind, sang another song, of which I shall tell you by and by. I do not think he was one of them. They came out to the windows, to the doors, into all the streets and byways to hear him as he went past.

M. le Maire will, however, be good enough to remark that I did not understand all that I heard. In the middle of a phrase, in a word half breathed, a sudden barrier would rise. For a time I laboured after their meaning, trying hard and vainly to understand; but afterwards I perceived that only when they spoke of Semur, of you who were gone forth, and of what was being done, could I make it out. At first this made me only more eager to hear; but when thought came, then I perceived that of all my longing nothing was satisfied. Though I was alone with the unseen, I comprehended it not; only when it touched upon what I knew, then I understood.

At first all went well. Those who were in the streets, and at the doors and windows of the houses, and on the Cathedral steps, where they seemed to throng, listening to the sounding of the bells, spoke only of this that they had come to do. Of you and you only I heard. They said to each other, with great joy, that the women had been instructed, that they had listened, and were safe. There was pleasure in all the city. The singers were called forth, those who were best instructed (so I judged from what I heard), to take the place of the warders on the walls; and all, as they went along sang that song: 'Our brothers have forgotten; but when we speak, they will hear.' How was it, how was it that you did not hear? One time I was by the river *porte* in a boat; and this song came to me from the walls as sweet as Heaven. Never have I heard such a song. The music was beseeching, it moved the very heart. 'We have come out of the unseen,' they sang; 'for love of you; believe us, believe us! Love brings us back to earth; believe us, believe us!' How was it that you did not hear? When I heard those singers sing, I wept; they beguiled the heart out of my bosom. They sang, they shouted, the music swept about all the walls: 'Love brings us back to earth, believe us!' M. le Maire, I saw you from the river gate; there was a look of perplexity upon your face; and one put his curved hand to his ear as if to listen to some thin far-off sound, when it was like a storm, like a tempest of music!

After that there was a great change in the city. The choirs came back from the walls marching more slowly, and with a sighing through all the air. A sigh, nay, something like a sob breathed through the streets. 'They cannot hear us, or they will not hear us.' Wherever I turned, this was what I heard: 'They cannot hear us.' The whole town, and all the houses that were teeming with souls, and all the street, where so many were coming and going, was full of wonder and dismay.

Old Lady Mary

Presently she found herself entering her own house.

It was all shut up and silent, – not a window lighted along the whole front of the house which used to twinkle and glitter with lights. It soothed her somewhat to see this, as if in evidence that the place had changed with her. She went in silently, and the darkness was as day to her. Her own rooms were all shut up, yet were open to her steps, which no external obstacle could limit. There was still the sound of life below stairs, and in the housekeeper's room a cheerful party gathered round the fire. It was there that she turned first with some wistful human attraction towards the warmth and light rather than to the still places in which her own life had been passed. Mrs Prentiss, the housekeeper, had her daughter with her on a visit and the daughter's baby lay asleep in a cradle placed upon two chairs outside the little circle of women round the table – one of whom was Jervis, Lady Mary's maid. Jervis sat and worked and cried, and mixed her words with little sobs. 'I never thought as I should have had to take another place,' she said. 'Brown and me, we made sure of a little something to start upon. He's been here for twenty years, and so have you, Mrs Prentiss; and me, as nobody can say I wasn't faithful night and day.'

'I never had that confidence in my lady to expect anything,' Prentiss said.

'Oh, mother, don't say that: many and many a day you've said, when my lady dies ——'

'And we've all said it,' said Jervis. 'I can't think how she did it, nor why she did it; for she was a kind lady, though appearances is against her.'

'She was one of them, and I've known a many, as could not abide to see a gloomy face,' said the housekeeper. 'She kept us all comfortable for the sake of being comfortable herself, but no more.'

'Oh, you are hard upon my lady!' cried Jervis, 'and I can't bear to hear a word against her, though it's been an awful disappointment to me.'

'What's you or me, or any one,' cried Mrs Prentiss, 'in comparison of that poor little thing that can't work for her living like we can; that is left on the charity of folks she don't belong to? I'd have forgiven my lady anything if she'd done what was right by Miss Mary. You'll get a place, and a good place; and me, they'll leave me here when the new folks come as have taken the house. But what will become of her, the darling? and not a penny, nor a friend, nor one to look to her? Oh, you selfish old woman! oh, you heart of stone! I just hope you are feeling it where you're gone,' the housekeeper cried.

But as she said this, the woman did not know who was looking at her with wide wistful eyes, holding out her hands in appeal, receiving every word as if it had been a blow. Though she knew it was useless, Lady Mary could not help it. She cried out to them, 'Have pity upon me! have pity upon me! I am not cruel, as you think,' with a keen anguish in her voice, which seemed to be sharp enough to pierce the very air and go up to the skies. And so, perhaps, it did; but never touched the human atmosphere in which she stood a stranger. Jervis was threading her needle when her mistress uttered that cry, but her hand did not tremble, nor did the thread deflect a hair's-breadth from the straight line. The young mother alone seemed to be moved by some faint disturbance. 'Hush!' she said; 'is he waking?' looking towards the cradle. But as the baby made no further sound, she too returned to her sewing; and they sat bending their heads over their work round the table, and continued their talk. The room was very comfortable, bright, and warm, as Lady Mary had liked all her rooms to be. The warm firelight danced upon the walls; the women talked in cheerful tones. She stood outside their circle, and looked at them with a wistful face. Their notice would have been more sweet to her as she stood in that great humiliation, than in other times the look of a queen.

'But what is the matter with baby?' the mother said, rising hastily.

It was with no servile intention of securing a look from that little prince of life that she who was not of this world had stepped aside forlorn, and looked at him in his cradle. Though she was not of this world, she was still a woman, and had nursed her children in her arms. She bent over the infant by the soft impulse of nature, tenderly, with no interested thought. But the child saw her; was it possible? He turned his head towards her, and flickered his baby hands, and cooed with that indescribable voice that goes to every woman's heart. Lady Mary felt such a thrill of pleasure go through her, as no incident had given her for long years. She put out her arms to him as the mother snatched him from his little bed; and he, which was more wonderful, stretched towards her in his innocence, turning away from them all.

'He wants to go to some one,' cried the mother. 'Oh look, look, for God's sake! who is there that the child sees?'

'There's no one there – not a soul. Now dearie, dearie, be reasonable. You can see for yourself there's not a creature,' said the grandmother.

'Oh, my baby, my baby! He sees something we can't see,' the young woman cried. 'Something has happened to his father, or he's going to be taken from me!' she said, holding the child to her in a sudden passion. The other women rushed to her to console her – the mother with reason and Jervis with poetry. 'It's the angels whispering, like the song says.' Oh the pang that was in the heart of the other whom they could not hear! She stood wondering how it could be – wondering with an amazement beyond words, how all that was in her heart, the love and the pain, and the sweetness and bitterness, could all be hidden – all hidden by that air in which the women stood so clear! She held out her hands, she spoke to them, telling who she was, but no one paid any attention; only the little dog Fido, who had been basking by the fire, sprang up, looked at her, and, retreating slowly backwards till he reached the wall, sat down there and looked at her again, with now and then a little bark of inquiry. The dog saw her. This gave her a curious pang of humiliation, yet pleasure. She went away out of that little centre of human life in a great excitement and thrill of her whole being. The child had seen her and the dog; but, oh heavens! how was she to work out her purpose by such auxiliaries as these?

She went up to her old bedchamber with unshed tears heavy about her eyes, and a pathetic smile quivering on her mouth. It touched her beyond measure that the child should have that confidence in her. 'Then God is still with me,' she said to herself. Her room, which had been so warm and bright, lay desolate in the stillness of the night; but she wanted no light, for the darkness was no darkness to her. She looked round her for a little, wondering to think how far away from her now was this scene of her old life, but feeling no pain in the sight of it – only a kind indulgence for the foolish simplicity which had taken so much pride in all these infantile elements of living. She went to the little Italian cabinet which stood against the wall, feeling now at least that she could do as she would, – that here there was no blank of human unconsciousness to stand in her way. But she was met by something that baffled and vexed her once more. She felt the polished surface of the wood under her hand, and saw all the pretty ornamentation, the inlaid work, the delicate carvings, which she knew so well. They swam in her eyes a little, as if they were part of some phantasmagoria about her, existing only in her vision. Yet the smooth surface resisted her touch; and when she withdrew a step from it, it stood before her solidly and square, as it had stood always, a glory to the place. She put forth her hands upon it, and could have traced the waving lines of the exquisite work, in which some artist soul had worked itself out in the old times; but though she thus saw it and felt, she could not with all her endeavours find the handle of the drawer, the richly wrought knob of ivory, the little door that opened into the secret place. How long she stood by it, attempting again and again to find what was as familiar to her as her own hand, what was before her, visible in every line, what she felt with fingers which began to tremble, she could not tell. Time did not count with her as with common men. She did not grow weary, or require refreshment or rest, like those who were still of this world. But at length her head grew giddy and her heart failed. A cold despair took possession of her soul. She could do nothing then – nothing; neither by help of man, neither by use of her own faculties, which were greater and clearer than ever before. She sank down upon the floor at the foot of that old toy, which had pleased her in the softness of her old age, to which she had trusted the fortunes of another; by which, in wantonness and folly, she had sinned, she had sinned! And she thought she saw standing round her companions in the land she had left, saying. 'It is impossible, impossible!' with infinite pity in their eyes; and the face of Him who had given her permission to come, yet who had said no word to her to encourage her in what was against nature. And there came into her heart a longing to fly, to get home, to be back in the land where her fellows were, and her appointed place. A child lost, how pitiful that is! without power to reason and divine how help will come; but a soul lost, outside of one method of existence, withdrawn from the other, knowing no way to retrace its steps, nor how help can come! There had been no bitterness in the passing from earth to the land where she had gone; but now there came upon her soul, in all the power of her new faculties, the bitterness of death. The place which was hers she had forsaken and left, and the place that had been hers knew her no more.

The Land of Darkness

The waste stretched far as eyes could see. It was wild and terrible, with neither vegetation nor sign of life. Here and there were heaps of ruin, which had been villages and cities; but nothing was in them save reptiles and crawling poisonous life, and traps for the unwary wanderer. How often I stumbled and fell among these ashes and dust-heaps of the past – through what dread moments I lay, with cold and slimy things leaving their trace upon my flesh – the horrors which seized me, so that I beat my head against a stone, – why should I tell? These were nought; they touched not the soul. They were but accidents of the way.

At length, when body and soul were low and worn out with misery and weariness, I came to another place, where all was so different from the last, that the sight gave me a momentary solace. It was full of furnaces and clanking machinery and endless work. The whole air round was aglow with the fury of the fires, and men went and came like demons in the flames, with red-hot melting metal, pouring it into moulds and beating it on anvils. In the huge workshops in the background there was a perpetual whir of machinery – of wheels turning and turning, and pistons beating, and all the din of labour, which for a time renewed the anguish of my brain, yet also soothed it; for there was meaning in the beatings and the whirlings. And a hope rose within me that with all the forces that were here, some revolution might be possible – something that would change the features of this place and overturn the worlds. I went from workshop to workshop, and examined all that was being done and understood – for I had known a little upon the earth, and my old knowledge came back, and to learn so much more filled me with new life. The master of all was one who never rested, nor seemed to feel weariness, nor pain, nor pleasure. He had everything in his hand. All who were there were his workmen, or his assistants, or his servants. No one shared with him in his councils. He was more than a prince among them – he was as a god. And the things he planned and made, and at which in armies and legions his workmen toiled and laboured, were like living things. They were made of steel and iron, but they moved like the brains and nerves of men. They went where he directed them, and did what he commanded, and moved at a touch. And though he talked little, when he saw how I followed all that he did, he was a little moved towards me, and spoke and explained to me the conceptions that were in his mind, one rising out of another, like the leaf out of the stem and the flower out of the bud. For nothing pleased him that he did, and necessity was upon him to go on and on.

'They are like living things,' I said – 'they do your bidding whatever you command them. They are like another and a stronger race of men.'

'Men!' he said, 'what are men? the most contemptible of all things that are made – creatures who will undo in a moment what it has taken millions of years, and all the skill and all the strength of generations to do. These are better than men. They cannot think or feel. They cannot stop but at my bidding, or begin unless I will. Had men been made so, we should be masters of the world.'

'Had men been made so, you would never have been – for what could genius have done or thought? – you would have been a machine like all the rest.'

'And better so!' he said, and turned away; for at that moment, watching keenly as he spoke the action of a delicate combination of movements, all made and balanced to a hair's breadth, there had come to him suddenly the idea of something which made it a hundredfold more strong and terrible. For they were terrible these things that lived yet did not live, which were his slaves, and moved at his will. When he had done this, he looked at me, and a smile came upon his mouth: but his eyes smiled not, nor ever changed from the set look they wore. And the words he spoke were familiar words, not his, but out of the old life. 'What a piece of work is a man!' he said; 'how noble in reason, how infinite in faculty! in form and moving how express and admirable! And yet to me what is this quintessence of dust?' His mind had followed another strain of thought, which to me was bewildering, so that I did not know how to reply. I answered like a child, upon his last word.

'We are dust no more,' I cried, for pride was in my heart – pride of him and his wonderful strength, and his thoughts which created strength, and all the marvels he did – 'those things which hindered are removed. Go on, go on – you want but another step. What is to prevent that you should not shake the universe, and overturn this doom, and break all our bonds? There is enough here to explode this grey fiction of a firmament, and to rend those precipices and to dissolve that waste – as at the time when the primeval seas dried up, and those infernal mountains rose.'

He laughed, and the echoes caught the sound and gave it back as if they mocked it. 'There is enough to rend us all into shreds,' he said, 'and to shake, as you say, both heaven and earth, and these plains and those hills.'

'Then why,' I cried in my haste, with a dreadful hope piercing through my soul – 'why do you create and perfect, but never employ? When we had armies on the earth we used them. You have more than armies. You have force beyond the thoughts of man: but all without use as yet.'

'All,' he cried, 'for no use! All in vain! – in vain!'

'O master!' I said, 'great, and more great, in time to come. Why? – why?'

He took me by the arm and drew me close.

'Have you strength,' he said, 'to bear it if I tell you why?'

I knew what he was about to say. I felt it in the quivering of my veins, and my heart that bounded as if it would escape from my breast. But I would not quail from what he did not shrink to utter. I could speak no word, but I looked him in the face and waited – for that which was more terrible than all.

He held me by the arm, as if he would hold me up when the shock of anguish came. 'They are in vain,' he said, 'in vain – because God rules over all.'

His arm was strong; but I fell at his feet like a dead man.

How miserable is that image, and how unfit to use! Death is still and cool and sweet. There is nothing in it that pierces like a sword, that burns like fire, that rends and tears like the turning wheels. O life, O pain, O terrible name of God, in which is all succour and all torment! What are the pangs and tortures to that, which ever increases in its awful power, and has no limit, nor any alleviation, but whenever it is spoken penetrates through and through the miserable soul? O God, whom once I called my Father! O Thou who gavest me being, against whom I have fought, whom I fight to the end, shall there never be anything but anguish in the sound of Thy great name?'

DR JEKYLL AND MR HYDE
&
TOD LAPRAIK

ROBERT LOUIS STEVENSON

Stevenson (1850–94), like George MacDonald, was fascinated by the unconscious: but his interest is in the divisions it reveals in man. For him it is man's primal and hidden (Hyde-en) energy which, repressed by reason, Victorian respectability and the modern split of the public from the private self, turns destructive. Stevenson knew that division in himself, and in the Edinburgh society of which the London setting of *Dr Jekyll and Mr Hyde* (1886) is an image. He even said his fiction was the product of a Hyde-like 'Brownie' of the subconscious, 'whom I keep locked in a back garret, while I get all the praise' – the 'I' here being his 'Jekyll'. *Dr Jekyll and Mr Hyde* had enormous popularity among a readership largely unconscious of its reflection on themselves.

The extract here sufficiently outlines the basic plot of the story, which lacks but its approaching end as Jekyll finds himself changing involuntarily into Hyde. This is Jekyll's written explanation of what we have so far seen others trying to decipher from outside, and is found by them only when they have broken into his study at the moment of his death.

The extract shows respectable and analytical Jekyll talking about his engineering of Hyde as though Hyde was a being separate from himself. Chemical experiments rather than moral choices are made the apparent source of Hyde's appearance. To the last, even when we see him turning into Hyde, Jekyll is to try to maintain that distance. What we watch in this passage is his moral degradation from the pressure of 'a certain impatient gaiety of disposition' to the murderous glee of Hyde, without any sense of the difference; and all conducted as though he, Jekyll, were an impartial spectator separate from it. The darker vision of the novel is one in which no polarisations of human nature are possible, and even innocence (a lovely child, a gracious old man, both violated by Hyde) may be inextricably implicated with evil.

This last vision is also seen in the short story here, 'Tod Lapraik' (from chapter XV of *Catriona* (1893). The suffering saints of the Kirk on the Bass Rock, and Prophet Peden, are replaced by the malevolent gull and the dancing thing in the shape of Tod Lapraik. The morally indefinite Tam Dale now acts as prison guard on the elect, now flees the island convinced of his sinfulness, now returns as governor of the place. The evil projected by Tod Lapraik seeps into the Rock and affects all who sojourn there. The two parts of the story seem separated, but the first contains a reservoir of sin that spills into the second, just as Tod Lapraik on the shore and the thing on the rock prove conjoined. At the same time the hellish creature is like Hyde an expression of the exultant and mad energies of the body and spirit that Peden and the saints violently deny: the joy of this wild thing, "'Joy o' hell I daursay: joy whatever'", takes it beyond easy moral categorisation. The strength of the tale is that all this is conveyed indirectly, through a strong sense of locality, and, far from being superstitious, is rigorously matter-of-fact.

❧

DR JEKYLL AND MR HYDE: HENRY JEKYLL'S
FULL STATEMENT OF THE CASE

❧

I WAS born in the year 18 – to a large fortune, endowed besides with excellent parts, inclined by nature to industry, fond of the respect of the wise and good among my fellow-men, and thus, as might have been supposed, with every guarantee of an honourable and distinguished future. And indeed the worst of my fault was a certain impatient gaiety of disposition, such as has made the happiness of many, but such as I found it hard to reconcile with my imperious desire to carry my head high, and wear a more than commonly grave countenance before the public. Hence it came about that I concealed my pleasures; and that when I reached years of reflection, and began to look round me and take stock of my progress and position in the world, I stood already committed to a profound duplicity of life. Many a man would have even blazoned such irregularities as I was guilty of; but from the high views that I had set before me, I regarded and hid them with an almost morbid sense of shame. It was thus rather the exacting nature of my aspirations than any particular degradation in my faults, that made me what I was and, with even a deeper trench than in the majority of men, severed in me those provinces of good and ill which divide and compound man's dual nature. In this case, I was driven to reflect deeply and inveterately on that hard law of life, which lies at the root of religion and is one of the most plentiful springs of distress. Though so profound a double-dealer, I was in no sense a hypocrite; both sides of me were in dead earnest; I was no more myself when I laid aside restraint and plunged in shame, than when I laboured, in the eye of day, at the furtherance of knowledge or the relief of sorrow and suffering. And it chanced that the direction of my scientific studies, which led wholly towards the mystic and the transcendental, reacted and shed a strong light on this consciousness of the perennial war among my members. With every day, and from both sides of my intelligence, the moral and the intellectual, I thus drew steadily nearer to that truth, by whose partial discovery I have been doomed to such a dreadful shipwreck: that man is not truly one, but truly two. I say two, because the state of my own knowledge does not pass beyond that point. Others will follow, others will outstrip me on the same lines; and I hazard the guess that man will be ultimately known for a mere polity of multifarious, incongruous and independent denizens. I for my part, from the nature of my life, advanced infallibly in one direction and in one direction only. It was on the moral side, and in my own person, that I learned to recognise the thorough and primitive duality of man; I saw that, of the two natures that contended in the field of my consciousness, even if I could rightly be said to be either, it was only because I was radically both; and from an early date, even before the course of my scientific discoveries had begun to suggest the most naked possibility of such a miracle, I had learned to dwell with pleasure, as a beloved daydream, on the thought of the separation of these elements. If each, I told myself, could but be housed in separate identities, life would be relieved of all that was unbearable; the unjust might go his way, delivered from the aspirations and remorse of his more upright twin; and the just could walk steadfastly and securely on his upward path, doing the good things in which he found his pleasure, and no longer exposed to disgrace and penitence by the hands of this extraneous evil. It was the curse of mankind that these incongruous faggots were thus bound together – that in the agonised womb of consciousness, these polar twins should be continuously struggling. How, then, were they dissociated?

I was so far in my reflections when, as I have said, a side light began to shine upon the subject from the laboratory table. I began to perceive more deeply than it has ever yet been stated, the trembling immateriality, the mist-like transience, of this seemingly so solid body in which we walk attired. Certain agents I found to have the power to shake and to pluck back that fleshly vestment, even as a wind might toss the curtains of a pavilion. For two good reasons, I will not enter deeply into this scientific branch of my confession. First, because I have been made to learn that the doom and burthen of our life is bound forever on man's shoulders, and when the attempt is made to cast it off, it but returns upon us with more unfamiliar and more awful pressure. Second, because as my narrative will make alas! too evident, my discoveries were incomplete. Enough, then, that I not only recognised my natural body for the mere aura and effulgence of certain of the powers that made up my spirit, but managed to compound a drug by which these powers should be dethroned from their supremacy, and a second form and countenance substituted, none the less natural to me because they were the expression, and bore the stamp, of lower elements in my soul.

I hesitated long before I put this theory to the test of practice. I knew well that I risked death; for any drug that so potently controlled and shook the very fortress of identity, might by the least scruple of an overdose or at the least inopportunity in the moment of exhibition, utterly blot out that immaterial tabernacle which I looked to it to change. But the temptation of a discovery so singular and profound, at last overcame the suggestions of alarm. I had long since prepared my tincture; I purchased at once, from a firm of wholesale chemists, a large quantity of a particular salt which I knew, from my experiments, to be the last ingredient required; and late one accursed night, I compounded the elements, watched them boil and smoke together in the glass, and when the ebullition had subsided, with a strong glow of courage, drank off the potion.

The most racking pangs succeeded: a grinding in the bones, deadly nausea, and a horror of the spirit that cannot be exceeded at the hour of birth or death. Then these agonies began swiftly to subside, and I came to myself as if out of a great sickness. There was something strange in my sensations, something indescribably new and, from its very novelty, incredibly sweet. I felt younger, lighter, happier in body; within I was conscious of a heady recklessness, a current of disordered sensual images running like a mill race in my fancy, a solution of the bonds of obligation, an unknown but not an innocent freedom of the soul. I knew myself, at the first breath of this new life, to be more wicked, tenfold more wicked, sold a slave to my original evil; and the thought, in that moment, braced and delighted me like wine. I stretched out my hands, exulting in the freshness of these sensations; and in the act, I was suddenly aware that I had lost in stature.

THE TALE OF TOD LAPRAIK

My faither, Tam Dale, peace to his banes, was a wild sploring lad in his young days, wi' little wisdom and less grace. He was fond of a lass and fond of a glass, and fond of a ran-dan; but I could never hear tell that he was muckle use for honest employment. Frae ae thing to anither, he listed at last for a sodger, and was in the garrison of this fort, which was the first way that ony of the Dales cam to set foot upon the Bass. Sorrow upon that service! The governor brewed his ain ale; it seems it was the warst conceivable. The rock was proveesioned frae the shore with vivers, the thing was ill-guided, and there were whiles when they büt to fish and shoot solans for their diet. To crown a', thir was the Days of the Persecution. The perishin' cauld chalmers were a' occupeed wi' sants and martyrs, the saut of the yerd, of which it wasna worthy. And though Tam Dale carried a firelock there, a single sodger, and likit a lass and a glass, as I was sayin', the mind of the man was mair just than set with his position. He had glints of the glory of the kirk; there were whiles when his dander rase to see the Lord's sants misguided, and shame covered him that he should be hauldin' a can'le (or carrying a firelock) in so black a business. There were nights of it when he was here on sentry, the place a' wheesht, the frosts o' winter maybe riving in the wa's, and he would hear ane o' the prisoners strike up a psalm, and the rest join in and the blessed sounds rising from the different chalmers – or dungeons, I would raither say – so that this auld craig in the sea was like a pairt of Heev'n. Black shame was on his saul; his sins hove up before him muckle as the Bass, and above a', that chief sin, that he should have a hand in hagging and hashing at Christ's Kirk. But the truth is that he resisted the spirit. Day cam, there were the rousing campainions, and his guid resolves depairtit.

In thir days, dwalled upon the Bass a man of God, Peden the Prophet was his name. Ye'll have heard tell of Prophet Peden. There was never the wale of him sinsyne, and it's a question wi' mony if there ever was his like afore. He was wild's a peat-hag, fearsome to look at, fearsome to hear, his face like the day of judgment. The voice of him was like a solan's and dinnled in folk's lugs, and the words of him like coals of fire.

Now there was a lass on the rock, and I think she had little to do, for it was nae place for dacent weemen; but it seems she was bonny, and her and Tam Dale were very well agreed. It befell that Peden was in the gairden his lane at the praying when Tam and the lass cam by; and what should the lassie do but mock with laughter at the sant's devotions? He rose and lookit at the twa o' them, and Tam's knees knoitered thegether at the look of him. But whan he spak, it was mair in sorrow than in anger. 'Poor thing, poor thing!' says he, and it was the lass he lookit at, 'I hear you skirl and laugh,' he says, 'but the Lord has a deid shot prepared for you, and at that surprising judgment ye shall skirl but the ae time!' Shortly thereafter she was daundering on the craigs wi' twa-three sodgers, and it was a blawy day. There cam a gowst of wind, claught her by the coats, and awa' wi' her, bag and baggage. And it was remarkit by the sodgers that she gied but the ae skirl.

Nae doubt this judgment had some weicht upon Tam Dale; but it passed again, and him nane the better. Ae day he was flyting wi' anither sodger-lad. 'Deil hae me!' quo' Tam, for he was a profane swearer. And there was Peden glowering at him, gash an' waefu'; Peden wi' his lang chafts an' luntin' een, the maud happit about his kist, and the hand of him held out wi' the black nails upon the finger-nebs – for he had nae care of the body. 'Fy, fy, poor man!' cries he, 'the poor fool man! *Deil hae me*, quo' he; an' I see the deil at his oxter.' The conviction of guilt and grace cam in on Tam like the deep sea; he flang doun the pike that was in his hands – 'I will nae mair lift arms against the cause o' Christ!' says he, and was as gude's word. There was a sair fyke in the beginning, but the governor, seeing him resolved, gied him his dischairge, and he went and dwallt and married in North Berwick, and had aye a gude name with honest folk frae that day on.

It was in the year seeventeen hunner and sax that the Bass cam in the hands o' the Da'rymples, and there was twa men soucht the chairge of it. Baith were weel qualified, for they had baith been sodgers in the garrison, and kennt the gate to handle solans, and the seasons and values of them. Forbye that they were baith – or they baith seemed – earnest professors and men of comely conversation. The first of them was just Tam Dale, my faither. The second was ane Lapraik, whom the folk ca'd Tod Lapraik maistly, but whether for his name or his nature I could never hear tell. Weel, Tam gaed to see Lapraik upon this business, and took me, that was a toddlin' laddie, by the hand. Tod had his dwallin' in the lang loan benorth the kirkyaird. It's a dark, uncanny loan, forbye that the kirk has aye had an ill name since the days o' James the Saxt and the deevil's cantrips played therein when the Queen was on the seas; and as for Tod's house, it was in the mirkest end, and was little likit by some that kenned the best. The door was on the sneck that day, and me and my faither gaed straucht in. Tod was a wabster to his trade; his loom stood in the but. There he sat, a muckle fat, white hash of a man like creish, wi' a kind of a holy smile that gart me scunner. The hand of him aye cawed the shuttle, but his een was steekit. We cried to him by his name, we skirled in the deid lug of him, we shook him by the shouther. Nae mainner o' service! There he sat on his dowp, an' cawed the shuttle and smiled like creish.

'God be guid to us,' says Tam Dale, 'this is no' canny!'

He had jimp said the word, when Tod Lapraik cam to himsel'.

'Is this you, Tam?' says he. 'Haith, man! I'm blithe to see ye. I whiles fa' into a bit dwam like this,' he says; 'it's frae the stamach.'

Weel, they began to crack about the Bass, and which of them twa was to get the warding o't, and by little and little cam to very ill words, and twined in anger. I mind weel, that as my faither and me gaed hame again, he came ower and ower the same expression, how little he likit Tod Lapraik and his dwams.

'Dwam!' says he. 'I think folk hae brunt for dwams like yon.'

Aweel, my faither got the Bass, and Tod had to go wantin'. It was remembered sinsyne what way he had ta'en the thing. 'Tam,' says he, 'ye hae gotten the better o' me aince mair, and I hope,' says he, 'ye'll find at least a' that ye expeckit at the Bass.' Which have since been thought remarkable expressions. At last the time came for Tam Dale to take young solans. This was a business he was weel used wi', he had been a craigsman frae a laddie, and trustit nane but himsel'. So there was he, hingin' by a line an' speldering on the craig face, whaur it's hieest and steighest. Fower tenty lads were on the tap, hauldin' the line and mindin' for his signals. But whaur Tam hung there was naething but the craig, and the sea below, and the solans skirling and flying. It was a braw spring morn, and Tam whustled as he claught in the young geese. Mony's the time I heard him tell of this experience, and aye the swat ran upon the man.

It chanced, ye see, that Tam keekit up, and he was awaur of a muckle solan, and the solan pyking at the line. He thocht this by-ordinar and outside the creature's habits. He minded that ropes was unco saft things, and the solan's neb and the Bass Rock unco hard, and that twa hunner feet were raither mair than he would care to fa'.

'Shoo!' says Tam. 'Awa', bird! Shoo, awa' wi' ye!' says he.

The solan keekit doun into Tam's face, and there was something unco in the creature's ee. Just the ae keek it gied, and back to the rope. But now it wroucht and warstl't like a thing dementit. There never was the solan made that wroucht as that solan wroucht; and it seemed to understand its employ brawly, birzing the saft rope between the neb of it and a crunkled jag o' stane.

There gaed a cauld stend o' fear into Tam's heart. 'This thing is nae bird,' thinks he. His een turnt backward in his heid and the day gaed black about him. 'Uf I get a dwam here,' he thocht, 'it's by wi' Tam Dale.' And he signalled for the lads to pu' him up.

And it seemed the solan understood about signals. For nae sooner was the signal made than he let be the rope, spried his wings, squawked out loud, took a turn flying, and dashed straucht at Tam Dale's een. Tam had a knife, he gart the cauld steel glitter. And it seemed the solan understood about knives, for nae suner did the steel glint in the sun than he gied the ae squawk, but laigher, like a body disappointit, and flegged aff about the roundness of the craig, and Tam saw him nae mair. And as sune as that thing was gane, Tam's heid drapt upon his shouther, and they pu'd him up like a deid corp, dadding on the craig.

A dram of brandy (which he went never without) broucht him to his mind, or what was left of it. Up he sat.

'Rin, Geordie, rin to the boat, mak' sure of the boat, man – rin!' he cries, 'or yon solan'll have it awa',' says he.

The fower lads stared at ither, an' tried to whillywha him to be quiet. But naething would satisfy Tam Dale, till ane o' them had startit on aheid to stand sentry on the boat. The ithers askit if he was for down again.

'Na,' says he, 'and neither you nor me,' says he, 'and as sune as I can win to stand on my twa feet we'll be aff frae this craig o' Sawtan.'

Sure eneuch, nae time was lost, and that was ower muckle; for before they won to North Betwick Tam was in a crying fever. He lay a' the simmer; and wha was sae kind as come speiring for him but Tod Lapraik! Folk thocht afterwards that ilka time Tod cam near the house the fever had worsened. I kenna for that; but what I ken the best, that was the end of it.

It was about this time o' the year; my grandfaither was out at the white fishing; and like a bairn, I büt to gang wi' him. We had a grand take, I mind, and the way that the fish lay broucht us near in by the Bass, whaur we forgathered wi' anither boat that belanged to a man Sandie Fletcher in Castleton. He's no' lang deid neither, or ye could speir at himsel'. Weel, Sandie hailed.

'What's yon on the Bass?' says he.

'On the Bass?' says grandfaither.

'Ay,' says Sandie, 'on the green side o't.'

'Whatten kind of a thing?' says grandfaither. 'There canna be naething on the Bass but just the sheep.'

'It looks unco like a body,' quo' Sandie, who was nearer in.

'A body!' says we, and we nane of us likit that. For there was nae boat that could have broucht a man, and the key o' the prison yett hung ower my faither's heid at hame in the press bed.

We keepit the twa boats closs for company, and crap in nearer hand. Grandfaither had a gless, for he had been a sailor, and the captain of a smack, and had lost her on the sands of Tay. And when we took the gless to it, sure eneuch there was a man. He was in a crunkle o' green brae, a wee below the chaipel, a' by his lee-lane, and lowped and flang and danced like a daft quean at a waddin'.

'It's Tod,' says grandfaither, and passed the gless to Sandie.

'Ay, it's him,' says Sandie.

'Or ane in the likeness o' him,' says grandfaither.

'Sma' is the differ,' quo' Sandie. 'Deil or warlock, I'll try the gun at him,' quo' he, and broucht up a fowling-piece that he aye carried, for Sandie was a notable famous shot in a' that country.

'Haud your hand, Sandie,' says grandfaither; 'we maun see clearer first,' says he, 'or this may be a dear day's wark to the baith of us.'

'Hout!' says Sandie, 'this is the Lord's judgments surely, and be damned to it!' says he.

'Maybe ay, and maybe no,' says my grandfaither, worthy man! 'But have you a mind of the procurator Fiscal, that I think ye'll have forgathered wi' before,' says he.

This was ower true, and Sandie was a wee thing set ajee. 'Aweel, Edie,' says he, 'and what would be your way of it?'

'Ou, just this,' says grandfaither. 'Let me that has the fastest boat gang back to North Berwick, and let you bide here and keep an eye on Thon. If I canna find Lapraik, I'll join ye, and the twa of us'll have a crack wi' him. But if Lapraik's at hame, I'll rin up the flag at the harbour, and ye can try Thon Thing wi' the gun.'

Aweel, so it was agreed between them twa. I was just a bairn, an' clum in Sandie's boat, whaur I thocht I would see the best of the employ. My gradsire gied Sandie a siller tester to pit in his gun wi' leid draps, bein' mair deidly again bogles. And then the ae boat set aff for North Berwick, an' the tither lay whaur it was and watched the wanchancy thing on the brae-side.

A' the time we lay there it lowped and flang and capered and span like a teetotum, and whiles we could hear it skelloch as it span. I hae seen lassies, the daft queans, that would lowp and dance a winter's nicht, and still be lowping and dancing when the winter's day cam in. But there would be folk there to hauld them company, and the lads to egg them on; and this thing was its lee-lane. And there would be a fiddler diddling his elbock in the chimney-side; and this thing had nae music but the skirling of the solans. And the lassies were bits o' young things wi' the reid life dinnling and stending in their members; and this was a muckle, fat, creishy man, and him fa'n in the vale o' years. Say what ye like, I maun say what I believe. It was joy was in the creature's heart; the joy o' hell, I daursay: joy whatever. Mony a time I have askit mysel', why witches and warlocks should sell their sauls (whilk are their maist dear possessions) and be auld, duddy, wrunkl't wives, or auld, feckless, doddered men; and then I mind upon Tod Lapraik dancing a' thae hours by his lane in the black glory of his heart. Nae doubt they burn for it in muckle hell, but they have a grand time here of it, whatever! – and the Lord forgie us!

Weel, at the hinder end, we saw the wee flag yirk up to the mast-heid upon the harbour rocks. That was a' Sandie waited for. He up wi' the gun, took a deleeberate aim, an' pu'd the trigger. There cam a bang and then ae waefu' skirl frae the Bass. And there were we, rubbin' our een and lookin' at ither like daft folk. For wi' the bang and the skirl the thing had clean disappeared. The sun glinted, the wind blew, and there was the bare yerd whaur the Wonder had been lowping and flinging but ae second syne.

The hale way hame I roared and grat wi' the terror of that dispensation. The grawn folk were nane sae muckle better; there was little said in Sandie's boat but just the name of God; and when we won in by the pier, the harbour rocks were fair black wi' the folk waitin' us. It seems they had fund Lapraik in ane of his dwams, cawing the shuttle and smiling. Ae lad they sent to hoist the flag, and the rest abode there in the wabster's house. You may be sure they likit it little; but it was a means of grace to severals that stood there praying in to themsel's (for nane cared to pray out loud) and looking on thon awesome thing as it cawed the shuttle. Syne, upon a suddenty, and wi' the ae dreidfu' skelloch, Tod sprang up frae his hinderlands and fell forrit on the wab, a bluidy corp.

When the corp was examined the leid draps hadna played buff upon the warlock's body; sorrow a leid drap was to be fund; but there was grandfaither's siller tester in the puddock's heart of him.

The Gold of Fairnilee

ANDREW LANG

Andrew Lang (1844–1912), friend of Stevenson, was a famous journalist and essayist in the period 1880–1910; he was also a pioneer folklorist and anthropologist, author of such books as *Custom and Myth* (1884) and *Myth, Ritual and Religion* (1887). His interest in popular culture was deep-rooted. Yet *The Gold of Fairnilee* (1888) is the only one of his fairy tales in which it is seen: in his comic fairy tales 'The Princess Nobody' (1884), *Prince Prigio* (1889) and *Prince Ricardo of Pantouflia* (1893) he follows much more the tradition of the sophisticated and witty English literary fairy tale as seen in Thackeray's *The Rose and the Ring* (1855). In *The Gold of Fairnilee* Lang unites his earliest experiences with his deep interest in folk narrative to produce the finest of his fairy tales.

The Gold of Fairnilee is a return by Lang to his Scottish Borders roots, in which he combines the tales of 'Thomas Rymer' and 'Tam Lin' in the story of the son of a sixteenth-century Borders knight. Randal (also suggestive of 'Lord Randal') and his mother lose his father at Flodden, but Randal has as consolation the friendship of the captured English girl Jeanie. One day his impulsiveness leads to Randal being taken by the fairies. In his absence famine falls on the land: but when Jeanie brings Randal back he comes with magic which leads to the discovery of a cache of ancient gold and the family's renewed prosperity.

There are several currents in the two beautiful chapters here. In the first we have 'Tam Lin' mixed with Christianity: using the sign of the cross to rescue Randal from the dwarf makes the ambiguous Fairyland of 'Tam Lin' part-devilish, from a Victorian Christian perspective. Yet Fairyland's 'glamour' is real too: only after years of delight there, when he found the magical, and ironically no less glamorous water, did Randal see it 'as it really was'. The story admits a variety of meaning. The journey down the well into Fairyland is one into the unconscious; and it is part of an archetypal rite of passage by which the hero descends into darkness to emerge in mature strength. There are contradictions in the outlook of the story: but their presence testifies to its range and depth.

❧

THE GOLD OF FAIRNILEE: THE WHITE ROSES

❧

Jeanie sat down beside the well. She wished her three wishes: to see Randal, to win him back from Fairyland, and to help the people in the famine. Then she knelt on the grass, and looked down into the well-water. At first she saw nothing but the smooth black water, with little waves trembling in it. Then the water began to grow bright within, as if the sun was shining far, far below. Then it grew as clear as crystal, and she saw through it, like a glass, into a new country – a beautiful country with a wide green plain, and in the midst of the plain a great castle, with golden flags floating from the tops of all the towers. Then she heard a curious whispering noise that thrilled and murmured, as if the music of all the trees that the wind blows through the world were in her ears, as if the noise of all the waves of every sea, and the rustling of heather-bells on every hill, and the singing of all birds were sounding, low and sweet, far, far away. Then she saw a great company of knights and ladies, dressed in green, ride up to the castle; and one knight rode apart from the rest, on a milk-white steed. They all went into the castle gates; but this knight rode slowly and sadly behind the others, with his head bowed on his breast.

Then the musical sounds were still, and the castle and the plain seemed to wave in the water. Next they quite vanished, and the well grew dim, and then grew dark and black and smooth as it had been before. Still she looked, and the little well bubbled up with sparkling foam, and so became still again, like a mirror, till Jeanie could see her own face in it, and beside her face came the reflection of another face, a young man's, dark, and sad, and beautiful. The lips smiled at her, and then Jeanie knew it was Randal. She thought he must be looking over her shoulder, and she leaped up with a cry, and glanced round.

But she was all alone, and the wood about her was empty and silent. The light had gone out of the sky, which was pale like silver, and overhead she saw the evening star.

Then Jeanie thought all was over. She had seen Randal as if it had been in a glass, and she hardly knew him: he was so much older, and his face was so sad. She sighed, and turned to go away over the hills, back to Fairnilee.

But her feet did not seem to carry her the way she wanted to go. It seemed as if something within her were moving her in a kind of dream. She felt herself going on through the forest, she did not know where. Deeper into the wood she went, and now it grew so dark that she saw scarcely anything; only she felt the fragrance of briar-roses, and it seemed to her that she was guided towards these roses. Then she knew there was a hand in her hand, though she saw nobody, and the hand seemed to lead her on. And she came to an open place in the forest, and there the silver light fell clear from the sky, and she saw a great shadowy rose tree, covered with white wild roses.

The hand was still in her hand, and Jeanie began to wish for nothing so much in the world as to gather some of these roses. She put out her hand and she plucked one, and there before her stood a strange creature – a dwarf, dressed in yellow and red, with a very angry face.

'Who are you,' he cried, 'that pluck my roses without my will?'

'And who are *you*?' said Jeanie, trembling, 'and what right have you on the hills of this world?'

Then she made the holy sign of the cross, and the face of the elf grew black, and the light went out of the sky.

She only saw the faint glimmer of the white flowers, and a kind of shadow standing where the dwarf stood.

'I bid you tell me,' said Jeanie, 'whether you are a Christian man, or a spirit that dreads the holy sign,' and she crossed him again.

Now all grew dark as the darkest winter's night. The air was warm and deadly still, and heavy with the scent of the fairy flowers.

In the blackness and the silence, Jeanie made the sacred sign for the third time. Then a clear fresh wind blew on her face, and the forest boughs were shaken, and the silver light grew and gained on the darkness, and she began to see a shape standing where the dwarf had stood. It was far taller than the dwarf, and the light grew and grew, and a star looked down out of the night, and Jean saw Randal standing by her. And she kissed him, and he kissed her, and he put his hand in hers, and they went out of the wood together. They came to the crest of the hill and the cairn. Far below them they saw the Tweed shining through an opening among the trees, and the lights in the farm of Peel, and they heard the night-birds crying, and the bells of the sheep ringing musically as they wandered through the fragrant heather on the hills.

Out of Fairyland

You may fancy, if you can, what joy there was in Fairnilee when Randal came home. They quite forgot the hunger and the hard times, and the old nurse laughed and cried over her bairn that had grown into a tall, strong young man. And to Lady Ker it was all one as if her husband had come again, as he was when first she knew him long ago; for Randal had his face, and his eyes, and the very sound of his voice. They could hardly believe he was not a spirit, and they clasped his hands, and hung on his neck, and could not keep their eyes off him. This was the end of all their sorrow, and it was as if Randal had come back from the dead; so that no people in the world were ever so happy as they were next day, when the sun shone down on the Tweed and the green trees that rustle in the wind round Fairnilee. But in the evening, when the old nurse was out of the way, Randal sat between his mother and Jean, and they each held his hands, as if they could not let him go, for fear he should vanish away from them again. And they would turn round anxiously if anything stirred, for fear it should be the two white deer that sometimes were said to come for people escaped from Fairyland, and then these people must rise and follow them, and never return any more. But the white deer never came for Randal.

So he told them all his adventures, and all that had happened to him since that midsummer night, seven long years ago.

It had been with him as it was with Jean. He had gone to the Wishing Well, and wished to see the Fairy Queen and Fairyland. And he had seen the beautiful castle in the well, and a beautiful woman's face had floated up to meet his on the water. Then he had gathered the white roses, and then he heard a great sound of horses' feet, and of bells jingling, and a lady rode up, the very lady he had seen in the well. She had a white horse, and she was dressed in green, and she beckoned to Randal to mount on her horse, with her before him on the pillion. And the bells on the bridle rang, and the horse flew faster than the wind.

So they rode and rode through the summer night, and they came to a desert place, and living lands were left far behind. Then the Fairy Queen showed him three paths, one steep and narrow, and beset with briars and thorns: that was the road to goodness and happiness, but it was little trodden or marked with the feet of people that had come and gone.

And there was a wide smooth road that went through fields of lilies, and that was the path of easy living and pleasure.

The third path wound about the wild hill-side, through ferns and heather, and that was the way to Elfland, and that way they rode. And still they rode through a country of dark night, and they crossed great black rivers, and they saw neither sun nor moon, but they heard the roaring of the sea. From that country they came into the light, and into the beautiful garden that lies round the castle of the Fairy Queen. There they lived in a noble company of gallant knights and fair ladies. All seemed very mirthful, and they rode, and hunted, and danced; and it was never dark night, nor broad daylight, but like early summer dawn before the sun has risen.

There Randal said that he had quite forgotten his mother and Jean, and the world where he was born, and Fairnilee.

But one day he happened to see a beautiful golden bottle of a strange shape, all set with diamonds, and he opened it. There was in it a sweet-smelling water, as clear as crystal, and he poured it into his hand, and passed his hand over his eyes. Now this water had the power to destroy the 'glamour' in Fairyland, and make people see it as it really was. And when Randal touched his eyes with it, lo, everything was changed in a moment. He saw that nothing was what it had seemed. The gold vanished from the embroidered curtains, the light grew dim and wretched like a misty winter day. The Fairy Queen, that had seemed so happy and beautiful in her bright dress, was a weary, pale woman in black, with a melancholy face and melancholy eyes. She looked as if she had been there for thousands of years, always longing for the sunlight and the earth, and the wind and rain. There were sleepy poppies twisted in her hair, instead of a golden crown. And the knights and ladies were changed. They looked but half alive; and some, in place of their gay green robes, were dressed in rusty mail, pierced with spears and stained with blood. And some were in burial robes of white, and some in dresses torn or dripping with water, or marked with the burning of fire. All were dressed strangely in some ancient fashion; their weapons were old-fashioned, too, unlike any that Randal had ever seen on earth. And their banquets were not of dainty meats, but of cold, tasteless flesh, and of beans, and pulse, and such things as the old heathens, before the coming of the Gospel, used to offer to the dead. It was dreadful to see them at such feasts, and dancing, and riding, and pretending to be merry with hollow faces and unhappy eyes.

And Randal wearied of Fairyland, which now that he saw it clearly looked like a great unending stretch of sand and barren grassy country, beside a grey sea where there was no tide. All the woods were of black cypress trees and poplar, and a wind from the sea drove a sea-mist through them, white and cold, and it blew through the open courts of the fairy castle.

So Randal longed more and more for the old earth he had left, and the changes of summer and autumn, and the streams of Tweed, and the hills, and his friends. Then the voice of Jeanie had come down to him, sounding from far away. And he was sent up by the Fairy Queen in a fairy form, as a hideous dwarf, to frighten her away from the white roses in the enchanted forest.

But her goodness and her courage had saved him, for he was a christened knight, and not a man of the fairy world. And he had taken his own form again beneath her hand, when she signed him with the Cross, and here he was, safe and happy, at home at Fairnilee.

THE WASHER OF THE FORD

FIONA MACLEOD

William Sharp (1855–1905), alias Fiona Macleod, was the eldest son of a wealthy Paisley merchant and his Swedish-descended wife. Sharp rebelled against the stifling respectabilities and the moral and 'manly' demands made on him by his family and society, but despite his energies could never settle to anything, and eventually wore himself to death. His summers he spent in the Highlands, his winters in London or abroad. He felt himself a misplaced Celt, and in 1894 became a leader of the Celtic revival centred in Edinburgh. It was from 1894 to 1897 that he wrote most of his Celtic novels and stories, under the name Fiona Macleod. This was no pseudonym: Sharp had felt increasingly that he was two people in one skin, and that his female side, for him the better one, was the source both of a yearning for a Gaelic paradise he called 'the Green Life', and of the inspiration for his stories.

Fiona published two collections of fantasy stories, *The Sin-Eater and Other Tales* (1895) and *The Washer of the Ford* (1895), many of them set in the imagined Dark Ages of Celtic myth. Like James Macpherson, whose *Ossian* she edited in 1896, Macleod freely translated from Gaelic originals. Sometimes, as in 'The Dan-nan-Ron' or 'The Sin-Eater', Macleod leaves the fates of her central characters to the harsh workings of what she calls the 'winged destiny': in other stories we find either Christianity or a spiritual presence within nature more central. 'The Washer of the Ford', which Macleod thought 'my most imaginative work', is the chosen story here because it dramatises the conflict of the two. Most evidently it is an allegory of the shift from pagan to Christian vision, as Torcall the blind heathen harper learns of the redemption of his sins. But there are deeper currents suggested by the obscurities of behaviour in the first part. What became of the mourning for Aodh-of-the-Songs, and what explains the doings in the boat? Here we touch on primal or mythic patterns of compulsion that Macleod spoke of as 'deep elementals', which are only temporarily snared in any one net of story. Here too her stories live within the subconscious, and move like wild dreams.

THE WASHER OF THE FORD

When Torcall the Harper heard of the death of his friend, Aodh-of-the-Songs, he made a vow to mourn for him for three seasons – a green time, an apple time, and a snow time.

There was sorrow upon him because of that death. True, Aodh was not of his kindred, but the singer had saved the harper's life when his friend was fallen in the Field of Spears.

Torcall was of the people of the north – of the men of Lochlin. His song was of the fjords and of strange gods, of the sword and the war-galley, of the red blood and the white breast, of Odin and Thor and Freya, of Balder and the Dream-God that sits in the rainbow, of the starry North, of the flames of pale blue and flushing rose that play around the Pole, of sudden death in battle, and of Valhalla.

Aodh was of the south isles, where these shake under the thunder of the western seas. His clan was of the isle that is now called Barra, and was then Aoidû; but his mother was a woman out of a royal rath in Banba, as men of old called Eiré or Eireann. She was so fair that a man died of his desire of her. He was named Ulad, and was a prince. 'The Melancholy of Ulad' was long sung in his land after his end in the dark swamp, where he heard a singing, and went laughing glad to his death. Another man was made a prince because of her. This was Aodh the Harper, out of the Hebrid Isles. He won the heart out of her, and it was his from the day she heard his music and felt his eyes flame upon her. Before the child was born, she said, 'He shall be the son of love. He shall be called Aodh. He shall be called Aodh-of-the-Songs.' And so it was.

Sweet were his songs. He loved, and he sang, and he died.

And when Torcall that was his friend knew this sorrow, he rose and made his vow, and went out for evermore from the place where he was.

Since the hour of the Field of Spears he had been blind. Torcall Dall he was upon men's lips thereafter. His harp had a moonshine wind upon it from that day, it was said: a beautiful strange harping when he went down through the glen, or out upon the sandy machar by the shore, and played what the wind sang, and the grass whispered, and the tree murmured, and the sea muttered or cried hollowly in the dark.

Because there was no sight to his eyes, men said he saw and he heard. What was it he heard and he saw that they saw not and heard not? It was in the voice that sighed in the strings of his harp, so the saying was.

When he rose and went away from his place, the Maormor asked him if he went north, as the blood sang; or south, as the heart cried; or west, as the dead go; or east, as the light comes.

'I go east,' answered Torcall Dall.

'And why so, Blind Harper?'

'For there is darkness always upon me, and I go where the light comes.'

On that night of the nights, a fair wind blowing out of the west, Torcall the Harper set forth in a galley. It splashed in the moonshine as it was rowed swiftly by nine men.

'Sing us a song, O Torcall Dall!' they cried.

'Sing us a song, Torcall of Lochlin,' said the man who steered. He and all his company were of the Gael: the Harper only was of the Northmen.

'What shall I sing?' he asked. 'Shall it be of war that you love, or of women that twine you like silk o' the kine; or shall it be of death that is your meed; or of your dread, the Spears of the North?'

A low sullen growl went from beard to beard.

'We are under *ceangal*, Blind Harper,' said the steersman, with downcast eyes because of his flaming wrath; 'we are under bond to take you safe to the mainland, but we have sworn no vow to sit still under the lash of your tongue. 'Twas a wind-fleet arrow that sliced the sight out of your eyes: have a care lest a sudden sword-wind sweep the breath out of your body.'

Torcall laughed a low, quiet laugh.

'Is it death I am fearing now – I who have washed my hands in blood, and had love, and known all that is given to man? But I will sing you a song, I will.'

And with that he took his harp, and struck the strings.

There is a lonely stream afar in a lone dim land:
It hath white dust for shore it has, white bones bestrew the strand:
The only thing that liveth there is a naked leaping sword;
But I, who a seer am, have seen the whirling hand
    Of the Washer of the Ford.

A shadowy shape of cloud and mist, of gloom and dusk, she stands,
    The Washer of the Ford:
She laughs, at times, and strews the dust through the hollow of her hands.
She counts the sins of all men there, and slays the red-stained horde –
The ghosts of all the sins of men must know the whirling sword
    Of the Washer of the Ford.
She stoops and laughs when in the dust she sees a writhing limb:
'Go back into the ford,' she says, 'and hither and thither swim;
Then I shall wash you white as snow, and shall take you by the hand,
And slay you here in the silence with this my whirling brand,
And trample you into the dust of this white windless sand' –
    This is the laughing word
    Of the Washer of the Ford
    Along that silent strand.

There was silence for a time after Torcall Dall sang that song. The oars took up the moonshine and flung it hither and thither like loose shining crystals. The foam at the prow curled and leaped.

Suddenly one of the rowers broke into a long, low chant ——

Yo, eily-a-ho, ayah-a-ho, eily-ayah-a-ho,
    Singeth the Sword
Eily-a-ho, ayah-a-ho, eily-ayah-a-ho,
    Of the Washer of the Ford!

And at that all ceased from rowing. Standing erect, they lifted up their oars against the stars, and the wild voices of them flew out upon the night ——

Yo, eily-a-ho, ayah-a-ho, eily-ayah-a-ho,
    Singeth the Sword
Eily-a-ho, ayah-a-ho, eily-ayah-a-ho,
    Of the Washer of the Ford!

Torcall Dall laughed. Then he drew his sword from his side and plunged it into the sea. When he drew the blade out of the water and whirled it on high, all the white shining drops of it swirled about his head like a sleety rain.

And at that the steersman let go the steering-oar and drew his sword, and clove a flowing wave. But with the might of his blow the sword spun him round, and the sword sliced away the ear of the man who had the sternmost oar. Then there was blood in the eyes of all there. The man staggered, and felt for his knife, and it was in the heart of the steersman.

Then because these two men were leaders, and had had a blood-feud, and because all there, save Torcall, were of one or the other side, swords and knives sang a song.

The rowers dropped their oars; and four men fought against three.

Torcall laughed, and lay back in his place. While out of the wandering wave the death of each man clambered into the hollow of the boat, and breathed its chill upon its man, Torcall the Blind took his harp. He sang this song, with the swirling spray against his face, and the smell of blood in his nostrils, and the feet of him dabbling in the red tide that rose there.

> Oh 'tis a good thing the red blood, by Odin his word!
> And a good thing it is to hear it bubbling deep.
> And when we hear the laughter of the Sword,
> Oh, the corbies croak, and the old wail, and the women weep!
>
> And busy will she be there where she stands,
> Washing the red out of the sins of all this slaying horde;
> And trampling the bones of them into white powdery sands,
> And laughing low at the thirst of her thirsty sword –
>   The Washer of the Ford!

When he had sung that song there was only one man whose pulse still beat, and he was at the bow.

'A bitter black curse upon you, Torcall Dall!' he groaned out of the ooze of blood that was in his mouth.

'And who will you be?' said the Blind Harper.

'I am Fergus, the son of Art, the son of Fergus of the Dûns.'

'Well, it is a song for your death I will make, Fergus mac Art mhic Fheargus: and because you are the last.'

With that Torcall struck a wild sob out of his harp, and he sang –

> Oh, death of Fergus, that is lying in the boat here,
>   Betwixt the man of the red hair and him of the black beard,
> Rise now, and out of thy cold white eyes take out the fear,
>   And let Fergus mac Art mhic Fheargus see his weird!
>
> Sure, now, it's a blind man I am, but I'm thinking I see
>   The shadow of you crawling across the dead.
> Soon you will twine your arm around his shaking knee,
>   And be whispering your silence into his listless head.
>
> And that is why, O Fergus ——

But here the man hurled his sword into the sea, and with a choking cry fell forward; and upon the white sands he was, beneath the trampling feet of the Washer of the Ford.

II

It was a fair wind that blew beneath the stars that night. At dawn the mountains of Skye were like turrets of a great Dûn against the east.

But Torcall the blind Harper did not see that thing. Sleep, too, was upon him. He smiled in that sleep, for in his mind he saw the dead men, that were of the alien people, his foes, draw near the stream that was in a far place. The shaking of them, poor tremulous frostbit leaves they were, thin and sere, made the only breath there was in that desert.

At the ford – this is what he saw in his vision – they fell down like stricken deer with the hounds upon them.

'What is this stream?' they cried in the thin voice of rain across the moors.

'The River of Blood,' said a voice.

'And who are you that are in the silence?'

'I am the Washer of the Ford.'

And with that each red soul was seized and thrown into the water of the ford; and when white as a sheep-bone on the hill, was taken in one hand by the Washer of the Ford and flung into the air, where no wind was and where sound was dead, and was then severed this way and that, in four whirling blows of the sword from the four quarters of the world. Then it was that the Washer of the Ford trampled upon what fell to the ground, till under the feet of her was only a white sand, white as powder, light as the dust of the yellow flowers that grow in the grass.

It was at that Torcall Dall smiled in his sleep. He did not hear the washing of the sea; no, nor any idle plashing of the unoared boat. Then he dreamed, and it was of the woman he had left, seven summer-sailings ago in Lochlin. He thought her hand was in his, and that her heart was against his.

'Ah, dear beautiful heart of woman,' he said, 'and what is the pain that has put a shadow upon you?'

It was a sweet voice that he heard coming out of sleep.

'Torcall, it is the weary love I have.'

'Ah, heart o' me, dear! sure 'tis a bitter pain I have had too, and I away from you all these years.'

'There's a man's pain, and there's a woman's pain.'

'By the blood of Balder, Hildyr, I would have both upon me to take it off the dear heart that is here.'

'Torcall!'

'Yes, white one.'

'We are not alone, we two in the dark.'

And when she had said that thing, Torcall felt two baby arms go round his neck, and two leaves of a wild-rose press cool and sweet against his lips.

'Ah! what is this?' he cried, with his heart beating, and the blood in his body singing a glad song.

A low voice crooned in his ear: a bitter-sweet song it was, passing-sweet, passing-bitter.

'Ah, white one, white one,' he moaned; 'ah, the wee fawn o' me! Baby o' foam, bonnie wee lass, put your sight upon me that I may see the blue eyes that are mine too and Hildyr's.'

But the child only nestled closer. Like a fledgling in a great nest she was. If God heard her song, He was a glad God that day. The blood that was in her body called to the blood that was in his body. He could say no word. The tears were in his blind eyes.

Then Hildyr leaned into the dark, and took his harp, and played upon it. It was of the fonnsheen he had learned, far, far away, where the isles are.

She sang: but he could not hear what she sang.

Then the little lips, that were like a cool wave upon the dry sand of his life, whispered into a low song: and the wavering of it was like this in his brain ——

Where the winds gather
   The souls of the dead,
O Torcall, my father,
   My soul is led!

In Hildyr-mead
   I was thrown, I was sown:
Out of thy seed
   I am sprung, I am blown!

But where is the way
   For Hildyr and me,
By the hill-moss grey
   Or the grey sea?

For a river is here,
   And a whirling Sword —
And a Woman washing
   By a Ford!

With that, Torcall Dall gave a wild cry, and sheathed an arm about the wee white one, and put out a hand to the bosom that loved him. But there was no white breast there, and no white babe: and what was against his lips was his own hand red with blood.

'O Hildyr!' he cried.

But only the splashing of the waves did he hear.

'O white one!' he cried.

But only the scream of a sea-mew, as it hovered over that boat filled with dead men, made answer.

III

All day the Blind Harper steered the galley of the dead. There was a faint wind moving out of the west. The boat went before it, slow, and with a low, sighing wash.

Torcall saw the red gaping wounds of the dead, and the glassy eyes of the nine men.

'It is better not to be blind and to see the dead,' he muttered, 'than to be blind and to see the dead.'

The man who had been steersman leaned against him. He took him in his shuddering grip and thrust him into the sea.

But when, an hour later, he put his hand to the coolness of the water, he drew it back with a cry, for it was on the cold, stiff face of the dead man that it had fallen. The long hair had caught in a cleft in the leather where the withes had given.

For another hour Torcall sat with his chin in his right hand, and his unseeing eyes staring upon the dead. He heard no sound at all, save the lap of wave upon wave, and the *suss* of spray against spray, and a bubbling beneath the boat, and the low, steady swish of the body that trailed alongside the steering oar.

At the second hour before sundown he lifted his head. The sound he heard was the sound of waves beating upon rocks.

At the hour before sundown he moved the oar rapidly to and fro, and cut away the body that trailed behind the boat. The noise of the waves upon the rocks was now a loud song.

When the last sunfire burned upon his neck, and made the long hair upon his shoulders ashine, he smelt the green smell of grass. Then it was too that he heard the muffled fall of the sea, in a quiet haven, where shelves of sand were.

He followed that sound, and while he strained to hear any voice the boat grided upon the sand, and drifted to one side. Taking his harp, Torcall drove an oar into the sand, and leaped on to the shore. When he was there, he listened. There was silence. Far, far away he heard the falling of a mountain-torrent, and the thin, faint cry of an eagle, where the sun-flame dyed its eyrie as with streaming blood.

So he lifted his harp, and, harping low, with a strange, wild song on his lips, moved away from that place, and gave no more thought to the dead.

It was deep gloaming when he came to a wood. He felt the cold green breath of it.

'Come,' said a voice, low and sweet.

'And who will *you* be?' asked Torcall the Harper, trembling because of the sudden voice in the stillness.

'I am a child, and here is my hand, and I will lead you, Torcall of Lochlin.'

The blind man had fear upon him.

'Who are you that in a strange place are for knowing who I am?'

'Come.'

'Ay, sure, it is coming I am, white one; but tell me who you are, and whence you came, and whither we go.'

Then a voice that he knew sang:

> O where the winds gather
>   The souls of the dead,
> O Torcall, my father,
>   My soul is led!
>
> But a river is here,
>   And a whirling Sword –
> And a Woman washing
>   By a Ford!

Torcall Dall was as the last leaf on a tree at that.

'Were you on the boat?' he whispered hoarsely.

But it seemed to him that another voice answered: '*Yea, even so.*'

'Tell me, for I have blindness: Is it peace?'

'It is peace.'

'Are you man, or child, or of the Hidden People?'

'I am a shepherd.'

'A shepherd? Then, sure, you will guide me through this wood? And what will be beyond this wood?'

'A river.'

'And what river will that be?'

'Deep and terrible. It runs through the Valley of the Shadow.'

'And is there no ford there?'

'Ay, there is a ford.'

'And who will guide me across that ford?'

'She.'

'Who?'

'The Washer of the Ford.'

But hereat Torcall Dall gave a sore cry and snatched his hand away, and fled sidelong into an alley of the wood.

It was moonshine when he lay down, weary. The sound of flowing water filled his ears.

'Come,' said a voice.

So he rose and went. When the cold breath of the water was upon his face, the guide that led him put a fruit into his hand.

'Eat, Torcall Dall!'

He ate. He was no more Torcall Dall. His sight was upon him again. Out of the blackness shadows came; out of the shadows, the great boughs of trees; from the boughs, dark branches and dark clusters of leaves; above the branches, white stars; below the branches, white flowers; and beyond these, the moonshine on the grass and the moonfire on the flowing of a river dark and deep.

'Take your harp, O Harper, and sing the song of what you see.'

Torcall heard the voice, but saw no one. No shadow moved. Then he walked out upon the moonlit grass; and at the ford he saw a woman stooping and washing shroud after shroud of woven moonbeams: washing them there in the flowing water, and singing low a song that he did not hear. He did not see her face. But she was young, and with long black hair that fell like the shadow of night over a white rock.

So Torcall took his harp, and he sang:

Glory to the great Gods, it is no Sword I am seeing;
Nor do I see aught but the flowing of a river.
And I see shadows on the flow that are ever fleeing,
And I see a woman washing shrouds for ever and ever.

Then he ceased, for he heard the woman sing:

Glory to God on high, and to Mary, Mother of Jesus,
Here am I washing away the sins of the shriven,
O Torcall of Lochlin, throw off the red sins that ye cherish
And I will be giving you the washen shroud that they wear in Heaven.

Filled with a great awe, Torcall bowed his head. Then once more he took his harp, and he sang:

O well it is I am seeing, Woman of the Shrouds,
That you have not for me any whirling of the Sword;
I have lost my gods, O woman, so what will the name be
Of thee and thy gods, O woman that art Washer of the Ford?

But the woman did not look up from the dark water, nor did she cease from washing the shrouds made of the woven moonbeams. The Harper heard this song above the sighing of the water:

It is Mary Magdalene my name is, and I loved Christ.
And Christ is the Son of God, and Mary the Mother of Heaven.
And this river is the river of death, and the shadows
Are the fleeing souls that are lost if they be not shriven.

Then Torcall drew nigher unto the stream. A melancholy wind was upon it.
'Where are all the dead of the world?' he said.
But the woman answered not.
'And what is the end, you that are called Mary?'
Then the woman rose.
'Would you cross the Ford, O Torcall the Harper?'
He made no word upon that. But he listened. He heard a woman singing faint and low, far away in the dark. He drew more near.
'Would you cross the Ford, O Torcall?'
He made no word upon that; but once more he listened. He heard a little child crying in the night.
'Ah, lonely heart of the white one,' he sighed, and his tears fell.
Mary Magdalene turned and looked upon him.
It was the face of Sorrow she had. She stooped and took up the tears.
'They are bells of joy,' she said. And he heard a faint, sweet ringing in his ears.
A prayer came out of his heart. A blind prayer it was, but God gave it wings. It flew to Mary, who took and kissed it, and gave it song.
'It is the Song of Peace,' she said. And Torcall had peace.
'What is best, O Torcall?' she asked, – rustling-sweet as rain among the trees her voice was. 'What is best? The sword, or peace?'
'Peace,' he answered; and he was white now, and was old.
'Take your harp,' Mary said, 'and go in unto the Ford. But, lo, now I clothe you with a white shroud. And if you fear the drowning flood, follow the bells that were your tears; and if the dark affright you, follow the song of the prayer that came out of your heart.'

So Torcall the Harper moved into the whelming flood, and he played a wild, strange air like the laughing of a child.

Deep silence there was. The moonshine lay upon the obscure wood, and the darkling river flowed sighing through the soundless gloom.

The Washer of the Ford stooped once more. Low and sweet, as of yore and for ever, over the drowning souls she sang her immemorial song.

PETER PAN

J. M. BARRIE

'I want always to be a little boy and to have fun.' Edwardian children's books are full of this feeling: for authors such as Kenneth Grahame, Rudyard Kipling or Edith Nesbit, childhood can at last be enjoyed for itself, freer from Victorian constraint and the emphasis on self-improvement. However, such feelings are found rather in the more luxuriant spiritual soil of the Home Counties where Barrie (1860–1937) lived than of Scotland from whence he came. Barrie's Peter Pan does not escape censure: he is 'gay and innocent and heartless', as the book version has it; his refusal to grow up is his loss as much as that of the children who do rejoin time. But *Peter Pan is* fun, and has been so enjoyed by (mainly middle-class) children till the present death of childhood itself. Who has not wanted to fly with the children? Who has not exulted in the Never Land? Barrie unsentimentally captures for us every best and worst impulse of a Never World we once lived in; if he admits danger, pain and loss in the shape of a Hook, or the possible deaths of Peter or Tinker Bell, it is only to confound their power.

Barrie had tried the theme before, in his *The Little White Bird* (1902) and does it again in *Peter Pan in Kensington Gardens* (1906), which describes a boy who leaves home and goes off with the fairies. He had also lived it, in the company of the Llewelyn Davies children with whom he made up elaborate adventures for himself and them to play. He returned to it in his more moral and Scots-rooted play *Mary Rose* (1920) in which an emotionally immature girl is taken by the fairies to a Hebridean isle for twenty-five years and finds her son gone on her return. It is a theme close to Barrie personally, stuck between vanishing boy and defective adult, but it is also a universal myth of return. As a myth, it is independent of any particular embodiment. Barrie continually revised the play, which was not published till 1931; he rewrote it as a book in 1911; he licensed others to recreate it in their own versions. In the preface to his 1931 *Plays* he wrote, 'I have no recollection of having written it'. The very words of the play are as elusive as Peter Pan, they slip, shimmer and change direction as Peter is now mischievous fairy urchin, heroic leader, paterfamilias, sexual infant and Pan, spirit at the heart of life itself.

The play may be called Scottish in its dream-like quality. After all, Never Land is the stuff of a dream in Peter's head: but the oddities and changes of the whole play dissolve the structures of reason and the solid world, just as happens in George MacDonald's work. Scottish also is the play's theme of identity, where Hook doubts himself, Mr Darling tries to be a dog, the children have 'home' selves and 'Never' selves, and where Peter Pan does not know who he is or where his parents are.

The extract here is the third and central act of the play. It is a self-contained adventure, with Peter at the height of his power, when the children have been brought to Never Land and before Wendy has asserted her rival authority. The Never Land, here as throughout, is both a shared dream and Peter's make-believe. Like Barrie, he can alter the scenery at will. No sooner does he mention the victims left on the rock than one appears – so abruptly that the games he has previously been imagining, end literally suspended; he creates the pirates, he imitates Hook's voice so well because all these are Pan; he engineers all the adventures and changes sides 'if he is winning too easily'. He makes believe his inability to swim or fly to create a scene of heroic self-denial with Wendy; and kite and Never Bird float by at his whim. We watch a narrative with characters of oddly literary speech having apparent feelings and intentions like 'real' people, but our belief in the fiction is undermined because almost every character, action and word is a changing piece of scenery in the mind of Peter. And Peter? Well, he is the spirit of nature – isn't he? Or is he someone else's dream? And what of us?

Peter Pan

Act III

THE MERMAIDS' LAGOON: *It is the end of a long playful day on the lagoon. The sun's rays have persuaded him to give them another five minutes, for one more race over the waters before he gathers them up and lets in the moon. There are many Mermaids here, going plop-plop, and one might attempt to count the tails did they not flash and disappear so quickly. At times a lovely Girl leaps in the air seeking to get rid of her excess of scales, which fall in a silver shower as she shakes them off. From the coral grottoes beneath the lagoon, where are the Mermaids' bed-chambers, comes fitful music.*

One of the most bewitching of these blue-eyed creatures is lying lazily on Marooner's Rock, combing her long tresses and noting effects in a transparent shell. Peter and his Band are in the water unseen behind the rock, whither they have tracked her as if she were a trout, and at a signal ten pairs of arms come whack upon the mermaid to enclose her. Alas, this is only what was meant to happen, for she hears the signal (which is the crow of a cock) and slips through their arms into the water. It has been such a near thing that there are scales on some of their hands. They climb on to the rock, crestfallen

WENDY (*preserving her scales as carefully as if they were rare postage stamps*) I did so want to catch a mermaid.

PETER (*getting rid of his*) It is awfully difficult to catch a mermaid.

The Mermaids at times find it just as difficult to catch him, though he sometimes joins them in their one game, which consists in lazily blowing their bubbles into the air and seeing who can catch them. The number of bubbles Peter has flown away with! When the weather grows cold Mermaids migrate to the other side of the world, and he once went with a great shoal of them half the way

They are such cruel creatures, Wendy, that they try to pull boys and girls like you into the water and drown them.

WENDY (*too guarded by this time to ask what he means precisely by 'like you', though she is very desirous of knowing*) How hateful!

She is slightly different in appearance now, rather rounder, while John and

Michael are not quite so round. The reason is that when new lost children arrive at his underground home Peter finds new trees for them to go up and down by, and instead of fitting the tree to them he makes them fit the tree. Sometimes it can be done by adding or removing garments, but if you are bumpy, or the tree is an odd shape, he has things done to you with a roller, and after that you fit. The other Boys are now playing King of the Castle, throwing each other into the water, taking headers and so on; but these two continue to talk

PETER Wendy, this is a fearfully important rock. It is called Marooner's Rock. Sailors are marooned, you know, when their captain leaves them on a rock and sails away.

WENDY Leaves them on this little rock to drown?

PETER (*lightly*) Oh, they don't live long. Their hands are tied, so that they can't swim. When the tide is full this rock is covered with water, and then the sailor drowns.

Wendy is uneasy as she surveys the rock, which is the only one in the lagoon and no larger than a table. Since she last looked around a threatening change has come over the scene. The sun has gone, but the moon has not come. What has come is a cold shiver across the waters which has sent all the wiser Mermaids to their coral recesses. They know that evil is creeping over the lagoon. Of the Boys Peter is of course the first to scent it, and he has leapt to his feet before the words strike the rock ——

'And if we're parted by a shot
We're sure to meet below.'

The games on the rock and around it end so abruptly that several Divers are checked in the air. There they hang waiting for the word of command from Peter. When they get it they strike the water simultaneously, and the rock is at once as bare as if suddenly they had been blown off it. Thus the Pirates find it deserted when their dinghy strikes the rock and is nearly stove in by the concussion. They are Smee and Starkey, with Tiger Lily, their captive, bound hand and foot

SMEE Luff, you spalpeen, luff! What we have got to do is to hoist the redskin on to the rock and leave her there to drown.

To one of her race this is an end darker than death by fire or torture, for it is written in the laws of the Piccaninnies that there is no path through water to the happy hunting ground. Yet her face is impassive; she is the daughter of a chief and must die as a chief's daughter; it is enough

STARKEY (*chagrined because she does not mewl*) No mewling. This is your reward for prowling round the ship with a knife in your mouth.

TIGER LILY (*stoically*) Enough said.

SMEE (*who would have preferred a farewell palaver*) So that's it! On to the rock with her, mate.

STARKEY (*experiencing for perhaps the last time the stirrings of a man*) Not so rough, Smee; roughish, but not so rough.

SMEE (*dragging her on to the rock*) It is the Captain's orders.

> *A stave has in some past time been driven into the rock, probably to mark the burial place of hidden treasure, and to this they moor the dinghy*

WENDY (*in the water*) Poor Tiger Lily!

STARKEY What was that?

> *The Children bob*

PETER (*who can imitate the Captain's voice so perfectly that even the author has a dizzy feeling that at times he was really Hook*) Ahoy there, you lubbers!

STARKEY It is the Captain; he must be swimming out to us.

SMEE (*calling*) We have put the redskin on the rock, Captain.

PETER Set her free.

SMEE But Captain ——

PETER Cut her bonds, or I'll plunge my hook in you.

SMEE This is queer!

STARKEY (*unmanned*) Let us follow the Captain's orders.

> *They undo the thongs and Tiger Lily slides between their legs into the lagoon, forgetting in her haste to utter her war-cry, but Peter utters it for her, so naturally that even the Lost Boys are deceived. It is at this moment that the voice of the true Hook is heard*

HOOK (*off*) Boat ahoy!

SMEE (*relieved*) It is the Captain.

> *Hook is swimming, and they help him to scale the rock. He is in gloomy mood*

STARKEY Captain, is all well?

SMEE He sighs.

STARKEY He sighs again.

SMEE (*counting*) And yet a third time he sighs. (*With fore-boding*) What's up, Captain?

HOOK (*who has perhaps found the large rich damp cake untouched*) The game is up. Those boys have found a mother!

STARKEY Oh evil day!

SMEE What is a mother?

WENDY (*horrified*) He doesn't know!

HOOK (*sharply*) What was that?

> *Peter makes the splash of a mermaid's tail*

STARKEY One of them mermaids.

HOOK Dost not know, Smee? A mother is ... (*He finds it more difficult to explain than he had expected, and looks about him for an illustration. He finds one in a great bird which drifts past in a nest as large as the roomiest basin*) There is a lesson in mothers for you! The nest must have fallen into the water, but would the bird desert her eggs?

Peter, who is now more or less off his head, makes the sound of a bird answering in the negative. The nest is borne out of sight

STARKEY Maybe she is hanging out here to protect Peter?

Hook's face clouds still further and Peter just manages not to call out that he needs no protection

SMEE (*not usually a man of ideas*) Captain, could we not kidnap these boys' mother and make her our mother?

HOOK Obesity and bunions, 'tis a princely scheme. We will seize the children, make them walk the plank, and Wendy shall be our mother!

WENDY Never!

Another splash from Peter

HOOK What say you, bullies?

SMEE There is my hand on't.

STARKEY And mine.

HOOK And there is my hook. Swear.

All swear

But I had forgot; where is the redskin?

SMEE (*shaken*) That is all right, Captain; we let her go.

HOOK (*terribly*) Let her go?

SMEE 'Twas your own orders, Captain.

STARKEY (*whimpering*) You called over the water to us to let her go.

HOOK Brimstone and gall, what cozening is here? (*Disturbed by their faithful faces*) Lads, I gave no such order.

SMEE 'Tis passing queer.

HOOK (*addressing the immensities*) Spirit that haunts this dark lagoon tonight, dost hear me?

PETER (*in the same voice*) Odds, bobs, hammer and tongs, I hear you.

HOOK (*gripping the stave for support*) Who are you, stranger, speak.

PETER (*who is only too ready to speak*) I am Jas Hook, Captain of the *Jolly Roger*.

HOOK (*now white to the gills*) No, no, you are not.

PETER Brimstone and gall, say that again and I'll cast anchor in you.

HOOK If you are Hook, come tell me, who am I?

PETER A codfish, only a codfish.

HOOK (*aghast*) A codfish?

SMEE (*drawing back from him*) Have we been captained all this time by a codfish?

STARKEY It's lowering to our pride.

HOOK (*feeling that his ego is slipping from him*) Don't desert me, bullies.

PETER (*top-heavy*) Paw, fish, paw!

> *There is a touch of the feminine in Hook, as in all the greatest pirates, and it prompts him to try the guessing game*

HOOK Have you another name?

PETER (*falling to the lure*) Ay, ay.

HOOK (*thirstily*) Vegetable?

PETER No.

HOOK Mineral?

PETER No.

HOOK Animal?

> *Peter has a hurried consultation with Tootles*

PETER Yes.

HOOK Man?

PETER (*with scorn*) No.

HOOK Boy?

PETER Yes.

HOOK Ordinary boy?

PETER No!

HOOK Wonderful boy?

PETER (*to Wendy's distress*) Yes!

HOOK Are you in England?

PETER No.

HOOK Are you here?

PETER Yes.

HOOK (*beaten, though he feels he has very nearly got it*) Smee, you ask him some questions.

SMEE (*rummaging his brains*) I can't think of a thing.

PETER Can't guess, can't guess! (*Foundering in his cockiness*) Do you give it up?

HOOK (*eagerly*) Yes.

PETER All of you?

SMEE and Starkey Yes.

PETER (*crowing*) Well, then, I am Peter Pan!

> *Now they have him*

HOOK Pan! Into the water, Smee, Starkey, mind the boat. Take him dead or alive!

PETER (*who still has all his baby teeth*) Boys, lam into the pirates!

For a moment the only two we can see are in the dinghy, where John throws himself on Starkey. Starkey wriggles into the lagoon and John leaps so quickly after him that he reaches it first. The impression left on Starkey is that he is being attacked by the Twins. The water becomes stained. The dinghy drifts away. Here and there a head shows in the water, and once it is the head of the Crocodile. In the growing gloom some strike at their friends, Slightly getting Tootles in the fourth rib while he himself is pinked by Curly. It looks as if the Boys were getting the worst of it, which is perhaps just as well at this point, because Peter, who will be the determining factor in the end, has a perplexing way of changing sides if he is winning too easily. Hook's iron claw makes a circle of black water round him from which opponents flee like fishes. There is only one prepared to enter that dreadful circle. His name is Pan. Strangely, it is not in the water that they meet. Hook has risen to the rock to breathe, and at the same moment Peter scales it on the opposite side. The rock is now wet and as slippery as a ball, and they have to crawl rather than climb. Suddenly they are face to face. Peter gnashes his pretty teeth with joy, and is gathering himself for the spring when he sees he is higher up the rock than his foe. Courteously he waits; Hook sees his intention, and taking advantage of it claws twice. Peter is untouched, but unfairness is what he can never get used to, and in his bewilderment he rolls off the rock. The Crocodile, whose tick has been drowned in the strife, rears its jaws, and Hook, who has almost stepped into them, is pursued by it to land. All is quiet on the lagoon now, not a sound save little waves nibbling at the rock, which is smaller than when we last looked at it. Two Boys appear with the dinghy, and the Others, despite their wounds, climb into it. They send the cry 'Peter – Wendy' across the waters, but no answer comes

NIBS They must be swimming home.

JOHN Or flying.

FIRST TWIN Yes, that is it. Let us be off and call to them as we go.

The dinghy disappears with its load, whose hearts would sink it if they knew of the peril of Wendy and her captain. From near and far away come the cries 'Peter – Wendy' till we no longer hear them. Two small figures are now on the rock, but they have fainted. A Mermaid, who has dared to come back in the stillness, stretches up her arms and is slowly pulling Wendy into the water to drown her. Wendy starts up just in time

WENDY Peter!

He rouses himself and looks around him

Where are we, Peter?

PETER We are on the rock, but it is getting smaller. Soon the water will be over it. Listen!

They can hear the wash of the relentless little waves

WENDY We must go.

PETER Yes.

WENDY Shall we swim or fly?

PETER Wendy, do you think you could swim or fly to the island without me?

WENDY You know I couldn't, Peter; I am just a beginner.

PETER Hook wounded me twice. (*He believes it; he is so good at pretend that he feels the pain, his arms hang limp*) I can neither swim nor fly.

WENDY Do you mean we shall both be drowned?

PETER Look how the water is rising!

They cover their faces with their hands. Something touches Wendy as lightly as a kiss

PETER (*with little interest*) It must be the tail of the kite we made for Michael; you remember it tore itself out of his hands and floated away. (*He looks up and sees the kite sailing overhead*) The kite! Why shouldn't it carry you? (*He grips the tail and pulls, and the kite responds*)

WENDY Both of us!

PETER It can't lift two. Michael and Curly tried.

She knows very well that if it can lift her it can lift him also, for she has been told by the Boys as a deadly secret that one of the queer things about him is that he is no weight at all. But it is a forbidden subject

WENDY I won't go without you. Let us draw lots which is to stay behind.

PETER And you a lady, never!

The tail is in Wendy's hands, and the kite is tugging hard. She holds out her mouth to Peter, but he knows they cannot do that

Ready, Wendy!

The kite draws her out of sight across the lagoon

The waters are lapping over the rock now, and Peter knows that it will soon be submerged. Pale rays of light mingle with the moving clouds, and from the coral grottoes is to be heard a sound, at once the most musical and the most melancholy in the Never Land, the Mermaids calling to the moon to rise. Peter is afraid at last, and a tremor runs through him, like a shudder passing over the lagoon; but on the lagoon one shudder follows another till there are hundreds of them, and he feels just the one

(*With a drum beating in his breast as if he were a real boy at last*) To die will be an awfully big adventure.

The blind rises again, and the lagoon is now suffused with moonlight. He is on the rock still, but the water is over his feet. The nest is borne nearer, and the

Bird, after cooing a message to him, leaves it and wings her way upwards. Peter, who knows the bird language, slips into the nest, first removing the two eggs and replacing them in Starkey's hat, which has been left on the stave. The hat drifts away from the rock, but he uses the stave as a mast. The wind is driving him toward the open sea. He takes off his shirt, which he had forgotten to remove while bathing, and unfurls it as a sail

Peter's vessel tacks, and he passes from sight, naked and victorious. The Bird returns and sits on the hat

A Voyage to Arcturus
&
The Haunted Woman

DAVID LINDSAY

David Lindsay (1876–1945), London insurance broker turned novelist of the sublime, is now best-known for his amazing interplanetary fantasy *A Voyage to Arcturus* (1920); but his more earth-based *The Haunted Woman* (1922) has also been successfully republished. Neither of these novels enjoyed more than one poor-selling edition in Lindsay's lifetime, and he spent the next twenty-three years of growing indigence struggling to write and rewrite increasingly unpublishable metaphysical fiction. Lindsay's dour courage and will cannot be denied, nor can the intense if misshapen force that instils his work. He was that unusual creature in this materialist century, a fierce ascetic who sought the sublime through refusals of the sensible world. He felt his greatest literary debt was to George MacDonald, but while the two have mysticism and imaginative genius in common, the sacramentalist MacDonald was no world-denier. Lindsay's vision finds starkest expression in *A Voyage to Arcturus*, where even love and the highest impulses of the spirit are rejected as the deceits of the devil. In *The Haunted Woman*, Lindsay is readier to suggest that love at its truest penetrates beneath the frauds of convention and can open a hidden door to a deeper spiritual reality.

The extract from *A Voyage to Arcturus* here describes an adventure of the 'strongman' hero Maskull, brought to the exotic planet Tormance from earth by two strange men, Krag and Nightspore, and then abandoned. Here he has come to Swaylone's Island of tormenting spiritual music with Gleameil, longing-ridden wife of his fisherman friend Polecrab; and he has met the island's musician Earthrid by his terrible lake-harp Irontick, which he plays on with his thoughts. Maskull's ultimate education is to be that everything in the planet, including Earthrid's searing music, is either a fraud or a perversion of the good by the planet's apparent deity Crystalman, and that his real search is for the true god Muspel or Surtur, who is utterly beyond all phenomena: having learned which, Maskull dies, and his deeper or unconscious self, revealed as Nightspore, takes over and completes the journey towards Muspel. In this passage we see Maskull unconsciously making himself a channel for Muspel's power: his giant will, at once the product of a fierce omnivorousness and the engine propelling him towards Muspel, is here in jagged sympathy with his unknown god. Earthrid, however powerful a musician of his lake-harp, is still a weak creature of surfaces: but the music that surges through Maskull rips open the entire landscape in a vision both of world-destruction and the raw unconscious.

In the extract from *The Haunted Woman*, which again involves searing music, the reluctant lovers Isbel Loment and Henry Judge have found in Judge's ancient Sussex house Runhill Court a secret way into another world, where their repressed feelings change temporarily to passion. The house, as frequently in modern fiction, is in part a symbol of mind, with the hidden stairway to the lost tower rooms the sub- or super-conscious. But that unconscious is not merely their own. The house they see becomes the house as it was fourteen centuries before when the Saxon Ulf lived in it; and the strange spring landscape they see outside it is a magic realm to which Ulf was reputedly transported. Ulf is in one sense 'there', but the person with the violin is also transcendental, a way to a still deeper world that lies through music and self-negation (Judge is eventually to die when he manages to see the musician's face).

A VOYAGE TO ARCTURUS

'The shocks you are preparing may kill us,' said Gleameil, in a low, taut voice, 'but we shall die, seeing *beauty*.'

Earthrid looked at her with a dignified expression.

'Neither you, nor any other person, can endure the thoughts which I put into my music. Still, you must have it your own way ... It needed a woman to call it "beauty". But if this is beauty, what is ugliness?'

'That I can tell you, Master,' replied Gleameil, smiling at him. 'Ugliness is old, stale life, while yours every night issues fresh from the womb of nature.'

Earthrid stared at her, without response.

'Teargeld is rising,' he said at last. 'And now you shall see – though not for long.'

As the words left his mouth, the full moon peeped over the hills in the dark eastern sky. They watched it in silence, and soon it was wholly up. It was larger than the moon of Earth, and seemed nearer. Its shadowy parts stood out in just as strong relief, but somehow it did not give Maskull the impression of being a dead world. Branchspell shone on the whole of it, but Alppain only on a part. The broad crescent which reflected Branchspell's rays alone was white and brilliant; but the part that was illuminated by both suns, shone with a greenish radiance which had almost solar power, and yet was cold and cheerless. On gazing at that combined light, he felt the same sense of disintegration that the afterglow of Alppain had always caused in him; but now the feeling was not physical, but merely aesthetic. The moon did not appear romantic to him, but disturbing and mystical.

Earthrid rose, and stood quietly for a minute. In the bright moonlight, his face seemed to have undergone a change. It lost its loose, weak, disagreeable look, and acquired a sort of crafty grandeur. He clapped his hands together meditatively two or three times, and walked up and down. The others stood together, watching him.

Then he sat down by the side of the lake, and leaning on his side, placed his right hand, open palm downwards, on the ground, at the same time stretching out his right leg, so that the foot was in contact with the water.

While Maskull was in the act of staring at him and at the lake, he felt a stabbing sensation right through his heart, as though he had been pierced by a rapier. He barely recovered himself from falling, and as he did so he saw that a spout had formed on the water, and was now subsiding again. The next moment he was knocked down by a violent blow in the mouth, delivered by an invisible hand. He picked himself up; and observed that a second spout had formed. No sooner was he on his legs, than a hideous pain hammered away inside his brain, as if caused by a malignant tumour. In his agony, he stumbled and fell again; this time on the arm which Krag had wounded. All his other mishaps were forgotten in this one, which half-stunned him. It lasted but a moment, and then sudden relief came, and he found that Earthrid's rough music had lost its power over him.

He saw him still stretched in the same position. Spouts were coming thick and fast on the lake, which was full of lively motion. But Gleameil was not on her legs. She was lying on the ground, in a heap, without moving. Her attitude was ugly, and he guessed she was dead. When he reached her, he discovered that she *was* dead. In what state of mind she had died, he did not know, for her face wore the vulgar Crystalman grin. The whole tragedy had not lasted five minutes.

He went over to Earthrid, and dragged him forcibly away from his playing.

'You have been as good as your word, musician,' he said. 'Gleameil is dead.'

Earthrid tried to collect his scattered senses.

'I warned her,' he replied, sitting up. 'Did I not beg her to go away? ... But she died very easily. She did not wait for the beauty she spoke about. She heard nothing of the passion, nor even of the rhythm. Neither have you.'

Maskull looked down at him in indignation, but said nothing.

'You should not have interrupted me,' went on Earthrid. 'When I am playing, nothing else is of importance. I might have lost the thread of my ideas. Fortunately, I never forget ... I shall start over again.'

'If music is to continue, in presence of the dead, I play next.'

The man glanced up quickly.

'That can't be.'

'It must be,' said Maskull decisively. 'I prefer playing to listening. Another reason is that you will have every night, but I have only tonight.'

Earthrid clenched and unclenched his fist, and began to turn pale.

'With your recklessness, you are likely to kill us both ... Irontick belongs to me, and until you have learnt how to play, you would only break the instrument.'

'Well, then, I will break it; but I am going to try.'

The musician jumped to his feet, and confronted him. 'Do you intend to take it from me by violence?'

'Keep calm! You will have the same choice that you offered us. I shall give you time to go away somewhere.'

'How will that serve me, if you spoil my lake? – You don't understand what you are doing.'

'Go, or stay!' responded Maskull. 'I give you till the water gets smooth again. After that, I begin playing.'

Earthrid kept swallowing. He glanced at the lake and back to Maskull.

'Do you swear it?'

'How long that will take, you know better than I; but till then you are safe.'

Earthrid cast him a look of malice, hesitated for an instant, and then moved away, and started to climb the nearest hill. Half-way up he glanced over his shoulder apprehensively, as if to see what was happening. In another minute or so, he had disappeared over the crest, travelling in the direction of the shore which faced Matterplay.

Later, when the water was once more tranquil, Maskull sat down by its edge, in imitation of Earthrid's attitude.

He knew neither how to set about producing his music, nor what would come of it. But audacious projects entered his brain, and he willed to create physical shapes – and, above all, one shape, that of Surtur.

Before putting his foot to the water, he turned things over a little in his mind.

He said, 'What *themes* are in common music, *shapes* are in this music. The composer does not find his theme by picking out single notes; but the whole theme flashes into his mind by inspiration. So it must be with shapes. When I start playing, if I am worth anything, the undivided ideas will pass from my unconscious mind to this lake, and then, reflected back in the dimensions of reality, I shall for the first time be made acquainted with them. So it must be.'

The instant his foot touched the water, he felt his thoughts flowing from him. He did not know what they were, but the mere act of flowing created a sensation of joyful mastery. With this was curiosity to learn what they would prove to be. Spouts formed on the lake, in increasing numbers; but he experienced no pain. His thoughts, which he knew to be music, did not issue from him in a steady, unbroken stream, but in great, rough gushes, succeeding intervals of quiescence. When these gushes came, the whole lake broke out into an eruption of spouts.

He realized that the ideas passing from him did not arise in his intellect, but had their source in the fathomless depths of his will. He could not decide what character they should have, but he was able to force them out, or retard them, by the exercise of his volition.

At first nothing changed around him. Then the moon grew dimmer, and a strange, new radiance began to illuminate the landscape. It increased so imperceptibly, that it was some time before he recognised it as the Muspel-light which he had seen in the Wombflash Forest. He could not give it a colour, or a name, but it filled him with a sort of stern and sacred awe. He called up the resources of his powerful will. The spouts thickened like a forest, and many of them were twenty feet high. Teargeld looked faint and pale; the radiance became intense; but it cast no shadows. The wind got up, but where Maskull was sitting, it was calm. Shortly afterwards it began to shriek and whistle, like a full gale. He saw no shapes, and redoubled his efforts.

His ideas were now rushing out on to the lake so furiously, that his whole soul was possessed by exhilaration and defiance. But still he did not know their nature. A huge spout shot up, and at the same moment the hills began to crack and break. Great masses of loose soil were erupted from their bowels, and in the next period of quietness, he saw that the landscape had altered. Still the mysterious light intensified. The moon disappeared entirely. The noise of the unseen tempest was terrifying, but Maskull played heroically on, trying to urge out ideas which would take shape. The hillsides were cleft with chasms. The water escaping from the tops of the spouts swamped the land; but where he was, it was dry.

The radiance grew terrible. It was everywhere, but Maskull fancied that it was far brighter in one particular quarter. He thought that it was becoming localised, preparatory to contracting into a solid form. He strained and strained …

Immediately afterwards, the bottom of the lake subsided. Its waters fell through, and his instrument was broken.

The Muspel-light vanished. The moon shone out again, but Maskull could not see it. After that unearthly shining, he seemed to himself to be in total blackness. The screaming wind ceased; there was a dead silence. His thoughts finished flowing towards the lake, and his foot no longer touched water, but hung in space.

He was too stunned by the suddenness of the change, to either think or feel. While he was still lying dazed, a vast explosion occurred in the newly opened depths beneath the lake bed. The water in its descent had met fire. Maskull was lifted bodily in the air, many yards high, and came down heavily. He lost consciousness …

When he came to his senses again, he saw everything. Teargeld was gleaming brilliantly. He was lying by the side of the old lake, but it was now a crater, to the bottom of which his eyes could not penetrate. The hills encircling it were torn, as if by heavy gunfire. A few thunder clouds were floating in the air at no great height, from which branched lightning descended to the earth incessantly, accompanied by alarming and singular crashes.

He got on his legs, and tested his actions. Finding that he was uninjured, he first of all viewed the crater at closer quarters, and then started to walk painfully towards the northern shore.

When he had attained the crest above the lake, the landscape sloped gently down for two miles to the sea. Everywhere he passed through traces of his rough work. The country was carved into scarps, grooves, channels, and craters. He arrived at the line of low cliffs overlooking the beach, and found that these also were partly broken down by landslips. He got down on to the sands, and stood looking over the moonlit, agitated sea, wondering how he should contrive to escape from this island of failure.

Then he saw Earthrid's body, lying quite close to him. It was on its back. Both legs had been violently torn off, and he could not see them anywhere. His teeth were buried in the flesh of his right forearm, indicating that the man had died in unreasoning physical agony. The skin gleamed green in the moonlight, but it was stained by darker discolorations, which were wounds. The sand about him was dyed by the pool of blood which had long since filtered through.

Maskull quitted the corpse in dismay, and walked a long way along the sweet-smelling shore. Sitting down on a rock, he waited for daybreak.

The Haunted Woman: The Music of Spring

They walked over to the right-hand door, which Judge, after turning the handle, at once kicked wide open with his foot … A sudden and unanticipated flood of brilliant sunshine, streaming through the room from an open window on the further side, momentarily blinded them, so that they staggered back with the shock.

Judge was the first to recover himself.

'It's all right, we can go in. The room's empty.'

Isbel hastened to the window. It was breast-high. There was no glass in it, but it possessed a stout wooden shutter, opening outwards, which at present was swung to its full extent squarely against the outside wall. The aperture of the window was so narrow that there was barely space for their two heads together, and she found her smooth cheek grazing his harsh one.

From out of doors came not only the sunlight but the song of birds, the loud sighing of the wind in its passage through trees, and an indescribable fresh, sweet smell, as of meadow grass, turned-up earth, and dew-drenched flowers. It seemed more like spring than autumn.

'Where are we, then?' was Isbel's first inquiry, uttered in a tone of bewilderment. 'How do we come to be so high up from the ground?'

'I don't recognize any of it. It's all new to me.'

From the foot of the house wall, forty feet below, the free country started.

Judge stared in vain for familiar landmarks – the more he gazed, the more puzzled he became. Not only had his own grounds disappeared, but neither in the foreground nor in the distance was there a single sign of human occupancy or labour. Look where he would, fields, hedgerows, roads, lanes, houses, had vanished entirely out of the landscape.

A bare hillside of grass and chalk, perhaps a couple of hundred feet high, fell away sharply from the house, to terminate in a miniature valley along which a brook, glittering in the sunlight, wound its way. Beyond it there was a corresponding hill up, but not so steep or high; and here the woods began; an undulating but unbroken forest appeard to extend right to the horizon, many miles distant. The intensely blue sky was adorned with cirrus-clouds, while the dazzling sun was high above their heads, about half a point to the right. Apart, altogether, from the strangeness of the scenery, anything less like a late afternoon in October would be hard to imagine; the forests were brilliantly green, many of the smaller, isolated trees in the valley were crowned with white blossom, while the air itself held that indefinable spirit of wild sweetness which is inseparable from a spring morning.

'Just look at that man!' said Isbel, suddenly.

He was sitting on the slope of the hill, directly opposite their window and not a stone's throw from them, but half hidden by the crest of the small hollow which he had selected for his perch, which explained why they had not previously noticed him. He sat motionless, facing the valley, with his back to the house; what he was doing there they could not imagine. It was his extraordinary attire which had evoked Isbel's exclamation. Only his head, the upper half of his back, and one out-stretched leg were visible; but the leg was encased in a sage-green trouser, tightly cross-gartered with yellow straps, the garment on his back resembled, as far as could be seen, a purple smock, and the hair of his hatless head fell in a thick, bright yellow mane as far as his shoulders.

Notwithstanding Isbel's amazement, she began to laugh.

'No wonder poor Mrs Richborough was startled! Is it a man, or a tulip?'

'He looks like an ancient Saxon come to life,' replied Judge, also laughing, but more moderately.

'Ulf, perhaps.'

'Very likely,' he agreed, without understanding her.

'Cry out and *ask* him if his name's Ulf.'

'But who was Ulf?'

'Don't you know? Why he's the man who built your house. The trolls ran away with him, poor fellow! and probably he's been sitting here ever since, yearning to get back home again ... Do call out.'

'You really want me to call?'

'If you don't I shall, and that will be immodest.'

Judge shouted at the top of his voice. The man neither responded nor turned his head.

'Again!' commanded Isbel, laughing. 'Louder – much louder! As if someone were running off with property of yours ...'

This time Judge roared, and then Isbel added her strange clanging cry twice or thrice, laughing between whiles; but still they were unable to attract his attention.

Temporarily abandoning the effort, she turned her head and glanced sideways at Judge, with an almost joyous expression.

'We can't be in October. That's hawthorn blooming ... and look at those beeches over there, with their pale-green, transparent leaves ... Hark! ...'

They kept quiet for a minute ... A distant cuckoo was calling. The cry was regularly repeated, at very short intervals.

Judge rubbed his eyes, in actual doubt whether he were awake or dreaming. 'It's spring, sure enough – but how can it be?'

'Oh, if we could only get down into it all!'

Both instinctively measured the wall beneath them with their eyes, but the distance to the ground was too great, the footholds were too precarious.

She leant further out, inhaling the sweet, fragrant air in deep breaths, and sighing it out again ... 'Beautiful! – beautiful! ...'

Then once more she became fascinated by the man.

'It can't be true. Such men don't exist – at least, nowadays. It's an optical illusion. If it were a real person he would answer us.'

Judge hailed him again, but still without result. A moment later, however, the man stopped to pick something up, and when he regained his sitting posture they caught a glimpse of a fiddle-shaped instrument in his hand, somewhat larger than a modern viola. Wasting no time in preliminaries, he swung his bow across it, and at once started to repeat the air they had heard already from the other room.

Isbel, drawing back a little, rested her elbow on the window-sill and her face on her elbow, in order better to concentrate her thoughts on the music. Judge retired altogether into the room, to make space for her. The tone of the instrument, notwithstanding its small size, was midway in depth between that of a violoncello and that of a contra-bass, and the low, slow scrape of its strings had a peculiarly disturbing effect upon her feelings. The theme had a strange, archaic flavour, as though it had come down through the centuries, yet it was so appropriate that Isbel could almost fancy it to be the voice of the landscape. It was hauntingly beautiful, and full of queer surprises; each long, sonorous note contained a world of music in itself, but it was the powerful, yet delicate and passionate *thought* slowly being developed as the air proceeded which stirred her so exceedingly.

While she stood listening, feelings which she had not had for ten years suddenly returned to her, and she realized, as in a flash, how far down the hill of life she had already travelled. The complex state of youth, composed of wildness, melancholy, audacity, inspiration, and hope, was momentarily restored to her, but only as a memory, as if for the purpose of mocking her. ... As the music finished, tears stood in her eyes, and her heart was choking, yet she was not unhappy ...

Judge approached her from behind ... 'Isbel!' ...

'It was like the voice of spring,' she said, without turning round. 'You are tortured, but you don't know what is happening to you.'

'Music must have been like that at one time.'

'Did you feel it, too?'

'It must be very, very old.' ... They hardly knew what they were saying to each other.

The Corn King and the Spring Queen

NAOMI MITCHISON

Naomi Mitchison, née Haldane (1899–) has been publishing her work for more than seventy years, but remains as radical and energetic in her outlook as when she began. Initially apparently destined to make a conventional society marriage and settle for wifely subservience, her inherited independence of nature, her open marriage to Dick Mitchison, her creativity, determination and sociability, and beyond these the sustaining context of the rebellious 1920s in which such qualities could come into their own, turned her to a life of untrammelled exploration of her own and all human nature through both her experience and her books. Fifty years before feminism, she was a feminist; like D. H. Lawrence she looked to the primal energies of human nature; from the beginning she explored the kind of socialist community which in civilised society was later fleetingly to be realised in the Israeli kibbutzim, but which she herself found in Africa. One of her strongest values is loyalty to a larger loving community. In her novel *Bull Calves* (1947), she visits the 'gene pool' of her own family in the eighteenth century; and she herself has become the adopted grandmother of an African tribe. She has lived in her own open society, ever available to visitors young and old, at Carradale House in Kintyre, her home since 1937.

The Corn King and the Spring Queen (1931) is arguably her best book; it was enthusiastically reviewed and voted best novel of 1931, ahead even of Virginia Woolf's *The Waves*. It has recently been reissued by Virago (1983) and by Canongate (1990). Begun in 1925, its theme of feminine self-definition is partly that of the author herself. It describes Erif Der (Red Fire backwards), young witch-queen of 'primitive' Marob on the northern Black Sea coast in the third century BC. Exiled from Marob for plotting against her husband Tarrik the Corn King, Erif Der travels to Sparta on the verge of its decline, to Greece, to decadent Egypt and thence back to Marob and Tarrik. On the way she learns through differing societies the values of civilisation and of intellect, but her experience teaches her that these things are fragile where they are not embedded in the values of a whole community, and where they are severed from the primal energies of nature and past tradition. The novel's scale is epic, its concern as much social as personal: what is the best society for the individual? Naomi Mitchison is no utopian, no evolutionary meliorist: the novel shows civilised societies in collapse, and in a sense Erif Der's journey is a rediscovery of the old, a kind of anti-clockwise movement symbolised in her inverted name. Equally, her passionate self-assertion, her Red Fire, can only come into its own when it is no longer subversive, but integrated with its community.

The extract here describes the Marob vegetation ritual to restore the year's fertility: it comes a third of the way through the book when Erif and Tarrik have come together for a time after her family's attempts to use her against him for their own ends. A series of blighted rituals in past years caused by their disharmony, is here cancelled with explosive power. What is fine in this portrait is the way Mitchison has blended casual reality with ritual, and has made convincing the suspension of their normal personalities by the king and queen; and how, in her attention to detail she has brought to life what in her source Sir James Frazer's *The Golden Bough* (chs.25,40,45–6) (1890-1915), is much more general. Most potent of all perhaps is the way that the action comes over both as a ritual enactment of what may happen naturally, and as an actual magical opening of the land by the power invested in the figures of the drama. And at the same time, this conjunction of plough and land is a symbol at the human level of the new togetherness of Tarrik and Erif. Unfortunately, it is not to last.

❧

The Corn King and the Spring Queen
☙

In the morning of Plowing Eve, every one went up to the fallow field in their best clothes. There were thick clay jars standing about, filled with a brownish drink that was made out of fermented wheat and only used on feast days. As it was rather nasty it was usually mixed with honey. Early in the day it had been raining, but by the latter part of the morning it had stopped, and the clouds rose and parted. The people stood and sat and lay about the edges of the damp field, with the coloured rods standing upright in it for the plowing marks. They got drunk, but this stuff, instead of making them softly drunk, as their usual herb-steeped mead did, made them drunk and hard and excited. After a time, in one and then another and another part of the ring round the field, the excitement grew and flared to a point, a violence, but, instead of wanting to fight, the man would want to shout, would begin shouting for the Corn King to come, for the plowing, for the year to begin. The shouting ran in waves, round and round. They clapped their hands on their thighs. The shouting took rhythm, became a double song of men and women, deep and shrill. It beat across the fallow field, and on to the plowshare at the side of it.

Now it was noon. At opposite sides the ring parted, huddled back on to itself as the song dropped to satisfied eagerness. From the south came the Spring Queen, with her eyes straight and held, unseeing, unsmiling, past men and women she knew well, brushing by her friend Disdallis, more apart than a bride, and so into the middle of the field. She sat down quietly there and hung her hands over her knees and dropped her head forward on to her wrists. She had a white dress with hundreds and hundreds of little coloured wool flowers fastened on to it all over by long wool stalks. As she walked slowly over the fallow field she was almost shapeless with the hanging mass of them, dropping over her fingers and down from the hem nearly over her feet. Her hair hung behind her in a tight single plait.

From the north end of the field came the Corn King, leading his white plow-oxen with painted horns. He himself wore a curious garment, long strips of coloured stuff over his naked body from neck to knee, belted at the waist, but splitting everywhere as he moved. Tarrik, wearing it, knew that his body was all shivering with no more than this between it and the March wind. All round the ring every one still wore furs and felt. Yet it was scarcely cold that he was. He did not look towards the Spring Queen, but yoked his oxen to the plow and began to drive them along the outer edge of the field. The ring of people were singing and dancing: the plow went in a square, inside their circle; it moved slowly past them like a knife-blade scraping along flesh. In the dance they too began to move slowly round the field, slower than the plow. Birds hovered, crows and seagulls, but did not dare to settle in the furrow for fear of the people. Tarrik pressed on the plow-beam, in, in to the hard, sticky, reluctant earth. After he had made and closed the full square about the field, he did not plow it all, only went parallel with his first lines and then suddenly inward on a sharp turn just as his immanent godhead and the sight of one of the plow marks might move him. After a time he began to talk to the Spring Queen in the middle, over his shoulder, in a loud, impersonal voice.

He talked about the plowing. He said: 'This is my field. Mine.' He said: 'Other things are mine. Everything I think of is mine, everything I name. Under the plow. They go under. The plow is a ship. It goes through thick water. It is bringing gold to Marob. I am the plow. It is my body. It is hard and strong. It leaps on the closed sod and plunges through. Soon comes the seed.' And every time he said one of these things the crowd would sigh after him. 'Plow hard! Plow deep!'

At first the Spring Queen said nothing. She seemed asleep. Then she raised her head a little from her knees and began to answer: 'Though you plow the field it is not your field. Why should the field hear? The closed soil has no pleasure of the plow, and cold and hard it will be to the seed. Why should the spring come?' But the people of Marob cried at her softly from the edges of the field: 'Spring Queen, be kind, be kind!'

So they went on until the middle of the afternoon. Tarrik was the plow, the seed, the warmth and force of growth. Erif was the hard, fallow field; the cold, reluctant spring. The words they said were in no set form or order, only, on every Plowing Eve since the beginning of Marob, the same kind of loud, unhurrying talk had gone on between the sweating Corn King and the still, shivering Spring Queen, with the same implications behind it. It would go on happening for countless years longer. This way, in Marob at least, the food and wealth of the people was made to grow. It was better not to make the talk into a plain repetition, a formula; the life might go out of it. Now as it went on the people divided up more and more, the women shouting at the Corn King to plow deep and hard, the men calling on the Spring Queen to be kind.

Tarrik had done all this at Plowing Eve since he was a boy. And afterwards, if he thought about it, he could never understand how he got the strength for the whole day, the plowing and dancing and shouting. When it was over he always slept dreamlessly and deliciously, yet not for longer than usual. He remembered that for the first few years he had been afraid, when the day came, that he would not be able to go through it rightly; but he always did. Now he had no fears. Only it was difficult to wait through the morning, after every one had left the Chief's house and gone up to the field, to wait there by himself, doing nothing, getting more and more aware of the smell and texture of the brown earth of the fallow field lying ready for him. He did not think of the day when he would begin to feel his strength go. Why should he? It was no part of him yet. As he plowed and talked and pressed and ached and held hard for the plow marks and felt the furrow opening and the wave of earth turning, the dark, torn clods and crumbs tumbling and settling, he knew that the Spring Queen was in the middle of the field and he was coming towards her. He had forgotten that she was also his wife, Erif Der.

This was her third Plowing Eve. The first time she had been a young girl, proud and confident and sure of her strength and her magic, deeply excited, but yet underneath always herself and her father's daughter, working for the moment with the seasons and with Tarrik, but ultimately not surrendered and prepared to work against Tarrik whenever she chose, later on, although at the moment she was doing the thing she liked, for fun. Last year it had been with her brother, Yellow Bull, and it had all seemed wrong and twisted. There had been something very queer about his plowing; even the oxen had noticed it, and she had seen at once through her half-shut eyes. And she was ill then, full of pains that suddenly took her and swept away everything else. She knew that she had fainted once or twice during her wait in the middle of the field, and once or twice she had heard herself speaking as she became fully conscious again, and was only thankful that the godhead was still with her enough to move through her senses. When she had realised that, she had let herself go into a sort of dim condition in which it possessed her and did and said the things for her, and she could look on and bear the pain that she thought then was coming from Tarrik's child, but was really the poison with which Yersha was trying to kill her.

This time she was relaxed again to her own godhead, but without pain. The child in her had not begun to stir yet. It was still tiny, a little queer worm at the base of her body, sending small messages of shock and disturbance. But also it was security. If everything else about her was appearance, if she grew so uncertain of her own existence that it became no difficult or unlikely step between life and death, then this thing which was her and yet not her, anchored her, nailed her down to some kind of reality. It was good to feel secure, good to be part of the seasons, budding and ripening with them.

She raised her head a little to give another answer and saw that the plow-oxen were quite near, that the fallow field was almost plowed. Suddenly Erif Der was unreasonably and beautifully glad. Her voice, as the crowd was hoping it would, grew louder. She was the spring and she would come with flowers and small leaves and lambs and a growing child. The plow came again across her field of vision and then turned inward towards her. She did not know at all how violently she was shivering. The painted horns of the oxen swung together and apart. She saw the Corn King's eyes over the backs of the beasts. The plow came at her. The singing stopped. At the last moment she leapt to her feet, ran under the horns of the oxen, between their panting flanks, and leapt the plowshare itself as it made the last furrow right through the centre of the fallow field, tearing apart the warmed, flattened grass where she had been sitting.

At once the singing began again, men and women together, and the ring swept inwards, nearer to the middle of the field and across the first belt of plowing, so that their feet trampled stickily into the brown, turned sods, the flesh of earth. 'The spring is awake!' they cried. 'Awake! Oh, awake and truly awake! The year is beginning again!'

ℱATHER ᴄMALACHY'S ᴄMIRACLE

BRUCE MARSHALL

Bruce Marshall (1899–1987) graduated in commerce and worked as a chartered accountant in Paris from 1926 to 1940, before retiring to the south of France; his novel-writing career began in 1925. In several of his novels he returns to the issue of the Catholic faith in the modern world. He is distinctive for his ability to combine deep faith together with a lively and comic sense of the unbelieving humanity which makes that faith a cross.

Father Malachy's Miracle (1931; rev. 1947) is one of the best-loved of Marshall's works, and his only fantasy of note. Set in Edinburgh, it is a witty and finely-written picture of a desperate priest in an increasingly materialistic society. Through his prayers, an obvious if ludicrous miracle is performed, yet nobody will believe it or attend to it, and in the end it is reversed. The priest Father Malachy concludes that he was presumptuous, and that God intended to teach him that it was "'equally another miracle that the majority of people should refuse to believe that it is a miracle'". For all that, the novel does operate as a picture of God's ignored majesty, and as an authentication of the foundations of Catholic belief. It belongs with other fantasies of Christian apology written at this time – with T. F. Powys's *Mr Weston's Good Wine* (1927), Charles William's *The Place of the Lion* (1931), and C. S. Lewis's *The Pilgrim's Regress* (1933), all of them written out of the sense that people were growing indifferent to Christian belief.

The extract describes the carrying out of a wager made by Father Malachy in exasperation with the worldly vicar (the Rev. Humphrey Hamilton) of the nearby Scottish Episcopalian church. It shows the author's ability to unite diverse and mutually jarring impressions in one whole: the ironically-named Garden of Eden and its absurd journey is juxtaposed with a scene of high adoration in the church, followed in turn by a banal breakfast and the fatuous public response to the miracle. The first half of Marshall's book is like this, a mixture of reverence and mirth, the sublime and the ordinary or vulgar; later, however, a harsher satiric view of human shallowness and greed becomes dominant.

❦

Father Malachy's Miracle

❧

'We have still another five minutes to wait,' said Father Malachy when they halted outside the main entrance to the Garden of Eden. 'It is, of course, possible that Almighty God would effect the miracle now if I were to ask Him nicely; but as I can see no purpose beyond our own personal comfort in doing so I think that I had better not. For all we know He may have some special grace to grant in Australia at this moment and it would be impolitic, in view of the nature of my request, to disturb Him before the hour agreed upon. In any case, Mr Humphrey Hamilton has not indicated to me the place to which he would wish the Garden of Eden to be transferred.'

'My dear Father, I *wish* to have the Garden of Eden transferred to nowhere. It is you who wish to have it transferred to somewhere in order that you may convince me that miracles are as possible in the present as they are supposed to have been in the past. I remember, however, that in your challenge to me you stipulated that I should choose the place; and as, in this case as in that of Saint Denis carrying his head, '*la distance n'y fait rien; c'est le premier pas qui coûte*,' I challenge you to transfer this building which we see in front of us to the top of the Bass Rock which lies, as we all know, in the Firth of Forth and slightly to the north-east of North Berwick.'

Canon Collins frowned inwardly as he heard the Reverend Humphrey Hamilton's challenge because the Bass Rock, although inhabited only by a lighthouse-keeper and his family, was in the diocese of Midlothian and he would have much preferred the Garden of Eden, if a-flying it would go, to make a thorough job of it and settle down on some desert *in partibus infidelium*; but he recognised that any suggestion on his part was out of the question and prayed to God that he would hear the prayer of His servant Malachy and cleanse the parish of Saint Margaret of Scotland from an establishment which hindered the sanctification of souls.

'Right,' said Father Malachy. 'The Bass Rock it shall be.' He pulled out his watch, glanced at it, put it back again. 'And as it is now twenty-seven minutes past I think I shall, with your permission, begin to recite the preliminary prayers. At half-past exactly I think that you will both of you be rewarded for your patience.'

And with these words Father Malachy took off his hat and handed it to Canon Collins and bowed his grey head in great and silent prayer. He did not see the few late couples passing up the steps of the Garden of Eden any more than he saw the curiosity with which they turned round to look at the unusual spectacle of three clergymen standing reverently on the pavement outside. He did not see the boy in uniform come tearing out and rush off up the street whistling for a taxi which wasn't there. He did not see and did not hear the trams as, all unconscious of the mystery which was then being hatched, they came clanging up from Leith and went clanging down into Leith. He did not see and he did not hear because his mind was shut to God and because he was praying that He would, of His Infinite Mercy, grant this little sign and wonder that men might again come to believe in Him and in the Truths which He had revealed to them. Through Jesus, by Mary, by Michael, by John the Baptist, by Peter and Paul he prayed, through them and by them and round them and over them to God; and at half-past eleven precisely the Garden of Eden stirred on its foundations, heaved tremendously, arose slowly and surely into the air and was absorbed by the night into a cluster of coloured lights which disappeared rapidly in the direction of North Berwick.

'*Gloria Patri, et Filio, et Spiritui Sancto,*' murmured Father Malachy when he opened his eyes and saw what had happened.

'*Sicut erat in principio, et nunc, et semper, et in saecula saeculorum. Amen,*' answered Canon Collins, seizing Father Malachy by the arm and rushing across the street to the presbytery before the policeman on point duty could arrest them.

VII

Ten minutes later three figures in shimmering white made their way to the altar of an empty church lit only by six tall candles. '*Te Deum Laudamus,*' intoned Father Malachy and Father O'Flaherty, invisible in the organ loft, pulled out the stops and let her rip. '… *te Dominum confitemur,*' took up Canon Collins and Father Neary. '*Te aeternum Patrem, omnis terra veneratur. Tibi omnes Angeli, tibi coeli, et universae potestates; Tibi Cherubim et Seraphim, incessabili voce proclamant: Sanctus, sanctus, sanctus, Dominus Deus Sabaoth.*'

On it went, the glorious canticle of Ambrose and Augustine, louder and louder it grew, the heavenly thunder of sheer praise, louder and louder until it seemed that the whole church must burst from matter into sound and go soaring to join the hymns which angels sang round the Throne of God, louder and louder until the praise quietened to prayer and the three priests dropped to their knees in humble commemoration of the Redemption of men by Jesus Christ. And then, rising, they sang to God that He might save His People and that they, who had trusted in Him, should not be confounded for ever.

And when it was all over the three figures in shimmering white went as silently as they had come and the candles were put out and the church became again a huge darkness lighted by a single ruby lamp.

CHAPTER VI

At a quarter to ten on Monday morning Father Malachy, having said Mass at nine, sat down to breakfast (Canon Collins and Fathers Neary and O'Flaherty, having said the earlier Masses, had already breakfasted) and, mindful of the example of Saint Aloysius and the game of billiards, turned a natural operation into a supernatural one by buttering his bread to the glory of the Father and stirring his tea to the glory of the Son and nicking the top off his egg to the glory of the Holy Ghost. But, try as he would, he could not think as exclusively of heavenly things as he wanted because the events of the last thirty-four hours and a quarter kept switching in upon his consciousness and so, excusing himself on the ground that his intention was meritorious and that the earthly matters exercising his attention were as other-worldly as it was possible for them to be, he gave up the exclusively heavenly as a bad job and allowed his thoughts to follow his inclinations.

And, indeed, it was no wonder that he indulged himself in this manner because the miracle, which had begun by being a personal affair between himself and God, had ended by becoming everybody's business. It appeared that an attendant of the Garden of Eden had been the first to notice that anything out of the ordinary had occurred. He had been sent, so he had told the policeman on point duty, by a patron of the establishment at twenty-six or twenty-seven minutes past eleven to get a taxi-cab and, returning at twenty-five minutes to twelve with one of Mr. Dan T. Munro's brightest and reddest, he had found a great square hole in the ground where the Garden of Eden used to be. It had taken him quite three minutes to realise that the Garden of Eden had actually been bodily removed from its customary location and another five to persuade the taxi-driver that he hadn't been 'trying to take a loan of him,' so that it had been seventeen minutes to twelve before he had informed the policeman of the mysterious disappearance; and the policeman had quite naturally said 'Awa' and tell that to the marines' an 'Havers, man' several times before consenting to accompany the boy and the taxi-driver to the spot from which they said that the Garden of Eden had disappeared. Then, after a few slow nods of the head and a 'Weel, weel' or two, the representative of the law had pulled a notebook from his hip pocket and proceeded to ask those heavy, practical questions which Caledonian constables always ask when something has happened to upset the public order. 'Was ye sure ye was inside when the gentleman sent ye outside for to get a taxi?' 'And what would the gentleman be like? Young or old, fair or dark?' 'Oh, and he was with a lady, was he? Would she be a real lady or – or yin o' yon?' 'And when he got outside, did he notice any suspeecious folk loitering about? Any folk that might be anarchists or communionists or likely to have a bomb on them?' 'So he had noticed three clairgies, had he? looking as holy as though they were praying at a Band o' Hope meeting. Weel, weel, it couldna be the clairgies now, could it?' 'Did he no mind of seeing somebody mair – mair seenister than a clairgie or a meenister?'

By this time, however, quite a crowd had collected and everyone familiar with the district agreed that the Garden of Eden had disappeared and that, all things considered, it was a mighty queer kind of flitting for folks to make. Some remembered having seen it the day before, some that morning and some as recently as an hour previously and some, whom the policeman had later described as 'a lot o' claverin' sweetie wives', said that they had seen lights flying through the air above the London Road, and three topers, who had been leaning against the closed door of the public house on the other side of the street, swore that they had seen all the windows of the Garden of Eden go bang up into the sky like the scenery in a pantomime, but had concluded, not unnaturally, that the vision had been inspired by their last 'double'. Several, however, testified to seeing three clairgies or three meenisters 'standing as though they were praying like' outside the Garden of Eden and a free-thinking soldier on leave from Redford Barracks said that, in his opinion, the clairgies had looked 'awfy like as though they were Roamin' Catholickies' and so the policeman, followed by an ever-increasing crowd, had been forced to cross the street and ring the bell of the presbytery of the church of Saint Margaret of Scotland. And he had had to ring not once but many times because the servants were all asleep on the fourth floor and because the priests had not yet returned from singing the solemn *Te Deum* in church. At last, however, the bell had been heard and Canon Collins, who had expected something of the sort, had restrained Father Malachy from opening the door and they had all gone up to the spare bedroom on the first floor and Father Neary, hugely enjoying the fun, had raised the window sash and asked the policeman below what he wanted. 'It's about the Garden of Eden,' the policeman had said. 'It seems to have fleed awa' and this laddie here says that he saw three clairgies standing outside it just before it got lost. I was wondering if you gentlemen knew anything about it.' 'Yes,' Father Malachy had answered, pulling Father Neary back from the window, 'we know all about it. At half-past eleven tonight I, Malachy Murdoch, monk and priest of the Order of Saint Benedict, caused, by the power of God, the Garden of Eden to be transported through the air to the Bass Rock.' 'Michty me,' the constable had exclaimed, 'and what for did ye do a thing like yon?' 'To show the people that God is still as Powerful as He was and that Christ is King of this world as well as of the next,' Father Malachy had replied, and a youthful heretic had begun to whistle the tune of a song of which the words ought to have been: 'When it's Dimanche in Deauville it's Sunday over here.'

Mr Bolfry

JAMES BRIDIE

James Bridie, pseudonym of Osborne Henry Mavor (1888–1951) trained and worked as a doctor in Glasgow before turning full-time playwright in 1938 following stage successes. Bridie's popularity came from his ability to create convincing characters, his sense of theatre, his witty use of the supernatural and his facility in touching with just the right depth on topical matters of belief and morality. He belongs to the 'drama of ideas' begun by Ibsen and Shaw: one reviewer called his *Mr Bolfry* (1943), set in the home of a Highland 'Wee Free' minister, 'Manse and Super Manse'. Only in the late 1950s, as the new theatre of Osborne, Beckett and Pinter took hold, did his star wane.

Many of Bridie's plays contain the supernatural, usually of Christian or biblical provenance. In his most popular play *Tobias and the Angel* (1930) he uses the apocryphal story of Tobit who was helped by the angel Raphael to defeat a devil and restore his family fortunes; in several plays, from *The Sunlight Sonata* (1928) to *The Baikie Charivari* (1952), the devil and the seven deadly sins are dramatised. Bridie's targets shifts from 1920s indifference to the later scientific humanism which would deny that the devil – or indeed anything supernatural – exists. But Bridie himself steers clear of a Christian line: his view is 'I have told a story ... out of which you can take your own meaning'.

Mr Bolfry may have been inspired by C. S. Lewis's highly popular *The Screwtape Letters: Letters from a Senior to a Junior Devil* (1942). But Bridie's play had only a brief stage life, possibly because, against the polarising atmosphere of the war, he gives his devil a run for his money, and because he will not give clear answers. This devil's Blakean view of the universe as continual conflict is at one with the nature of drama itself. The Rev. McCrimmon has repressed his energies with his spirit. Here Bridie's vision is close to that presented by Stevenson in *Dr Jekyll and Mr Hyde*. The main impulse of the play is to show the universe far vaster and more exciting than people suppose.

The extract from the play, which is set during the Second World War, comes after the devil Bolfry has been called up through the reading of a spell of invocation by the unbelieving young people in the house. Jean is the niece of the Rev. McCrimmon, and Cully and Cohen are soldiers billeted in the manse. This is the central scene, the moment of most energetic conflict and revelation. Later the characters try to explain it away in terms of dreaming, drink or mass suggestion, until a final supernatural event in front of them all – the departure of Mr Bolfry's umbrella in quest of its master – throws the matter open again. Bridie is showing how man resists reality: Mrs McCrimmon ends, "'It's a funny thing we should be surprised at seeing the Devil and him raging through the skies and blotting out the sun at this very hour. We're all such a nice kind of lot that we've forgotten there's any such person'".

MR BOLFRY

BOLFRY. ... Ah, there you are, McCrimmon.

[*Re-enter* MR *and* MRS MCCRIMMON. MRS MCCRIMMON *is carrying a Minister's gown and white Geneva bands.*]

Well, my dear Sir, time is getting on. Shall we adjourn to the Kirk?

MCCRIMMON. No.

BOLFRY. No? But, my dear fellow, I thought it was all arranged.

MCCRIMMON. No. This is a dream, of course; but there must be decency even in dreams. Waking or sleeping, I will have no phantasmagorical equivocator preaching in my Kirk.

BOLFRY. A dream, eh? You think this is all a dream?

MCCRIMMON. What else can it be?

BOLFRY. What is the difference between a dream and a supernatural happening?

MCCRIMMON. The question does not arise. This is nothing but a highly circumstantial dream. I shall laugh at it the morning.

BOLFRY. The sign of a supernatural event is that it obeys all the laws of

Nature except one. You will find that true of every supernatural event from the Burning Bush to the Resurrection.

MCCRIMMON. There is truth in that.

BOLFRY. Has your room changed? Have the people around you changed? Does the clock go on ticking? This is not a dream, Mr McCrimmon.

MCCRIMMON. I am troubled in my mind, but I can yet hold fast to what there is to grasp. I will have no spectre or Devil preaching in my church.

BOLFRY (*in a low and sinister voice*). By the Throne of Thunder and the Canopy of Eternal Night ...

MRS MCCRIMMON. Now, now, then, Mr Bolfry, there's no need to excite yourself. You can preach here quite well. See, here's the wee reading-desk, and I've brought the Minister's second-best gown and bands. Put the desk on the table, Mr Cohen.

[COHEN *puts a small reading-desk on the table.*]

There now, that's fine. For Sabbath after Sabbath we had the diet of worship in this wee room when the Kirk was being done for the dry rot. We'll pull the chairs round, and Mr Bolfry will give us the grand sermon, I'm sure.

JEAN. Yes, Mr Bolfry. It would be better. Give me the gown, Auntie.

BOLFRY. What is there in Creation or beyond it that cannot be wheedled by women?

[JEAN *and* MRS MCCRIMMON *close in on him and invest him in the gown and bands. He is a little tipsy. The others arrange the furniture for the Sermon.*]

MRS MCCRIMMON. Well, well, that's no' very polite talk. Put your arm through here and content yourself.

JEAN (*with the bands*). How does this go, Auntie?

MORAG. There's a wee thingummy that catches behind the collar. Look you, I'll do it.

[MORAG *fastens the bands, while* JEAN *walks round for a front view.* MRS MCCRIMMON *smooths the robe.*]

JEAN. You look absolutely beautiful.

[BOLFRY *goes to the fireplace and surveys himself in the picture-glass. The others sit down round the table in silence.* BOLFRY *turns and goes to the makeshift Pulpit.*]

BOLFRY. You will find my text in the Gospel according to William Blake, that Poet and Prophet who walked to the edge of Hampstead Heath and put his finger through the sky. 'Now is the dominion of Edom and the return of Adam to Paradise.'

CULLY. Ha! Ha!

BOLFRY. What are you laughing at?

CULLY. Paradise! I can't help it.

BOLFRY. You must not laugh at Paradise.

CULLY. Have a look at your Paradise … Hunger and filth and disease and murder.

BOLFRY. Have a look at your Bible and don't interrupt my Sermon. You sit there in your squalid, drab, killer's clothes, with your squalid, drab mind and see nothing but your little bodily rough-and-tumble in your little thieves' kitchen of a world. Look up! The real War is beyond and about it. The War between Good and Evil. The Holy War. It is a War not to destroy, but to create. It is like the war between man and woman. If there were no war, God would go to sleep. The Kingdom of Heaven would wilt and wither. Death would conquer both Good and Evil and there would be Nothing. It is unbearable that there should be nothing. The War must go on.

For what, you ask me, do these forces fight? Their War Aims are plain. My Führer fights for the New Disorder; for disorder is perpetual movement and movement is Life. The Enemy has stated clearly his Ten Points, from Mount Sinai in a thunder storm. [We must not allow our reverence to stray from one single object. We must not create works of Art, nor devote ourselves to them. We must not conceive or propagate any idea about God that is not strictly true. We must do no work on the seventh day of the week. We must respect the Family. We must not destroy life. We must be faithful to our first love and desire no other woman. We must not live on another man's efforts. We must not lie about our neighbours. We must want nothing that another man has.]

To these are added two more powerful commands, spoken quietly on a hot and dusty day. We must love the Holy Spirit with all our strength and we must love Tom, Dick and Harry as ourselves.

To effect these things is impossible. It is admitted by the teachers that to do them is impossible to man; and man is the cleverest thing we know. But to the Holy Spirit, they say, everything is possible. By its Grace, they say, and by forcing the soul through Fire and Water up to Crucifixion itself man will at last achieve the impossible, which will be Victory.

I, the Devil, am Fire and Water. I hoist the gallows and drive the pike between the ribs. Without an enemy, there can be no Victory. Honour me, then, for my part in your triumph. Honour me for the day when you spurn the clouds written with curses, when you stamp the stony laws to dust, 'loosing the eternal horses from the dens of night'.

MCCRIMMON. Rhetoric! Rhetoric! Rhetoric! The Fathers have confuted you hundreds of years back.

BOLFRY. So much the worse for them.

MCCRIMMON. You are talking a parcel of old-fashioned Dualistic sophistications. You are a Manichaean.

BOLFRY. You are a liar.

COHEN. Order, order!

MCCRIMMON. I do not take issue with you for that word, because you are my own heart speaking in a dream. But it is sorrowful I am that it should be so.

BOLFRY. You are better than your neighbours, Mr McCrimmon. They would say that because a truth was sorrowful or distasteful, or inconvenient, it was therefore not a truth. That is why they will not believe what I have come to tell you; that Victory may go the other way.

MCCRIMMON. What do you mean?

BOLFRY. That the Gates of Hell may prevail against the armies of the Cherubim. That Disorder may win the day. If that were not possible, why do you wrestle and pray?

MCCRIMMON. God forbid that it should be so.

BOLFRY. God forbade Adam to eat an apple.

JEAN. What will happen if you win this War?

BOLFRY. Man's genius will burst its bonds and leap to meet the sun. The living, glorious animal in you will riot in the fields, and the soul will laugh for joy, naked but not ashamed. Your Self will be triumphant.

When I win, Man will be an individual. You may love your neighbour if you like, but all that is highest in you tells him to keep his distance. You don't know him. You will never know him. You are no longer a thing in a herd, crouching against your neighbour's wool to keep you from the cold. You are a man. You are a woman.

Onward, Christian Soldiers, shuffling along shouldered with your heavy packs, and your blistered feet, and the fear of Hell in your eyes. It's a rocky road to Zion, and what will you find when you get there? Your officers lash you on with curses and punishment and flatter you with Hope. There is no Hope in my country. No man hopes for what he has.

What are the virtues that keep you going? Courage? Honesty? Charity? I have them too. Courage is the reaction to Fear. You are more afraid than I am. Honesty is the reaction to lies. Charity is the reaction to hate and suspicion. My honesty spurns your superstitions. My charity embraces both the sheep and the goats.

My flags are the Pride of the Eye and the Lust of the Flesh. Their other names are Art and Poetry, and where they wave the abomination of desolation can never be.

How long, O Lucifer, Son of the Morning, how long? How long will these fools listen to the quaverings of impotent old priests, haters of the Life they never know?

How long will they swaddle their strong limbs in dusty parchments?

How long will they shut out the sky from their eyes with prisons of cold stone?

I tell you that all you have and all you know is your Self. Honour your Self and set him free; for the Soul and the Body are one, and their only home is the World, and their only life is the Flesh and their only friend is the Devil.

Let the wild horses loose!

MCCRIMMON (*rising*). In nomine Patris Aeternis, Filii et Spiritus Sancti, conjuro te, Sathanas ...

BOLFRY. Latin, eh? You've gone Papist, have you? You don't know your own regiment, my man.

MCCRIMMON. Away with you! Away with you out of my house!

BOLFRY. Take care, McCrimmon.

MCCRIMMON (*more quietly*). If you are, as I think you are, a bad dream and the voice of my own heart speaking evil, I will tear you from my breast if I die for it.

BOLFRY. Stay where you are. You said there was truth in what I told you— 'The sign of a supernatural event is that it obeys all the laws of Nature except one.' Think of that before you act too rashly.

MCCRIMMON. You said you were here to free the Self from its shackles. I am my Self, and myself is a Minister of the Gospel. I will follow my inclination, look you. And what is my inclination? It is to have the thrapple of you out by the roots.

[MCCRIMMON *suddenly takes up* CULLY'*s knife. The* WOMEN *scream.* BOLFRY *backs out of his pulpit and towards the door.*]

BOLFRY. You are not very wise, McCrimmon. You are not very wise.

MORAG. Stay in the circle. He will have you. He will have you.

JEAN. Uncle, don't be a fool.

MRS MCCRIMMON. Oh, no! Oh, no!

CULLY. Let him be. It's all right. Conk and I will look after him.

BOLFRY. You will have it, will you? Come along, then. Let's see you hunt the Devil over the moor.

[MCCRIMMON *breaks from* CULLY *and* COHEN *and makes for*

BOLFRY. BOLFRY *throws the gown over* MCCRIMMON'S *head and makes for the door. In a moment* MCCRIMMON *recovers himself and, flinging the gown over his shoulder like a cloak, follows* BOLFRY *through the doorway.*]

COHEN. Come on, Cully. There'll be murder done.

[*He runs through the doorway.*]

CULLY. Murder? Of what?

[*He follows* COHEN.]

MRS MCCRIMMON. Oh, such a like night to be out! And in his slippers, too. Well, well. We'll away to our beds.

JEAN. But, Auntie ... But ...

MRS MCCRIMMON. Och, we're dreaming all this. And I've a hard day's work before me tomorrow when I wake up. And moreover, when I do wake up, I'd like to it be decent-like in my bed. Away to your bed, Morag, girl.

&

The Green Isle of the Great Deep
&
The Well at the World's End

&

NEIL GUNN

Author of twenty novels, many on Highland life and community, Neil Gunn (1891–1973) spent much of his life in Caithness, Inverness and Ross-shire. Trained as a Customs and Excise officer, he worked in the service from 1911 to 1937 before becoming a full time writer; by then he had already written six novels, including the successful *Morning Tide* (1930) and *Highland River* (1937). In all his novels up to *The Green Isle of the Great Deep* (1944) Gunn celebrates life rooted in tradition and nature. As he saw it, 'tradition is the environment in which the creative spirit is at home to itself'. His vision is sometimes quite close to that of Lewis Grassic Gibbon, whose trilogy of rural life in Aberdeenshire, *A Scots Quair*, appeared from 1932–34, a year before the author's death: both too were 'diffusionists', believing that civilisation is a decline from the primitive culture centres from which it started out. Gunn was in his post-war novels to follow, like Gibbon's Chris Guthrie, a process of separation from the countryside before eventual return: but Gunn was not so much a bedrock mystic of the land as Gibbon, and in his last novels *The Well at the World's End* (1951) and *The Other Landscape* (1954), the Highlands are more the background than the focus, the central characters are rather cultured eccentrics than native Highlanders and the regenerative force, where it is found, comes more from women, music and Eastern mysticism. After completing this spiritual journey through his novels, Neil Gunn stopped writing for the twenty years before his death.

Naomi Mitchison, Gunn's friend, thought *The Green Isle of the Great Deep* was written for her; and indeed her explorations of organized utopias versus societies founded on natural magic is not far from his. Gunn however said he wrote *The Green Isle* by 1941, with the Russian purges of the 1930s, the Nazi concentration camps and the particular horror of brain-washing strongly in mind. The book was an unexpectedly huge success, selling 18,000 copies by 1948, though after 1949 it was eclipsed by Orwell's *Nineteen Eighty-Four*. While its obvious antecedents are Yevgeny Zamiatin's *We* (trans. 1924) and Aldous Huxley's *Brave New World* (1932), its immediate origin is in Gunn's own *Young Art and Old Hector* (1942), in which he celebrates the growth of a Highland relationship that is to be at the heart of *The Green Isle*: by the end of the former novel Hector and Art are about to make the long-delayed journey to the river to fish, the river from where they will go to the Green Isle.

In the Green Isle Hector and Art find what looks like a paradise but is in fact a tyranny ruled by a renegade clique of intellectuals who have brain-washed most of the citizens to mindless automata. Here 'mind' has become divorced from 'body' with the ruling group living in their citified Seat of the Rock, and innocence has been turned to vacuity. The descent of Hector and Art into Hazel Pool as they enter the Green Isle is partly one into the unconscious, as in many other Scottish fantasies. Here that unconscious will war with the intellect and win, just as the natural and primal community that Hector and Art represent will over-throw the organized ant-society they find. Old Hector is caught and the layers of his mind stripped away by a Questioner: but in his Highland subconscious is found not defeat, but God, who now returns to the Green Isle to restore it to its true nature.

In the extract here from *The Green Isle*, Young Art and Old Hector have just fallen through Hazel Pool to the Green Isle. We do not yet know whether they are dead or have stumbled on some paradise; and at this stage the beauty of the countryside and the normality of Hector and Art play against an early sense of something not quite right. The hazel-nuts Art finds in his pocket are a magnificent cluster he pulled from a tree by Hazel Pool: much is to be made later of these as nuts first of knowledge, then of wisdom, and then of redeeming magic (God).

The extract from *The Well at the World's End* is the opening chapter. The issue in this novel, as in *The Green Isle*, is where life's magic (or water) is to be found. Gunn is fond of circles: Art and Hector make a circle of youth and age; Peter here is to go alone on an odyssey which will bring him back to his wife Fand ('found'). For she is the well, and his return to her represents a renewal of their relationship. In this story Gunn acknowledged that he was also describing the renewal of his own relationship with his wife Daisy. The theme in this passage is that you cannot have what you want just when you think you want it, just as the sun-mote will not be trapped in Fand's hand: you will only find what you do not expect. Here too Gunn is criticising the mind's attempts to bend the world to its patterns: Peter the professor must become once more a student of life. As in all Scottish fantasy it is only by going into the unconscious, into less structured experience (Peter's subsequent wandering), that one can arrive at truth.

❧

The Green Isle of the Great Deep

❧

'I don't know the place at all,' said Old Hector, 'though I seem to remember it, too. The sea looks a bit bluer than the sea at home at this time of the year. Are you quite dry?'

'I'm fine,' said Art in a small voice, for the place was altogether strange to him.

'The grass is as green as I have ever seen. And look! there are some cows up there. We should be coming to a house soon. Are you hungry?'

'I'm not that hungry,' said Art. 'See! There's a man yonder.' And he held still closer to Old Hector.

'He'll be herding likely,' nodded Old Hector. 'It must be fertile land, this. Indeed it looks the finest country ever I have seen. And I can remember being on the Black Isle once, in behind Conon in Easter Ross, where the fine farms slope to the sea, and you see the mountains far away beyond the gleaming firth. I thought it very beautiful yonder in the autumn, but it hardly touches this.'

'Look! he's coming down,' whispered Art.

'That's fine. We should know where we are soon.'

They watched the man as he strolled down onto the road in front of them.

'It's a fine day,' Old Hector greeted him, smiling politely.

The man gave them a queer quizzical look as if he were thinking on the surface of his face.

'We are strangers here,' continued Old Hector, 'as you can see. We belong to the Clachdrum country and I was wondering if you would be so kind as to tell us the way to it.'

When the man's eyes had run over them, he said, 'You will continue along this road for three days, and then you will come to the Seat on the Rock, and you will report yourselves there.'

'Thank you very much,' replied Old Hector. 'Maybe we are a long way from Clachdrum then?'

'You are,' said the man.

'Would you at least tell me, if you please, what the name of this land is?' The man's eyelids flickered. 'It is called The Green Isle.'

'Thank you,' said Old Hector, with a polite nod to cover the jump of his heart. 'It looks very fertile country. You have some fine cows up there.'

'I am the Coastwatcher here,' said the man.

'Oh indeed,' said Old Hector. 'You will forgive me for not recognising the uniform. Have you many wrecks here-about?'

'None,' said the Coastwatcher. 'But folk arrive in many ways.'

'I see,' said Old Hector vaguely. 'Well, I suppose we may as well be going on.' But still he lingered. 'It will take three days, you say, to reach the – the place?'

'Three days and nights to reach the Seat on the Rock. And each night you will stay at an Inn. You will follow this road and not leave it, nor eat what you may see.'

'How will we know the Inn?'

'It is in a town which you will always reach at evening and the road takes you there.'

'I see,' said Old Hector. 'Will I mention that you told me to call?'

'I have already taken a note of your arrival.' The last look he gave them was over his shoulder, but it still stopped short of the shallow laugh as he moved away.

'He seems a merry fellow,' remarked Old Hector to the air in front, as Art and himself walked on.

There was silence for a time.

'I did not like that man,' whispered Art, with a backward glance. 'Did you?'

'I thought by his voice at first that he came from Gairloch, but they are kind folk in Gairloch,' answered Old Hector, 'even if some of them are narrow.'

'I thought,' said Art, keeping what fear he could from his voice, 'that he was laughing at us.'

'I don't know that he knew he meant it,' said Old Hector. Then he looked down at Art and smiled. 'Do you know what I think he was laughing at?'

'What?'

'At my whiskers.'

Art ventured a small smile himself then. 'Maybe it was,' he said hopefully. 'Do you think it would be?'

'Why wouldn't it? I have the feeling that nobody has whiskers on him in this land.'

'I was thinking that myself,' said Art. 'Are there no ones with whiskers in Gairloch?'

Old Hector gave a quiet chuckle. 'There are,' he said, and to Art he looked again as he used to look.

'Was that a good one?'

'Fair to middling,' said Old Hector, and Art gave a little hop.

The country now began to open out, for they had come over the sea-ledge, and presently they paused to look at what they saw before them. And indeed it was a picture. A broad, slowly-uprising valley, with fields of grain having the sunny yellow in them that gold has missed; parks of green trees, glistening with red and yellow points that must surely be singing birds; a village of houses and each house white as sleep in the afternoon; cool green acres everywhere with sometimes a purple haze; paths winding up the slopes and figures moving on them; and, passing through all, the road that caught a pale gleam as it topped the ridge far away and disappeared with the sky.

Art looked up at Old Hector, whose face was like the face of a fisherman holding the tiller in times that need cool judgment. 'Do you know this place?' he asked.

'No,' answered Old Hector, 'it is strange to me, but we'll hold on.'

Art took a good grip of his hand, and after a while he asked, 'What are they?'

'They are clusters of grapes,' answered Old Hector. 'I once saw them in a shop in Inverness.'

'Are they good to eat?'

'They say they are, but I have never tasted them.'

'There's a woman coming down there with a basket.'

But the woman did not come onto the road; instead, she stopped a few paces up, her eyes opening wide.

'It's a fine day,' called Old Hector politely.

She lowered the basket to the ground and stood still and erect in order to take them in. Then she laughed. She was a young woman and her laugh was bright and shallow.

Old Hector held on his way.

'Who do you think she was?' whispered Art.

'I think,' said Old Hector, 'that she was the sister of that Coastwatcher.'

Soon they discovered that the glistening spots on the trees were not singing birds but apples and oranges. And they looked more happy and tempting in the clear air than any clusters of nuts. When they passed under a tree which hung over a grassy bank and Art looked up, the juice of the orange soaked into its glowing colour in a way that brought water from under his tongue.

'I could climb that tree easy,' he said. When suddenly he saw a man's face behind the tree, he lowered his own and walked on with Old Hector.

Men and women were busy in the village, carrying the baskets of fruit to a space standing back from the square and marked out by poles, up which vines grew before they flattened and spread their branches in a cool green ceiling, from which flecks of light filtered through and danced over bare arms and faces and fruit.

As they packed the fruit in lattice-crates, the talk and cries, with a chattering of laughter, got mixed with the dancing specks. The skin of their arms and faces glowed as in firelight.

Suddenly all the specks stood still, the gabble and the laughter ceased, and the eyes steadied on the advancing strangers, as if a stream had stopped flowing.

As they passed there was a ripple of laughter, and in no time the speckled stream was more noisily flowing than ever.

Feeling the laughter in his back, Art was attacked by an urgent desire to cry.

'Keep your heart up,' Old Hector rallied him. 'They don't mean any harm.'

'P-perhaps,' stuttered Art, 'they k-know no better.'

'You're the best fellow for a joke in a whole day's march,' nodded Old Hector.

Art was somewhat cheered at that, for he was always surprised to find he had made a joke. Often he had only to repeat what he had heard some old person say and it was enough.

'Is it a g-good one?' he asked.

'One of the very best,' nodded Old Hector, laughing in his nostrils. 'We'll keep our own end up whatever.'

Singing now reached them, thin and clear. Children's voices from a wide building with a great flat roof. They decided it must be the school. Art felt more frightened than he had yet been, and Old Hector had to quicken his step.

'I know what they were singing,' said Art, when they were well past.

'What was it?'

'It was about the farmer's wife who cut off the tails of the blind mice with a carving knife.'

'Was it?'

'It was. We got it in school.'

'It's an odd song to be singing in a place like this,' murmured, Old Hector thoughtfully. There was a moment when the clear bright voices had seemed to him innocent as the voices of angels.

As they were going out of the village they saw coming towards them a man who, though the oldest they had yet encountered, had not even a moustache on him. His face, however, was grave, and that was a welcome change.

'It's a fine day that's in it,' said Old Hector with his friendliest courtesy.

The man stood and looked at Old Hector and his thought worked just below the skin of his face.

'Every day is fine here,' he said.

'I'm thinking,' replied Old Hector, gathering his scattered wits, 'it's not much use us looking for Clachdrum in that case!'

The stranger did not smile.

'We were told,' proceeded Old Hector, and Art felt his hand working in its stress, 'that we were to report at the Seat on the Rock. Will it be far in front of us yet?'

'You will reach it on the third day.'

'We were in such a hurry,' said Old Hector, 'that we forgot to take anything with us.'

'Each night you will come to a town and you will stay in the Inn.'

'But we have nothing with us to pay for our keep?'

'You have enough.'

'Thank you,' said Old Hector, in the silence. 'We are much obliged to you.'

The man stood still, following them with his eyes until they had gone past.

Art was frightened to look back. 'I would like to go home,' he said.

Old Hector comforted him, saying that this was an adventure and that all life, from its beginning to its end, was an adventure.

'I'm thirsty,' said Art.

'And there's a well.'

The well was so crystal clear that Art could not see the water except where it was running out. But when he had drunk, he felt cool.

Old Hector wiped the water from his beard and sat down; 'It's good water, that,' he said. 'Very good.'

'It's a pity,' said Art, 'you didn't ask him if we could take an apple.'

'Are you very hungry?'

'I am,' said Art. 'I could be doing with something.' And, putting his hand thoughtlessly into his pocket, he found the nuts. Proud he was when Old Hector complimented him, and he ran around looking for a stone, but not a stone could he find. Then he remembered his teeth. But though he kept shifting the nut into new positions with his tongue, he could not crack it.

'Have you your knife?' asked Old Hector.

'I have,' said Art, and in a sudden fear gripped at the secret pocket. The knife was still there, and——'More nuts!'

They both remained still.

'The nuts of knowledge,' added Art in a hushed voice.

'Let us leave them yet a while,' said Old Hector. He took one of the other nuts and, cutting off its very tip, disclosed a thin line into which he pushed the point of the blade, levering it from side to side as he did so. The shell split in neat halves, and he offered the kernel to Art.

The kernel he brought forth for himself he sliced into small pieces, for his teeth, he said, were not too good.

When they had thus eaten six of the nuts they drank again.

'Are you feeling any better?'

'Not much,' answered Art.

As they moved on, Old Hector saw the shells lying on the road, so he returned and picked them up and shoved them into the roots of the grass.

They discussed this act, which neither of them had ever done before, as they continued on their way.

When at last they came to the crest, they saw another valley, broader and longer than the last, and far in the distance they saw a small white town, and remote beyond that the line of the horizon. The light was surely fading slightly, for now it was as if in all space there was only endless distance.

Old Hector began to tell Art a story, and the story was about a man who went on an adventure, and no matter what happened to him he refused to give in. The dangers he encountered were so fearsome and terrible that, by contrast, this adventure they were on was something to look forward to.

But Art did not look forward to it, and when at last in the half light they saw the town only a mile or two ahead, he stopped. He was terrified to go to the Inn.

Old Hector's reasoning now had no effect except a bad one, for the clearer the reason the worse Art got.

'Hush!' said Old Hector, following the boy as he ran up a little path by an orchard. The workers were all gone from the land and it was quiet. In a hollow at the top or back of the orchard was a great pile of straw. Art felt safe now, for he knew it was real straw by its smell.

'Look at that tree,' he said as they sat down to rest. It was a big tree and wide-branching, and the apples that grew on it were ruddy and gold in the evening light. The more Old Hector looked, the quieter the tree became, until its stillness held the beauty that being pure was strangely ominous, and into his mind came the words: *The tree of knowledge of good and evil.*

Presently he heard Art's low voice: 'What land do you think this is?'

'The Coastwatcher called it the Green Isle.'

'Do you think,' asked Art, 'it might be the Green Isle of the Great Deep?'

'How could it be? because the Green Isle of the Great Deep is Paradise.'

But as he gazed on the tree, Old Hector was sorely troubled.

The Well at the World's End

Peter Munro stared into the well that was so obviously dry.

'What an extraordinary thing!' he said, and his mouth remained slightly open in a face that shed its last trace of academic life.

His wife looked past his shoulder as if she could not always trust him to see what was before his nose, remarking thoughtfully, 'The old woman said there was water.' The pebbles on the well's bottom were blue and brown and beautifully clean, and it seemed to her that though the well had gone dry it still retained the memory of water, as pebbles in a cave the memory of the sea. It was shadowed by great clumps of fern and the bank was mottled with flakes of summer sunlight coming through the trees.

'Look!' Side-stepping both him and the well, she quickly parted some heavy fronds and exposed a delicate growth of maidenhair fern.

His brows gathered and his mouth closed, for she had at times a genius for being irrelevant. He stared at the well again, then looked about him for water with which to fill the small tin kettle in his hand. 'I can't understand it.'

She gave him a sidelong glance; saw a finger of sunlight picking out the occasional silver strand in his dark-brown hair, burnishing his well-cut nose and glancing off the sweat on his near cheek-bone. The grey-green tweed suited him and she would have to get the oil smear off his jaw – but not at the moment.

'I expect it's all this tourism,' he said with an irony as dry as the well. A wren let out an astonishing volume of song from hazel twigs on top of the bank. In a blue flash her eyes found the small brown body, as round as a penny and not much bigger.

'It's the first time I have ever gone to a door in the Highlands for a drop of water,' he said, 'and been told to fetch it myself from a dry well.' Then he started back along the path towards the main road.

It was his wife who had gone to the door, and she now withdrew her eyes from the maidenhair fern, from the roots of the hazel twigs where the wren was active as a mouse, and glanced up at the birch branches. Spangles of sunlight smote her eyes and the whole small glen went dappled and dizzy. Marching on in front went her athletic husband, and even he seemed to waver as the spangles flowed over his head and his shoulders and winked on the tin kettle.

But before he had gone thirty yards he stopped as though he had not yet told her what was wrong exactly and in detail. 'I'm not blaming the old woman,' he explained. 'She doesn't keep a cow, she said, and she has no milk. She hasn't even water. No wonder. People think they can call at any remote house and be helped to everything.'

'Never mind,' she said, 'it's a lovely day and we'll find water farther on.'

'That's not the point,' he said. 'However,' and he stalked on.

As he came by the main road and saw the top of the small cottage beyond the thorn hedge on the other side he stopped again. 'I have a good mind to go and ask her what she meant.'

'I wouldn't. She's a poor thing.'

'But why did she send us to the well?'

'You heard her telling me we could get water there and I thought it might perhaps be a nice place to make our tea.'

He looked at her.

'She would not have told us,' she said, 'unless she got water there herself. She's too old to keep a cow.'

'But how on earth could she get water———?' He gave her up and walked to the old car with which he had been struggling for an hour. The taste of the petrol jets was still in his mouth. He had got one leg in at the driving door, when he saw the old woman's head above the hedge. 'I'm afraid there's no water in your well,' he called.

'Oh yes,' she answered. 'There's always water in the well.'

'But we looked into it.'

She smiled. 'That well is never dry.'

He drew his leg out. She had a rosy wrinkled face like some memoried moony fruit, and the white cap that fringed it had corrugations round the edge like the ghost of a mutch.

It was too much. With the odd feeling of having hunted the wrong well in another world, he turned abruptly away and went striding down the same path looking for the right well. It was a hot day, and with the back of his oily hand he now smeared his brow. You had to hand it to women when it came to the irrational. But at least he would have the satisfaction of proving to himself … His feet brought him on the only path that ended, beyond doubt, at the same dry well.

It was astonishing. Before a thought more irrational than any woman's could quite touch his mind he argued it away. For a man can always see where the surface of water, however crystal, touches the sides of its container. There *is* a difference between air and water. All he had got to do was pick up a handful of dry pebbles from the bottom.

But he could not move and his eyes stared as though fascinated by some invisible spirit in the well. Then with the air of one on the brink of some extraordinary revelation he stooped and slowly put his hand down, and his hand went into water.

She saw him sitting by the well as she came with the tin kettle in her hand, and when she stood still the shaft of sunlight had time to hunt out flakes of yellow from her hair as it had hunted grey strands from his, though in age there was little between them. Her eyelids crinkled in thoughtful wonder, then she went on with watchful ease, ready beforehand for any kind of revelation.

He turned his head and glanced up her slim length to her face. There was something beyond humour in his expression, a marvelling, a critical looking at her that actually sent her eyes in a swift sweep over her clothes, as if something astonishing or ludicrous might have got exposed somewhere. After twenty years of married life this sort of incalculable moment between them could be as fresh and vivid as it had ever been.

He got up. 'Come here, Fand,' he said in the quiet voice that made her advance tentatively. 'Dip your kettle.'

'What is it?'

'Go on! Down with it.'

When the kettle touched the water she cried out as if she had been stung.

How beautiful, how incredible the waves of the crystal water! She got to her knees and watched them. The smile played in her eyes like the waves in the well. That they should have been deceived! The humour of it was a sheer gift, a fairy tale that shook her into laughter.

'Extraordinary,' said his voice above her. 'I can't get over it.'

Slowly she pushed the kettle under until it was full to the brim, then got to her feet and looked about her. 'We'll make the tea here.'

'Sit down. There's no hurry. Haven't we got two months?'

She sat down beside him.

NEIL GUNN

'Light,' he said.

'It made me dizzy for a moment when the spangles moved on you going along the path.'

'At first I laughed. That there should have been water in the well when we were so certain it was dry! Water so clear we thought it wasn't there! Then – all at once – the queer feeling came over me that we were at the beginning of an adventure – setting out to find the – the something in life that we think isn't there.'

'You have long been wanting to do that,' she said.

'Do what?'

'Go away and find the well at the world's end.'

At a rare moment she had a way of making an extravagant remark sound like practical sense. She was looking at a round fleck of light on her wrist. She opened her long bony hand and drew it back until the fleck lay on her palm. Slowly she began to close her fingers, then snapped them shut, but the sunbeam danced onto her knuckles.

Magnus
&
An Epiphany Tale

GEORGE MACKAY BROWN

George Mackay Brown (1921–96) lived almost all his life in Orkney, and the islands are the setting for most of his work. First a poet, Brown turned to the novel with *Greenvoe* (1972), on contemporary life, and then in *Magnus* (1973) to life in twelfth-century Orkney under earl and later saint Magnus. Brown also moved to the short story, with *A Calendar of Love* (1967); later collections included *A Time to Keep* (1969), *Hawkfall* (1974), *The Sun's Net* (1976), *Andrina* (1983) and *The Masked Fisherman* (1989). He also wrote books for children. Both in poetry and prose Brown has long stood in the forefront of Scots writing.

Love of Orkney and love of God are at the heart of Brown's work. As a Roman Catholic his joy in nature is sacramental: but he does not start from his faith so much as let it flare out from his acute sense of the this-ness of things. In this he is close to his favourite poet Gerard Manley Hopkins. There is no easy assurance, however; the vision is clear and hard, like the rocky scenery and the harsh sea; the tales are often of terrible loss, of evil, of strangled good, which are the mortal and fallen condition, set amidst the varied beauties of a changeless landscape. Time is at the heart of Brown's work, time remote and time near, time diurnal and time aging; time which destroys, enriches, mocks; time which, far off or too near to see, is in God's hand.

Brown had treated the story of St Magnus, whose death he thought 'the most vital event in all Orkney's rich history', several times before his novel. His source here is the twelfth-century *Orkneyinga Saga*. Magnus was by the overlord King of Norway made joint-earl of Orkney with his cousin Hakon, but through rivalry was killed; a pacifist and conciliator, Magnus put himself in God's hand. Brown describes Magnus's life as a piece of cloth being woven on a divine loom of light. The weaving catches up the stories of other martyrs and sacrifices throughout time, all within the eternally present Passion of Christ. The cloth is enriched with an aching sense of nature's passing beauty. Brown's novel is itself a new weaving of the story, its words, sentences and chapters fresh colours in the incessant loom of martyrdom.

In the extract from *Magnus*, Magnus is not yet joint-earl. He has just returned from a raiding expedition with the King of Norway against the men of Anglesey, in which he has shown himself a pacifist. His supernatural visitant here might of course be a delusion; as also when he speaks later in the church during Magnus's Gethsemane. After his visit, the short paragraphs begin to click like time.

The short story, 'An Epiphany Tale' (1980), is an example of Brown's fondness for the rhythms of folktale, and his impulse towards the elemental. This is his style at its barest and most symbolic. The story shows us the miracle of the world to which familiarity blinds us; but it also figures the glimpses of heaven with which we are occasionally visited. And because the Epiphany is Christ's manifestation of himself to the Gentiles in the form of the Magi, the promise here is of more lasting gifts.

❦

*M*AGNUS

❧

IT was said, concerning the holy martyr Magnus, that to gain his soul's kingdom he had to suffer five grievous temptations, and but that he was upheld then and ever and near the hour of his blessed martyrdom by a certain comforter that was sent to him, his soul might have been overborne by the evil one and brought down into the fires of hell.

This stranger appeared unto Magnus first at the time that the king of Norway was in the Orcades, busking him for a warcruise as far as Wales and Ireland (but none knew then what the king intended.) Magnus Erlendson was then a young man, and stood betwixt the arch and the king's ship, with the other young men, his companions, waiting on the king's word and command. While the other young men were disputing and laughing at the shore, with their hawks and harps and swords, Magnus stood apart and alone. The stranger came down it seemed to Magnus from the cloister and called him by his name, and said, 'The loom is set for thee now.' Magnus did not by any means understand the man's speech. The man put upon Magnus a look of much sweetness and gravity and said, 'Now that thou art a man, Magnus, thou must weave well upon the loom of the spirit. Thou canst weave whatsoever thou desirest, the white fold of blessedness, or darkness, or Joseph's coat of many colours.' Then Magnus said, 'Tell me thy name.' But the man would only say that he was the keeper of the loom, and that he was sent to guard the soul of Magnus from hurt. 'For,' saith he, 'there is another stranger that will presently appear unto thee, my dark opposite, the tempter. He will come to thee in many subtle disguises. The tempter and I are never far from one another. Nay, we are as close as twins. We wrestle forever upon the mountain of eternity, above the dark vale where dwell the tribes of men. This tempter will contrive if so he can to ruin thy loom, he will seek with many cunning devices to bring thy soul into hell. Look where he cometh now.' Magnus looked and saw approaching him from the door of the great hall Egil the chamberlain: who saith to Magnus that he brought great tidings. The king (said Egil) had decided on war. He would sail the *Sea Eagle* as far south as Ireland and Wales and Cornwall. Then Magnus asked what innocent throats were like to be cut that summer? And he asked what churches would have stone removed from stone, and what mills were like to be burnt? But Egil said, 'You must sail on the king's ship, Magnus. You are destined to be a hero and a great warrior. The king has done you a particular honour. He has made you his cup-bearer, you are to stand at the king's shoulder when he dines on shipboard.' Then Egil gave Magnus an axe for the war-cruise. 'This weapon,' he said, 'will bring you much fame and glory.' Magnus said that Egil should rather bring him a psalter down to the ship. He said that he would follow the king to the wars, for that the king was the anointed servant of God and so it behoved all subjects to obey him. Then, after Egil had departed in much wonderment, the stranger returned and said to the young man, 'The first white threads are in the loom now, Magnus. Your prayers, prayers uttered on your behalf, right actions, blessings put upon you, holy observances, penances, pilgrimages, all will be woven into the immaculate garment.'

Then the stranger bade Magnus go in peace to the war.

March fell, a cold wave of light, over the islands.

It laved the world.

It passed through the bodies of the young men and girls. It left them clean and trembling for love.

The wave surged on. The sun climbed. In April the body of Magnus took a first kindling, blurrings of warmth and light. A slow flush went over his body.

The beasts in the field quenched their black flames, one on another.

The hill was opened by the plough. Fire and earth had their way one with another. Was everywhere the loveliest spurting of seed and egg and spawn.

Girls felt into the rockpool, flowed, climbed out into the sun with sweet silver streaming bodies. They shrieked.

Magnus burned.

Hold Ragnarson's voice in the garden, 'What's wrong, Magnus? I can get you a girl. I know them all.'

Mans left the ox in the furrow. His fist trembled on the latch. Hild inside was baking bread. It was noon. Earth hands mingled with fire hands.

The cold voices in the stone web, *Simile factum est regnus caelorum homini regi qui fecit nuptias filio suo*. A certain king made a great wedding.

Magnus carried his tormented body into the church. Holy water glittered at fingers and forehead. He knelt. He prayed.

The tinkers left the cliff hollows brimming with the crushed smells of seapink, trefoil, daisy.

Hold Ragnarson again. 'What's wrong, Magnus? A young man in your position could have as many girls as he wanted.'

A wedding, then. Some of his friends – Hakon, Sigurd, Finn – were already married. The lusts of men are sanctified with ceremony.

'Magnus, there is a certain girl in Shetland called Ingerth Olafsdotter. Olaf has a large farm there. Ingerth is beautiful, chaste, modest. Think of it, Magnus. You are to be earl here in Orkney one day – there must be children to follow you ...' The mother's voice – Thora. She had seen the stirrings and burnings in him.

The sun went down. The lovers came out like moths. They tormented one another in the two-tongued invisible flame that burned between them in the first darkness. The mouth of Hold Ragnarson touched a white shoulder. The girl moaned between shame and desire.

At midnight a young man entered the rockpool, a dark solitary flame.

'My lord, the ship left Shetland on Friday, with Ingerth.' ... Hold Ragnarson's voice in the garden, envious and glad.

The fires of creation. Out of the mingled fires of men and women come new creatures to people the earth. This is a good ordinance of God. A certain king made a marriage feast. 'Magnus, thou art bidden now to the marriage.' ... 'No, but I cannot come, for that I am myself to be a bridegroom soon.' ... 'Magnus, thou art bidden to the marriage feast of Christ with his church' ... 'No, but I cannot come, for that I have to study statecraft and the duties of a ruler; but I wish well to the ceremony and the guests.' ... 'Magnus, thou art summoned.' ... 'No, but I have no suitable clothes to put on. See what I wear on my body – a garment scorched and stained with the burnings of desire.' ... 'Magnus, there is a coat being woven for thee for the wedding. I have told thee.'

Magnus awoke from the dream. The friend stood no longer in the room. The taste of ashes was in his mouth.

'My lord, Ingerth will leave the ship at noon.'

Contrariwise, the hideous fires of hell, even here on earth: these flame through the bodies of a man and a woman in lust unsanctified and uncreative. It may chance that, learning wisdom, this man and this woman exchange rings, and so turn lust into love, and enter kindly (with children growing about them) a slow winter of wisdom and withering. But if not, they are bound upon a wheel of torment that will carry them down into uttermost burning depths.

Magnus stood on the shore.

His mouth touched the sweet shivering mouth of the girl from the north. All around them the faces smiled. Erlend and Thora smiled. Hold Ragnarson winked lewdly. The bishop said that the wedding of Magnus and Ingerth would be celebrated immediately after Easter. Ingerth was taken by an old woman and a girl up to her chamber.

After the marriage, after the giving of rings, after the feast of harps and honey and wine, Magnus stood in the marriage chamber. Hold Ragnarson unthonged a shoe, and laughed, and nudged Magnus in the ribs, and went away into the darkness. The bride was brought by dimpling women to his door. The flame was in her. It wavered in her hands and breast and mouth. But from Magnus came no answering flame to mingle with hers. Now, at the moment of supreme earthly felicity, the fires that had tormented him were out.

Magnus looked at Ingerth hopelessly. He shook his head. The bed lay between them white and unbroken.

Magnus slept in his own room. He dreamed. He was in a place of burnings and ice. 'No,' said the voice of the friend beyond a fold of green wavering fire, 'but there is love indeed, and God ordained it, and it is a good love and necessary for the world's weal, and worthy are those who taste of it. But there are souls which cannot eat at that feast, for they serve another and a greater love, which is to these flames and meltings (wherein you suffer) the hard immortal diamond. Magnus, I call thee yet once more to the marriage feast of the king.' ... Magnus opened his eyes. He lay in his own room in the great Hall; but he that called himself 'the keeper of the loom' had vanished.

From that hour – it is said – Magnus enrolled himself in the company of the virgins.

Yet for the sake of state and of policy and of the high position into which he had been born, Magnus lived in the great Hall with Ingerth his bride.

And the fire that had long tormented the bridegroom began to harden to a cold precious flame.

Fire and fire burned in their different intensities.

The women saw, after a week, how it was with Ingerth. She was like a bee imprisoned in a burning window. Magnus saw it too. He wept for the bitter ordinances of time.

The bride stood often on the cliff looking over the sea northwards.

Subtle witherings began to appear in her flesh before the summer was over.

Yet they lived in the same house and grew in time to have a tender regard one for another.

Hold Ragnarson, checking his laughter, looked bewildered from one face to the other.

That winter Ingerth sat at her loom in the great chamber and made a heavy winter coat for her husband (the equinox was past, and the north wind was putting the first black gurls on the sea beyond Birsay.)

Magnus came up from the beach carrying a great halibut on his back. He had been fishing with Hold and Sigurd all morning.

Ingerth turned on him then eyes of longing and peace and love.

To Hold Ragnarson, since he continued to be perplexed at the cold marriage, Magnus one evening when they were alone together at the shore tried to explain – as best he could, and with many silences and hesitancies – what had happened.

'How shall I put it, my dear friend? It isn't that the rage of fire – which you so shrewdly observed in me in March and April – has died down. No, it is fiercer than ever. But it is no longer fixed on one object – the fertile conduit in the sweet flesh of woman – it has undergone a transmutation, it is diffused in a new feeling, a special regard for everyone who walks the earth, as if they all (even the tinkers on the road) were lords and princes. And this regard – it extends beyond human beings to the animals, it longs to embrace even water and stone. This summer I began to handle sea, shells, larks' eggs, a piece of cloth from the loom, with a delight I have never known before, not even as a child. You remember that morning last week when we fished with five Birsay men off Marwick Head. I had the helm myself. You remember that great lithe cod that was drawn in on the hook. Mans from Revay caught it. I was pierced with the beauty and the agony of the creature. But when I saw the practical hands of the fishermen setting to work at once with the knife, I knew that of course such cruelty is needful in the world. Pain is woven through and through the stuff of life. Ingerth is suffering now, because of me. I suffer too, because of Ingerth and everyone I have had dealings with. Is God to blame for all this suffering? What an empty question! Look at the agony on this crucifix I have round my neck. This crucifix is the forge, and the threshing-floor, and the shed of the net-makers, where God and man work out together a plan of utter necessity and of unimaginable beauty ...'

Hold Ragnarson smiled at the deep sincerity of his friend – expressed in falterings and sudden fluencies – and at the beauty of the images he uttered, as they walked together along the cliff verges of Marwick that sunset. He smiled with simulated understanding, but in truth he was more perplexed than ever.

*A*N *E*PIPHANY *T*ALE

There was once a small boy and he was deaf and dumb and blind.

He knew nothing about Christmas. All he knew was that it got cold at a certain time of the year. He would touch a stone with his fingers. His fingers burned with frost!

One day the boy was sitting on his mother's doorstep wrapped in a thick coat and scarf against the cold.

A stranger came and stood above him. There was a good smell from the stranger's hands and beard. It was different from the smell of the village people; the fishermen and the shepherds and their women and children and animals. The man smelt of sunrise.

The stranger touched the boy's ear. At once he could hear all the village sounds – the sea on the stones, his mother at the hearth baking scones, the seagulls, and the children playing in the field.

'No,' his mother was saying to the stranger, 'I don't want to buy a pan or a fork from your pack. No use speaking to the boy – he's deaf as a stone. Look, I'll give you a scone to eat. We're poor. I have no money to buy a thing.'

The boy didn't understand what the stranger and his mother said. The interchange of sounds seemed to him to be more wonderful than anything he could ever have imagined, and the most wonderful was the stranger's voice.

It said, 'Thank you for the bread, woman.'

Soon the stranger was no longer there. He had taken his rich silk smell and his clanging treasure away. The boy sat on the doorstep as the multitudinous harp of the world was stroked again and again. His mother kneaded dough on the board and stoked the peat fire.

Then the doors of his ears were closed once more. He laughed, silently.

Another smell drifted across the boy's nostrils, different from anything he had known. It was like incense of darkness, a circling of bright swift animals.

The second stranger touched the boy's eyes. They opened. The things he saw all at once amazed him with their beauty and variety. A few flakes of snow were falling on the dead ditch-grass. Gray clouds huddled along the sky. A cat crossed the road from a fishing-boat below with a small fish in its mouth.

Two people were arguing in the door. The white strenuous kind face must be his mother's. The black smiling face belonged to the stranger. Both were beautiful.

The boy's looked into the gloom of the house. The flames in the hearth were so beautiful it gave him a catch in the breath.

Clearly his mother was refusing to have anything to do with the objects the stranger was spreading out before her: soft shining fabrics, ivory combs, a few sheets with music and poems on them. The boy did not know what they were – each was marvellous and delightful in its different way.

At last his mother, exasperated, took a fish that had been smoking in the chimney. She gave it to the black man. He smiled. He tied up his pack. He turned to the boy and raised his hand in a gesture of farewell.

The boy's mother shook her head: as if to say, 'There's no point in making signs to this poor child of mine. He's been as blind as a worm from the day he was born.'

Then, to her amazement, the boy raised a blue wintry hand, and smiled and nodded farewell to the second stranger.

For an hour the boy's eyes gazed deep into the slowly-turning sapphire of the day. His mother moving between fire and board; the three fishermen handing a basket of fish from the stern of their boat to half-a-dozen shore-fast women; the gulls wheeling above; the thickening drift of flakes across the village chimneys; a boy and a girl throwing snowballs at each other – all were dances more beautiful than he could have imagined.

Then the luminous stone dulled and flawed. Between one bread dance and another, while his mother stood and wiped her flame-flushed brow at the window, she became a shadow. The boy was as sightless as he had ever been. He laughed, silently.

It was the most wonderful day the boy had ever known. And still the day wasn't over.

He was aware of a third presence at the door, lingering. This stranger brought with him smells of green ice, flashing stars, seal-pelts.

The mother, at her wits' end now, mixed with those smells of the pole her own smells of flour and butter and peat-smoke. The boy knew that his mother was angry; the smells came from her in fierce thrusting swirls.

It was enough to drive the most importunate pedlar away, but the man from the far north stood mildly at the threshold. The boy could imagine a bland quiet smile.

His mother's anger never lasted long. Another smell came to the boy's quivering nostrils: ale. His mother had poured a bottle of ale for the stranger, to refresh him for his journey. And now the smells of ice and fire and malt mingled gently in the doorway.

'I wonder,' thought the boy, 'what they're saying to each other? The same beautiful things as before, I expect. Their hands and their mouths will be making the same good shapes.'

It seemed a marvel to him that his ears and his eyes had been opened both in one day. How could any human being endure such ravishment of the senses, every hour of every day for many winters and summers?

The winter sun was down. The boy felt the first shadow on the back of his hand.

It was the time now for all the villagers to go indoors for the night. But this day they didn't go straight home. The fishermen and their wives and children came and lingered on the road outside the boy's door. He could smell the sweet milk breath of the children, and the sea breath of the men and the well-and-peat breath of the women. (Also he could smell the ashen breath of one old villager who would, he knew, be dead before the new grass.)

The villagers had come to stare at the stranger. The aroma of malt ebbed slowly. The boy felt the stone shivering; the stranger, having drunk, had put down his pewter mug on the doorstep.

Then he felt the touch of a finger on his locked mouth. He opened it. All his wonder and joy and gratitude for this one festival day gathered to his lips and broke out in a cry.

His mother dropped her baking bowl on the floor, in her astonishment. The bowl broke in a hundred pieces.

The old man who was soon to die said he had heard many rare sounds in his life, but nothing so sweet and pure as the boy's one cry.

The youngest villager was a child in her mother's arms that day. She remembered that sound all her life. Nothing that she heard ever afterwards, a lover's coaxing words, or a lark over a cornfield, or the star of birth that broke from the mouth of her own first child, no utterance seemed to be half as enchanting as the single incomprehensible word of the dumb boy.

Some of the stupider villagers said he had made no sound at all. How could he? – he had never spoken before, he would never utter a word again. A mouse had squeaked in the thatch, perhaps.

The stranger left in the last of the light. He joined two other darkling figures on the ridge.

The villagers dispersed to their houses.

The boy went indoors to the seat beside the fire. How flustered his mother was! What a day she had had! Her baking interrupted by three going-around men – her best blue china bowl in smithereens – her poor boy stricken with wonderment in the shifting net of flame shadows! She had never seen him like this before. He touched his ears, his eyes, his mouth, as if his body was an instrument that he must prepare for some great music.

And yet, poor creature, he was as dumb and deaf and blind as he had ever been.

The boy sat and let the flame-shadows play on him.

The mother washed her floury hands in the basin. Then she crossed the flagstone floor and bent over him and kissed him.

He sat, his stone head laved with hearth flames.

❧ ʟANARK ❧

ALASDAIR GRAY

Alasdair Gray (1934–), artist and writer, has lived for most of his life in Glasgow. He attended the Glasgow Art School (1952–57) and, until the success of *Lanark* in 1981, struggled to support himself (and after 1963 a family) through painting and drawing commissions, teaching and writing plays for radio and television. Since 1981 he has been able to devote himself to his writing with the assurance of publication: among his works are the collection of short fantastic tales *Unlikely Stories, Mostly* (1983) and the near-fantasy *Poor Things* (1992). *Lanark* however is his major work, and was almost singly responsible for the transformation of the Scottish novel in the 1980s. And since its appearance, much Scottish fantasy has had its form of clashing planes of textualised reality, which is called 'postmodernist'.

Lanark was begun as far back as 1952, as a semi-autobiographical account of a struggling Glasgow artist called Duncan Thaw who is finally driven to suicide. This was to become Books 1 and 2 of the eventual *Lanark: A Life in Four Books*, but Gray first tried unsuccessfully to have Book 1 published separately in 1963. At an early stage Gray intended to mix the Thaw story with another about a Kafkaesque afterworld with a central character called Lanark, which appeared as Books 3 and 4 of *Lanark* when published. But in *Lanark* the sequence of the books is disrupted to 3, 1, 2, 4 thus dislocating time and enfolding the Glasgow world of Thaw within the (devouring) world of Lanark.

The novel starts with Lanark living in the darkened city of Unthank. He gradually falls sick, like many others around him, of a disease of 'dragonhide', whereby the flesh is progressively covered by a hard scaly shell. Horrified at his world, he finds a way out of it through a giant pair of lips in a graveyard, and falls into a huge hospital institute beneath a mountain. There he is cured of his dragonhide and is then advanced from patient to doctor. He finds Rima, his girlfriend from the 'upper' world there, and heals her. In Book 4 Lanark and Rima dare to leave the institute (which hardly ever happens) and return to the town from which Lanark started; thereafter Lanark finds himself trying to cure the ills of the whole world. In the middle of this account we have Books 1 and 2, the 'realistic' story of Duncan Thaw in Glasgow, narrated to Lanark and Rima in the institute by an oracle, which tells Lanark that in a previous life he was Thaw. This makes Lanark's life the posthumous sequel to Thaw's: but by shifting the sequence Gray makes it possible to read this the other way round. Each world, that of Glasgow and Unthank, is 'after', or fantastic in relation to, the other – which is one form of the postmodernist vision of reality as a series of shifting planes of space, time and fiction.

The extract here is from Book 3, where the cured Lanark is introduced by Professor Ozenfant, chief doctor of the institute, to more extreme cases of his previous disease; and is also shown his future patient, Rima. Dragonhide is produced by failure to express the self and go out to others: it is a symbol in part of Scottish repression. The grotesque, Bosch-like, crustacean forms illustrate the distortions of the self produced by this repression: they are ironically highly visible and ornately idiosyncratic, where the sole object of the souls inside them has been with concealment and conformity. That they explode is at least a tribute to the vitality they have sought to deny. The hospital seeks to cure them by sympathetic treatment, and where it fails, devours the heat of their passing. The analogy throughout is digestive. Lanark has fallen through the mouth into the stomach of the world: but this is a world which consumes but does not excrete.

The idea of devouring pervades *Lanark*: the opposite of the repressive instinct, it seeks to engorge the self with others. This is to be the rapacious world of the city of Provan and the World council: it is also, to the repressed Duncan Thaw, the world that faces him in Glasgow. And it is part of the 'author' himself, who at one point tells Lanark that they both survive by '"seducing a living soul into our printed world and trapping it here long enough for us to steal the imaginative energy which gives us life"'. The story of Lanark surrounds and feeds off that of Thaw, without which it would not have the materials to live. In one way this is Gray's fantastic vision of what we call 'the consumer society'.

$\mathcal{L}$ANARK

Ozenfant went to the nearest tapestry and dragged it sideways, uncovering a circular glass screen in the wall behind. A slender microphone hung under it. He brought this to the divan pulling a fine cable after it, and sat down and said, 'Ozenfant speaking. Show me chamber twelve.'

The neon lights in the ceiling went out and a blurred image shone inside the screen, seemingly a knight in gothic armour lying on the slab of a tomb. The image grew distinct and more like a prehistoric lizard on a steel table. The hide was black, the knobbly joints had pink and purple quills on them, a bush of purple spines hid the genitals and a double row of spikes down the back supported the body about nine inches above the table. The head was neckless, chinless, and grew up from the collarbone into a gaping beak like the beak of a vast cuckoo. The face had no other real features, though a couple of blank domes stuck out like parodies of eyeballs. Munro said, 'The mouth is open.'

Ozenfant said, 'Yes, but the air trembles above it. Soon it shuts, and then *boom!*'

'When was he delivered?'

'Nine months, nine days, twenty-two hours ago. He arrived nearly as you see him, nothing human but the hands, throat and sternum mastoid. He seemed to like jazz, for he clutched the remnant of a saxophone, so I said, 'He is musical, I will treat him myself.' Unluckily I know nothing of jazz. I tried him with Debussy (who sometimes works in these cases) then I tried the nineteenth-century romantics. I pounded him with Wagner, overwhelmed him with Brahms, beguiled him with Mendelssohn. Results: negative. In despair I recede further and further, and who works in the end? Scarlatti. Each time I played *The Cortege* his human parts blushed as pink and soft as a baby's bottom.'

Ozenfant closed his eyes and kissed his fingertips to the ceiling. 'Well, matters remain thus till six hours ago when he goes wholly dragon in five minutes. Perhaps I do not play the clavichord well? Who else in this wretched institute would have tried?'

Munro said, 'You assume he blushed pink with pleasure. It may have been rage. Maybe he disliked Scarlatti. You should have asked.'

'I distrust speech therapy. Words are the language of lies and evasions. Music cannot lie. Music talks to the heart.'

Lanark moved impatiently. Light from the screen showed Ozenfant's mouth so fixed in a smile that it seemed expressionless, while the eyebrows kept moving in exaggerated expressions of thoughtfulness, astonishment or woe. Ozenfant said, 'Lanark is bored by these technicalities. I will show him more patients.'

He spoke to the microphone and a sequence of dragons on steel tables appeared on the screen. Some had glossy hides, some were plated like tortoises, some were scaled like fish and crocodiles. Most had quills, spines or spikes and some were hugely horned and antlered, but all were made monstrous by a detail, a human foot or ear or breast sticking through the dinosaur armour. A doctor sat on the edge of one table and studied a chessboard balanced on a dragonish stomach. Ozenfant said, 'That is McWham, who is also unmusical. He treats the dryly rational cases; he teaches them chess and plays interminable games. He thinks that if anyone defeats him their armour will fall off, but so far he has been too clever for them. Do you play any games, Lanark?'

'No.'

In another chamber a thin priest with intensely miserable eyes sat with his ear close to a dragonish beak.

'That is Monsignor Noakes, out only faith healer. We used to have lots of them: Lutherans, Jews, Atheists, Muslims, and others with names I forget. Nowdays all the hardened religious cases have to be treated by poor Noakes. Luckily we don't get many.'

'He looks unhappy.'

'Yes, he takes his work too seriously. He is Roman Catholic and the only people he cures are Quakers and Anglicans. Have you a religion, Lanark?'

'No.'

'You see a cure is more likely when doctor and patient have something in common. How would you describe yourself?'

'I can't.'

Ozenfant laughed. 'Of course you can't! I asked foolishly. The lemon cannot taste bitterness, it only drinks the rain. Munro, describe Lanark to me.'

'Obstinate and suspicious,' said Munro. 'He has intelligence, but keeps it narrow.'

'Good. I have a patient for him. Also obstinate, also suspicious, with a cleverness which only reinforces a deep, deep, immeasurably deep despair.'

Ozenfant said to the microphone, 'Show chamber one, and let us see the patient from above.'

A gleaming silver dragon appeared between a folded pair of brazen wings. A stout arm ending in seven brazen claws lay along one wing, a slender soft human arm along the other. 'You see the wings? Only unusually desperate cases have wings, though they cannot use them. Yet this one brings such reckless energy to her despair that I have sometimes hoped. She is unmusical, but I, a musician, have stooped to speech therapy and spoken to her like a vulgar critic, and she exasperated me so much that I decided to give her to the catalyst. We will give her to Lanark instead.'

A radio said *plin-plong*. Ozenfant took one from a waistcoat pocket and turned the switch. A voice announced that patient twelve was turning salamander.

Ozenfant said to the microphone, 'Quick! Chamber twelve.'

Chamber twelve was obscured by white vapours streaming and whirling from the dragon's beak, which suddenly snapped shut. Radiant beams shot from the domes in the head; the figure seemed to be writhing. Ozenfrant cried, 'No light, please! We will observe by heat alone.'

There was immediate blackness on which Lanark's dazzled eyes projected stars and circles before adjusting to it. He could hear Munro's quick dry breathing on one side and Ozenfant breathing through his mouth on the other. He said, 'What's happening?'

Ozenfant said, 'Brilliant light pours from all his organs – it would blind us. Soon you will see him by his heat.'

A moment later Lanark was startled to feel Ozenfant murmuring into his ear.

'The heat made by a body should move easily through it, overflowing the pores, penis, anus, eyes, lips, limbs and fingertips in acts of generosity and self-preservation. But many people are afraid of the cold and try to keep more heat than they give, they stop the heat from leaving though an organ or limb, and the stopped heat forges the surface into hard insulating armour. What part of you went dragon?'

'A hand and arm.'

'Did you ever touch them with your proper hand?'

'Yes. They felt cold.'

'Quite. No heat was getting out. But no heat was getting in! And since men feel the heat they receive more than the heat they create the armour makes the remaining human parts feel colder. So do they strip it off? Seldom. Like nations losing unjust wars they convert more and more of themselves into armour when they should surrender or retreat. So someone may start by limiting only his affections or lust or intelligence, and eventually heart, genitals, brain, hands and skin are crusted over. He does nothing but talk and feed, giving and taking through a single hole; then the mouth shuts, the heat has no outlet, it increases inside him until ... watch, you will see.' The blackness they sat in had been dense and total but a crooked thread of scarlet light appeared on it. This twitched and grew at both ends until it outlined the erect shape of a dragon with legs astride, arms outstretched, the hands thrusting against darkness, the great head moving from side to side. Lanark had a weird feeling that the beast stood before him in the room. There was nothing but blackness to compare it with, and it seemed vast. Its gestures may have been caused by pain but they looked threatening and triumphant. Inside the black head two stars appeared where eyes should be, then the whole body was covered with white and golden stars. Lanark felt the great gothic shape towering miles above him, a galaxy shaped like a man. Then the figure became one blot of gold which expanded into a blinding globe. There was a crash of thunder and for a moment the room became very hot. The floor heaved and the lights went on.

It took a while to see things clearly. The thunder had ended, but throughout the apartment instruments were jangling and thrumming in sympathy. Lanark noticed Munro still sitting beside him. There was sweat on his brow and he was industriously polishing his spectacles with a handkerchief. The blank screen was cracked from side to side but the microphone hung neatly under it. Ozenfant stood at a distance examining a fiddle. 'See!' he cried. 'The A-string has snapped. Yet some assert that a Stradivarius is without a soul.'

Munro said, 'I am no judge of salamanders, but that vibration seemed abnormally strong.'

'Indeed yes. There were over a million megatherms in that small blast.'

'Surely not!'

'Certainly. I will prove it.'

Ozenfant produced his radio and said, 'Ozenfant will speak with engineer Johnson ... Johnson, hello, you have received our salamander; what is he worth? ... Oh, I see. Anyway, he cracked my viewing lens, so replace it soon, please.'

Ozenfant pocketed the radio and said briskly, 'Not quite a million megatherms, but it will suffice for a month or two.' He bent and hoisted up a harp which had fallen on its side. Lanark said sharply, 'That heat is used?'

'Of course. Somehow we must warm ourselves.'

'That is atrocious!'

'Why?'

Lanark started stammering then forced himself to speak slowly. 'I knew people deteriorate. That is dismal but not surprising. But for cheerful healthy folk to profit by it is atrocious!'

'What would you prefer? A world with a cesspool under it where the helplessly corrupt would fall and fester eternally? That is a very old-fashioned model of the universe.'

'And very poor housekeeping,' said Munro, standing up. 'We could cure nobody if we did not utilize our failures. I must go now. Lanark, your department and mine have different staff clubs but if you ever leave the institute we will meet again. Professor Ozenfant is your adviser now, so good luck, and try not to be violent.'

Lanark was so keen to learn if the last remark was a joke that he stared hard into Munro's calm benign face and let his hand be gravely shaken without saying a word. Ozenfant murmured, 'Excellent advice.'

He uncovered a door and Munro went through it.

Ozenfant returned to the centre of the room chuckling and rubbing his hands. He said, 'You noticed the sweat on his brow? He did not like what he saw; he is a rigorist, Lanark. He cannot sympathize with our disease.'

'What is a rigorist?'

'One who bargains with his heat. Rigorists do not hold their heat in, they give it away, but only in exchange for fresh supplies. They are very dependable people, and when they go bad they crumble into crystals essential for making communication circuits, but when you and I went bad we took a different path. That is why an exploding salamander exalts us. We feel in our bowels the rightness of such nemesis. You were exalted, were you not?'

'I was excited, and I regret it.'

'Your regret serves no purpose. And now perhaps you wish to meet your patient.'

Ozenfant lifted the corner of another tapestry, uncovered a low circular door and said, 'Her chamber is through here.'

'But what have I to do?'

'Since you are only able to talk, you must talk.'

'What about?'

'I cannot say. A good doctor does not carry a remedy to his patient, he lets the patient teach him what the remedy is. I drove someone salamander today because I understood my cure better than my invalid. I often make these mistakes because I know I am very wise. You know you are ignorant, which should be an advantage.'

Lanark stood with his hands in his pockets, biting his lower lip and tapping the floor with one foot. Ozenfant said, 'If you do not go to her I will certainly send the catalyst.'

'What is the catalyst?'

'A very important specialist who comes to lingering cases when other treatments have failed. The catalyst provokes very rapid deterioration. Why are you reluctant?'

'Because I am afraid!' cried Lanark passionately, 'You want to mix me with someone else's despair, and I hate despair! I want to be free, and freedom is freedom from other people!' Ozenfant smiled and nodded. He said 'A very dragonish sentiment! But you are no longer a dragon. It is time you learned a different sentiment.'

After a while the smile left Ozenfant's face, leaving it startlingly impassive. He let go the tapestry, went to the carpenter's bench and picked up a fretsaw.

He said sharply, 'You feel I am pressing you and you dislike it. Do what you please. But since I myself have work to do I will be glad if you waste no more of my time.'

He bent over the guitar. Lanark stared frustratedly at the corner of the tapestry. It depicted a stately woman labelled *Correctio Conversio* standing on a crowned and sprawling young man labelled *Tarquinius*. At last he pulled this aside, stepped through the door and went down the corridor beyond.

The Grimm Sisters

LIZ LOCHHEAD

Liz Lochhead's creativity has changed direction several times in her life (1947-). After school in Motherwell, when it seemed natural for her to go on to university to read English, she instead decided upon Glasgow School of Art; during her diploma course she turned to poetry, producing her first collection, *Memo for Spring*, in 1972; then in 1978 she began to transform her poems into performance readings; and from there she moved to writing plays. A sense of life as a mixture, without boundaries, runs through her life and her work. Her Newarthill childhood was in an industrial village right on the edge of the countryside; at night her mother would mingle bedtime stories from the Greek myths with incidents from her own experience during the war. Liz Lochhead's poetry is full of crossed planes of reality that express her sense of life's fullness and elusiveness.

The poems here, from *The Grimm Sisters* (1981) were mostly written while she was on a Writer's Exchange Fellowship at Glendon College, Toronto from 1978–79. Her interest in fantasy here is as a means of breaking down the boundaries of reality, but she also subverts fairy tales themselves as false patriarchal templates for women's experience. Each of the poems uses the fairy stories as intermittent background mixed with modern urban experience, their narratives altered or run into one another ('Rapunz-stiltskin'). Like Alasdair Gray, one of her close friends, she splices multi-realities together; though the darker vision of *Lanark* is not hers.

In the poems here the 'theme' is the struggle to break free from convention, of which the fairy tale is a paradigm. The fairy tale becomes a narrative prison which is to be escaped, or a stasis to be subverted.

Rapunzel in the tower is shut in by her own expectations: she wants the conventional prince to break out of the story and cliché and thus release her, but he fails and lies to her, and she can only destroy herself. The poem fuses 'Rapunzel', 'Rumpelstiltskin' (inverted), a television quiz show, 'Little Red Riding Hood' and the voice of an urbane moll. In 'Tam Lin's Lady', the down-to-earth voice of one girl plays against the fairy tale assumptions of another. Each one lives in the prison of her own reality, but the speaker has the edge when she puts the disenchantment of Tam Lin (from the old witch his mother) beside the subsequent disenchantment of the girl (from her illusions). All the poems explore the fraudulence of the romantic cliché, set youthful idealism beside the cynicism of advancing age, ask readers to break free of set patterns of living.

THE GRIMM SISTERS

Three Twists

1. *Rapunzstiltskin*

& just when our maiden had got
good & used to her isolation,
stopped daily expecting to be rescued,
had come to almost love her tower,
along comes This Prince
with absolutely
all the wrong answers.
Of course she had not been brought up to look for
originality or gingerbread
so at first she was quite undaunted
by his tendency to talk in strung-together cliché.
'Just hang on and we'll get you out of there'
he hollered like a fireman in some soap opera
when she confided her plight (the old
hag inside etc. & how trapped she was);
well, it was corny but
he did look sort of gorgeous
axe and all.

So there she was, humming & pulling
all the pins out of her chignon,
throwing him all the usual lifelines
till, soon, he was shimmying in & out
every other day as though
he owned the place, bringing her
the sex manuals & skeins of silk
from which she was meant, eventually,
to weave the means of her own escape.
'All very well & good,' she prompted,
'but when exactly?'
She gave him till
well past the bell on the timeclock.
She mouthed at him, hinted,
she was keener than a T.V. quizmaster
that he should get it right.
'I'll do everything in my power' he intoned, 'but
the impossible (she groaned) might
take a little longer.' He grinned.
She pulled her glasses off.
'All the better
to see you with my dear?' he hazarded.
She screamed, cut off her hair.
'Why, you're beautiful?' he guessed tentatively.
'No, No, No!' she
shrieked & stamped her foot so
hard it sank six cubits through the floorboards.
'I love you?' he came up with
as finally she tore herself in two.

11: *Beauty &*

The Beast
he was hot
he grew horns
he had you
screaming mammy daddy screaming blue
murder.
From one sleepy thought

of how like a mane his hair ...
next thing
he's furred & feathered, pig bristled,
warted like a toad
puffed & jumping –
the green cling of those
froggy fingers
will make you shudder yet.
Then his flesh gone
dead. Scaled as a handbag.
He was that old crocodile
you had to kiss

yes, Rosebud, I
suppose you were right.
Better than hanging around
a hundred years for Someone
to hack his way through the thorns
for the shoe that fits
for chance to have you cough up
the poisoned apple
wodged in your gullet.
So you (anything for a quiet
life) embrace the beast, endure.

Three days & nights, three patient years,
you'll win I'm sure.
But who'd have guessed
paying your dues would mean
the whole wham bam menagerie?

Oh, but soon
(her hair grew lang her breath grew strang)
you'll
(little One-Eye for little Three-Eyes, the
Bearded Lady)
Yes, sweet Beauty, you'll
match him
horror for horror.

III: *After Leaving The Castle*

On the first night
the lady lay in the dark with her lover
awake all night
afraid her husband would pursue her.

On the second night
the lady lay awake in the arms of her lover
her tongue and teeth idly
exploring the cold of his earring.

On the third night
the lady lay awake afraid
her husband would never come after.

On the fourth night
the lady thought as she drifted off to sleep
how monotonous it was going to be
to live on rabbit stew forever
& she turned a little away
from snoring, the smell of wild garlic.

When they passed him on the road
on the fifth day,
she began to make eyes at the merchant.

Tam Lin's Lady

'Oh I forbid you maidens a'
who wear gowd in your hair –
to come or go by Carterhaugh
for young Tam Lin is there.'

So you met him in a magic place?
O.K.
But that's a bit airy fairy for me.
I go for the specific – you could, for instance,
say that when he took you for a coffee
before he stuck you on the last bus
there was one of those horrible congealed-on
plastic tomatoes on the table ... oh don't

ask me
I don't know why everything has to be so sordid these days ...
I can take *some* sentiment –
tell me how charmed you were
when he wrote both your names and a heart in spilt coffee –
anything except that he carved them on the elder tree.
But have it your own way.
Picking apart your personal
dream landscape of court and castle and greenwood
isn't really up to me.
So call it magical. A fair country.
Anyway you were warned.

And if, as the story goes nine times out of ten –
he took you by the milk white hand & by the grassgreen sleeve
& laid you on that bonnie bank & asked of you no leave,
well, so what?
You're not the first to fall for it,
good green girdle and all –
with your schooltie rolled up in your pocket
trying to look eighteen. I know.
All perfectly forgiveable.
Relax.

What I do think was a little dumb
if you don't mind me saying so
was to swallow that old one about you being
the only one who could save him.

Oh I see – there was this lady
he couldn't get free of.
Seven years and more he said he'd sacrificed himself
and if you didn't help him he'd end up
a fairy for ever! Enslaved.

Or worse still in hell without you.

Well, well.
So he stopped you from wandering in the forest
and picking pennyroyal and foxgloves
and making appointments and borrowing money for the abortion.
He said all would be well

If only you'd trust him just this once
and go through
what he was honest enough to admit in advance
would be hell and highwater for you.

So he told you which relatives to pander to
and which to ignore.
How to snatch him from the Old One
and hold on through thick and thin
through every change that happened.
Oh but it was terrible!
It seemed earlier, you see,
he'd been talking in symbols (like
adder-snake, wild savage bear
brand of bright iron red-hot from the fire)
and as usual the plain unmythical truth was worse.
At any rate you were good and brave, you did
hang on, hang on tight.
And in the end of course
everything turned out conventionally right
with the old witch banished to her corner lamenting,
cursing his soft heart and the fact she couldn't keep him,
and everyone sending out for booze for the wedding.

So we're all supposed to be happy?
But how about you, my fallen fair maiden
now the drama's over, tell me
how goes the glamourie?
After the twelve casks of good claret wine
and the twelve and twelve of muskadine,
tell me
what about you?
How do you think Tam Lin will take
all the changes you go through?

Six Disenchantments

The mirror you are
tells me too often
I am not beautiful.

The warm room you were once
was a good place to be.
Oh catch me saying
the walls of the room were warm fingers stroking
but it was clean and decent,
it was the kind of place that let me warm myself.
I spent a lot of time in it
scribbling and humming, rearranging
at my leisure
the objects on the mantelshelf.

The rocket you are
still takes off occasionally
with a bump and a woosh in the night.
Always, its always the surprise of my life
and I have to hang on tight.

You say the scissors I am
are too keen on cutting.

You say the teacher I am
is a terrible version of a cartoon schoolmarm
too straightlipped and square shouldered
all pinstripes and pencil skirt, spike heels, she's
strictly
too lewd to be true
and you can't be sure what punishment
she wants to exact from you.
So you thumb your nose and tell her
her boys will all grow up too soon
leave school and throw their schoolcaps
over the moon.

God
the brickwall you are these days
it doesn't even crack when you smile.
Believe me I spent a lot of time
working with my fingernails at mortar and lime
before I started to bash and
batter my head at it, that brick wall.
Now, even when I stop,
it doesn't stop hurting at all.

THE BRIDGE

IAIN BANKS

Only son of an Admiralty officer father and a mother who was an ex-professional ice skater, Iain Banks (1954–) was brought up in North Queensferry, Gourock and Greenock, read English Literature with Philosophy and Psychology at Stirling University, and did several technical and clerical jobs until the success of his 'shocking' *The Wasp Factory* in 1984. He now lives in Fife, and alternates writing a novel or more a year with enjoying the company of his friends. To date he has written fifteen novels, seven of a science-fictional character under the *alter ego* 'Iain M. Banks', one veering towards horror *(The Wasp Factory)* and one part-fantasy, *The Bridge* (1986), which he considers his best book. He views himself as primarily a writer of science fiction – of which he is Scotland's sole major exponent to date. His first interest, he maintains, is in the construction of good plots; his last in being 'deep'. He has no consistent vision or philosophy to grind, for his interests lie much more in the immediate excitements of invention and imaginative collision; or, as he puts it, "'I just like to write about weird shit, basically'".

The Forth Rail Bridge has had many praises, but none quite like *The Bridge*. Even though Banks often turns the Bridge to use as a symbol, whether of society, the body of a girl, or the mind itself, still he returns to the fascination of the massively redundant construction of the thing, the vast spans and girders that soar above and beneath sight; he has made it far larger than it actually is in testimony to the power of its image over him, not least from his childhood in its shadow. Here he is the science fiction writer with a fascination for technical mastery, the ambitious shaping of matter by colonialist intelligence. And that is the character of much of the book: it is the exploration of a world, or rather several worlds, since Banks's energetic imagination drives him to explore context after context, from the story of a Broad Scots Conan the barbarian in a vulgarised landscape of fairy tale and myth to the chequered love-life of an Edinburgh businessman. What leaves the book still fantasy is that Banks offers few explanations, mixes different realities and texts in just the subconscious or rather postmodernist mode that we have already seen in Gray, of whom Banks has said, 'I don't think *The Bridge* would be the way it is at all if it wasn't for *Lanark*'.

The 'story' is of a man who has a car crash on the Forth Road Bridge and 'visits' the Bridge while in a coma in hospital: his eventual journey away from the Bridge ends in his return to consciousness. But while of course the Bridge is 'therefore' his subconscious mind, it has all the imagined substantiality of real existence. The extract here however is taken from near the end of his journey, long after he has left the Bridge: he has passed through a country riven by war, and has left a city where he was waiter to a degenerate Field Marshal, and now realities are beginning to merge, just as he, the character in the strange landscape of this story, will merge in the hospital bed with his Edinburgh *alter ego*. Here he meets a character very like one encountered much earlier in a dream, who was then lashing the waves of the sea; and he silently meets and passes the barbaric hero we have seen in an intermittent sub-plot. The dreams are getting more multiple, he is more aware of himself making them, they are fractured, insubstantial, beginning to approach entropy, like the ruined Bridge he now sees, as he nears recovered consciousness.

❦

THE BRIDGE

❧

Low rolling hills under a dark sky; the undersurface of the lowering, ruddy clouds seems to mirror the gentle contours of the land below. The air is thick and heavy; it smells of blood.

It is soggy underfoot, but not with water. Whatever great battle was fought here, over these hills that seem to stretch for ever, it drenched the land with blood. There are bodies everywhere, of every animal and every colour and race of human, and many others besides. I find the small dark man eventually, attending the corpses.

He is dressed in rags; we last met in … Mocca? (Occam? Something like that), when he was beating the waves with his iron flail. Now it is bodies. Dead bodies; a hundred lashes each, if there's anything left to lash. I watch him for a while.

He is calm, methodical, beating each body exactly one hundred times, before proceeding to the next one. He shows no preference concerning species, sex, size or colour; he beats each with the same determined vigour; on the back if possible, but otherwise just as they lie. Only if they are fully armoured does he touch them, bending stiffly to pull back a visor or disconnect a chest-strap.

'Hello,' he says. I stand some distance away, in case he is under orders to whip everybody on the field, regardless.

'Remember me?' I ask him. He strokes his bloody lash.

'Can't say I do,' he says. I tell him about the city by the sea. He shakes his head. 'No, not me,' he says. He digs into his filthy robes for a moment, then comes out with a small rectangle of card. He wipes it with one strip of his rags, then holds it out. I step forward warily. 'Take it,' he nods. 'I was told to give it to you. Here.' He leans forward. I take the card, step back. It is a playing card; the three of diamonds.

'What's this for?' I ask him. He just shrugs, wipes his flail-hand on one tattered sleeve.

'Don't know.'

'Who gave it to you? How did they know ——'

'Is it really necessary to ask all these questions?' he says, shaking his head. I am shamed.

'I suppose not.' I hold up the playing card. 'Thanks.'

'You're welcome,' he says. I had forgotten how soft his voice was. I turn to go, then look back at him.

'Just one more thing.' I nod at the bodies littering the ground like fallen leaves. 'What happened here? What happened to all these people?'

He shrugs. 'They didn't listen to their dreams,' he says, then turns back to his task.

I set off again, for the distant line of light which fills the horizon like a streak of white gold.

I left the city in the dried sea basin and walked the railway track away from it, heading in the same direction as the Field Marshal's train before it was attacked. There was no pursuit, but I heard the sound of distant gunfire coming from the city as I walked.

The landscape changed gradually to become less harsh. I found water and, after a while, fruit on trees. The climate grew less bleak. I saw people sometimes, travelling alone like me, or in groups. I stayed away from them, and they avoided me. Once I found I could walk without danger, and find food and water, the dreams came every night.

It was always the same nameless man and the same city. The dreams came and went, repeating and repeating. I saw so much, but nothing clearly. Twice I think I almost had the man's name. I started to believe that my dreams were the genuine reality, and woke each morning beneath a tree or in the lee of some rocks, fully expecting to wake into another existence, a different life; just a nice clean hospital bed would be a start ... but no. I was always here, on temperate downlands that eventually became a battlefield, and where I have just met the man with the flail. Still, there is light at the end of the horizon.

I head for that light. It looks like the edge of these dank clouds; a long lidded eye of gold. At the top of a hill I look back on the small, misshapen man. He is still there, whipping at some fallen warrior. Perhaps I ought to have lain down and let him lash me; could death be the only way I might awake from this terrible, enchanted sleep?

That would require faith. I do not believe in faith. I believe it exists but I do not believe it works. I don't know what the rules are here; I can't risk throwing everything away on a long shot.

I come to the place where the clouds end and the dark downs give way to a low cliff. Beyond, there is sand.

An unnatural place, I think, looking up at the edge of dark cloud. It is too distinct, too uniform, the boundary between the shadowy downs with their fallen armies of dead and the golden waste of sand too precisely defined. A hot breath from off the sand blows away the stale, thick smells of the battlefield. I have a bottle of water, and some fruit. My waiter's jacket is thin, the Field Marshal's old coat dirty. I still have the handkerchief, like a favour.

I jump from the last hill over the hot sand, down into the golden slope, ploughing and sliding towards the floor of the desert. The air is hot and dry, devoid of the corrupting odours of the rolling battlefield behind me, but full of another sort of death; its promise in the very dryness of that air moving above a place where there is no water, no food, no shade.

I start walking.

Once I thought I was dying. I had walked and crawled, finding no shade. Finally I fell down the slip face of a dune and knew I could not rise from there without water, without liquid, without something. The sun was a white hole in the sky so blue it had no colour. I waited for clouds to form, but none came. Eventually dark, wide-winged birds appeared. They started to wheel above me, riding an unseen thermal; waiting.

I watched them, through half-glued eyes. The birds flew in a great spiral over the desert, as though there was some immense, invisible bolt suspended over me, and they were just scraps of black silk stuck to its spiralled plane, moving slowly as that vast column turned.

Then I see another man appear at the top of the dune. He is tall and muscular and dressed in some savage's light armour; his golden arms and legs are bare. He carries a huge sword, and a decorated helmet, which he holds in the crook of one arm. He looks transparent and unsubstantial, for all his bulk. I can see through his body: perhaps he is a ghost. The sword glitters in the sunlight, but dully. He sways as he stands there, not seeing me. He puts one hand shakily to his brow, then seems to talk to the helmet he holds. He half-walks, half-staggers down the slip face towards me, his booted feet and thickly muscled legs plunging through the baking sand. Still he does not appear to notice me. His hair is bleached by the sun; peeling skin covers his face and arms and legs. The sword drags in the sand behind him. He stops at my feet, staring into the distance, swaying. Has he come to kill me with that great sword? At least it might be quick.

He stands, still swaying, eyes fixed on the hazy distance. I would swear he is standing too close to me, too close to my feet; as though his own feet were somehow inside mine. I lie, waiting. He stands above, struggling to keep on his feet, one arm going out suddenly as he tries to balance himself. The helmet in the crook of his arm falls to the sand. The helmet's decoration, a wolf's head, cries out.

The warrior's eyes turn up into his head, going white. He crumples, falling towards me. I close my eyes, ready to be crushed.

I feel nothing. I hear nothing, either; he does not fall onto the sand beside me, and when I open my eyes there is no trace of him or the helmet he dropped. I stare into the sky again, at the entwined double-spiral of circling birds that are death.

I used the last of my strength to peel open my coat and jacket and bare my chest to the invisible, turning bolt in the sky. I lay, spreadeagled, for some time; two of the birds landed near me. I did not stir.

One of them swiped at my hand with its hooked beak, then jumped back. I lay still, waiting.

When they came for my eyes I took them by their necks. Their blood was thick and salty, but like the taste of life to me.

I see the bridge. At first I am certain it is a hallucination. Then I believe it might be a mirage, something which looks like the bridge reflected in the air and – to my parched, obsessed eyes -- taking on its form. I walk closer, through the heat and the slopes of clinging, flowing grains. I have the handkerchief over my head, shading me. The bridge shimmers in the distance, a long rough line of summits.

I come slowly closer to it throughout the day, resting only for a short while when the sun is at its height. Sometimes I climb to the tops of the long dunes, to reassure myself it is there. I am within a couple of miles before my confused eyes admit the truth to me; the bridge is in ruins.

The main sections are largely intact, though damaged, but the linking sections, those spans, those little bridges within bridges, they have collapsed or been destroyed, and large parts of the section extremities have disappeared along with them. The bridge looks less like a succession of laterally stretched hexagons and more like a line of isolated octagons. Its feet still stand, its bones still rise, but its linking arms, its connections – they have gone.

I see no movement, no sudden glints of light. The wind sighs sand over the edges of dunes, but no sound comes from the tall ochre skeleton of the bridge. It stands, blanched and gaunt and jagged in the sand, slow golden waves lapping at its granite plinths and lower buildings.

I enter its shadow at last, gratefully. The burning wind moans between the towering girders. I find a staircase, start to climb. It is hot and I am thirsty again.

I recognise this. I know where I am.

Everywhere is deserted. I see no skeletons but I find no survivors. The train deck holds a few old carriages and locomotives, rusted to the rails they stand upon; finally part of the bridge. Sand has blown up even here, shading yellow-gold into the edges of the rails and points.

My old haunt, indeed. I find Dissy Pitton's. It is a fallen place; the ropes which used to attach tables and chairs to ceiling have mostly been cut; the couches and seats and tables lie sprawled over the dusty floor like bodies from long ago. A few hang by one edge or corner; cripples among the dead. I walk to the Sea View Lounge.

I sat here once with Brooke. Right here. We looked out and he complained about the barrage balloons; then the planes flew past. The desert is bright under the high sun.

Dr Joyce's office; not his. I do not recognise any of this furniture, but then he was always moving. The blinds, blowing in and out gently behind the broken windows, look the same.

A long walk takes me to the Arrols' abandoned summer apartment. It is half-submerged in the sand. The door is open. Only the tops of the still sheet-covered pieces of furniture are visible. The fire is buried beneath the waves of sand; so is the bed.

I climb slowly back to the train deck and stand, looking out over the shimmering sands which surround the bridge. An empty bottle lies at my feet. I take it by the neck and throw it from the train deck. It curves, end over end, glinting in the sunlight, towards the sand.

CELLS OF KNOWLEDGE

SIAN HAYTON

Cells of Knowledge, Sian Hayton's first novel, was published in 1989 and received that year's Scotsman/Saltire First Book Award; the succeeding books of what became a trilogy – *Hidden Daughters* (1992) and *The Last Flight* (1993) – passed with less notice. Hayton made a foray into a contemporary semi-realistic novel with *The Governors* (1992), which is less assured. Born in Liverpool in 1944, she has spent much of her life in Scotland – in Glasgow, where she studied at the Royal Scottish Academy of Music and Drama, gained an M.Ed. (1977) and variously taught (in the field of developmental psychology) and acted, before beginning to write seriously in 1982.

Cells of Knowledge is set in the south west of Scotland in the late tenth century. But to the expected mix of struggling settlements, local kings, sea-raiders and the well-anchored tentacles of a missionary church, Hayton adds a giant Usbathaden and his daughters in a hidden and technologically sophisticated castle. If we consider the giant an impossibility, then we are also to consider the limitations of our own cell of knowledge, by which we know the past only in terms of its often scant leavings.

The book depicts men as those who make their reality limited or exclusive. The giant, who is a figure from myth, in part represents the folk heritage of the people the Christian monks reject. Instinctively the monks class him and his daughters as devils. Equally, the giant represses his daughters, because he knows that the marriage of any one of them to a mortal will be his death. In the end, it is the females who embrace the world so different from their own protected one, and accept time and die; the monks, apart from one Selyf who travels to the giant's castle, remain on the whole closed within their terrified certainties. Yet even here Hayton blurs the picture, allowing the often shrill monk who inserts continual marginal comments on the story measures of real generosity and understanding of the other, when what is best in his faith burns bright.

The passage here occurs after Kynan White-hair has with Marighal's help passed three of the courtship tests set by her giant father, and is at the feast to be given her as his bride-to-be. The underlying source is the folktale 'Nicht Nought Nothing', which has analogues going back to the story of Jason and Medea. Thus the apparent cell of the fiction opens out into another. And even then it is not so simple, for this story takes in futuristic science-fictional elements which have nothing to do with this source.

CELLS OF KNOWLEDGE

The giant raised his hand in a fist, and at that moment the door to the hall flew open and in strode the daughters, every one.

Each looked exactly like her sister, as Marighal had said. No man could have told one from the other, neither by dress nor by face, no matter how hard he might study. Each wore her red-gold hair in four tresses, two in front and two behind, and her skin was as white as the breast of a seagull at sunset, and her eyes were the green of deep water. Each one had cheeks red as the foxglove, and lips like the berries of the rowan. Her brow was wide and white and on her head there was a crown of gold filigree wire where crystals hung and quivered like dew on brambles at dawn. The kerchief beneath it and the shift were of finest linen, and her tunic was of red wool edged with gold and silver, and her mantle was of green edged with a deep fringe of gold and blue; green and red precious stones were set in it so that it swung as she walked. Beneath her shift her little feet peeped out and in with every step, and each was shod with the softest white leather, with gold flowers on the front, and on each hand she wore two rings of twisted gold wire with red and amber beads.

They came in, one after the other, all the sisters, and nowhere could I see a difference between them. Olwen, who had been my second mother; Leborchan the wise woman; Elayne the dimpled baby; Beatrude whom I had carried on my shoulders years before; and Essyllt the crone, all looked as much like my lady as she did herself – those named and many, many more. Before that night I had not known how many sisters were in that house, and as they ranged themselves across the hall and back again in three files my heart went white within me for fear that I would not know my lady. Suddenly the giant spoke at my ear with a voice like thunder, and I leapt in my chair like a wounded stag.

'There she is, Kynan White-hair. Go and choose your bride from among her sisters and lead her to her father's table. Bring her to my side so that we may drink to her health and prosperity.'

I stepped down and walked trembling along the files of women. Nothing in those smooth, white faces told me which was my lady. Each one of them stared ahead with green eyes as cold as glass, and would not look at me. The giant's voice came to me speaking to the company and bidding them to fill their cups. Then a flicker caught my eye and held it. I looked round and saw the fingers of a hand moving, and, looking closer I saw that the smallest finger of that hand was missing.

At once I knew my lady. I stepped up to her and taking her by the right hand I led her to her father's table. There I claimed her as my rightful bride before the whole company. The giant was not pleased by this and with a wave of his hand he restored the sisters to themselves so that Marighal alone wore the crown. The sisters took their places at the table opposite ours in order of age, and those who knew me smiled at me at last.

'Now we will have the entertainment,' said the giant, 'I ask your forbearance for the poverty of my efforts. Had I more time I would have brought musicians from Persia, jugglers from Iberia, and acrobats from the land of the burning sun, but my son-in-law is in such haste to consummate his marriage I have had to cheat you all. You will have to be content with a local artist.'

He clapped his hands and in came a poor old man with a small harp in his feeble arms. The people of the forest frowned at me as the giant had shown them, as if to say it was I alone that had cheated them. Yet the sisters and I knew well that if the master had willed it he could have brought any man he wished from any country in the world.

The bard sang in a feeble voice to an ill-tuned harp and was certainly the worst poet I ever heard. Even the giant grew tired of his poor voice, and his own mockery wearied him, for he said, 'This is poor stuff,' and sent the old man off with a wave of his hand.

'Let us all drink to the man and wife,' he cried, and all rose to obey him, with another dull shout. In all this time my lady had not looked at me, and even at the toast she stared ahead of her with a face like snow for paleness.

I felt that night that the sun stood still in his place below the edge of the world till the last guest had fallen asleep at the table. Indeed he was well up in the sky before the giant spoke up in his brazen voice to bid his guests wake and witness our vows. Marighal made her oath, and some of her sisters stood by as her helpers. Then to my amazement the giant stood for me when I made my vows to his daughter. Everyone there was now weary, except for the giant himself and he summoned servants to bring more food and drink. We rubbed our eyes and yawned, and tried once again to be joyful as guests at a wedding should.

But when the middle of the day was past the forest people said, 'Master, we have come to your feast as you bade us, but now, we beg you, give us leave to return to our homes. We have spent a day and a night in revelry with you and witnessed your daughter's oath and now we must go. We have flocks to gather, stacks to tend and for many of us the road home is long. Please dismiss us, we pray you.'

The giant lifted up his voice in rage and cursed them, saying, 'For all these generations I have protected you and kept your roads open when all were closed elsewhere. I have kept the pirates from your doors, and the Saxons from your meadows, and I have watched without tiring. Yet now, wretched ingratitude, you will not stay to see my daughter consummate her marriage. Are you to be like the scavenging wolves who smell a failing beast and wait with joy to see it stumble? Be off with you, if you must go, but be sure that there will be no more help from me if you leave me now. After this time, when the pirates march into your lands, and the men from the east put fire to your homes, and none will come to buy your rotting produce, you will remember me and regret that you did not give me more of your time.'

'Master,' said the people, and some wept at his words, 'by our hands you must believe us, we would stay if we could, nor can you compel us to stay longer than we agreed. Our beasts wait for us and without us they will starve. We wish you well, though you have been a hard master to us sometimes. We have been right pleased to come to your feast today, but we dare not stay longer, even though you cease to aid us. Farewell!'

They left, and suddenly the sisters rose from their places also and spoke in loud voices to each other before their father, which I had never seen before. My master was very angry and he struck the table.

'Go away, now! Go from me! Do not make me sit and listen to the rattle of your foolish mouths. Why do you pause? Is this not the time for which you have been waiting, some of you for generations? Why do you tarry now? Get your sister's bed ready at last.'

At that they fled, and left my wife and myself to wait on their return to release us. The giant said nothing to us, neither of rage nor of greeting, but he watched my lady as she sat eating and drinking wine. She was as calm as if she were watching on the moors alone and I wondered at her patience.

For myself I silently cursed the day that I had ever come to that hall, and raged at my craven father who had put me in this creature's power. At last the sisters returned and led us to our bed without a word. They undressed the bride till she stood in her fine shift beside the garlanded bed, and her hair hung unbraided down her back. Then they shut the doors of the bed and left us.

'What is to become of us? Your father will not permit us to leave, surely?'

She shook her head and put her finger to her lips, then dimmed the light and said, 'My father loves me, and I am sure this marriage has his good will,' but as she spoke she thrust her hand behind the tester and brought out a spy-globe. She twisted it in a way only she and her father knew and it fell into four parts in her hand, then she put it under the pillow. We lay in silence on the bed until we heard the humming of another which she also found and destroyed.

After that she turned the light up and said, 'Now I am sure it is safe for us to talk a little. We cannot stay long in this bed for the stones above us are not part of the wall. They are made so that when the first rays of the sun strike them they will descend and crush us as we lie. If this does not kill us then there are globes set all over the halls which will summon my father, but I know their working and can stop them. I have horses ready in the stable, and your battle-gear lies under the mattress. Now rest a while and we will leave at the darkest hour of the night.'

We dressed ourselves again, and she set about the globes with a thin silver knife. At last I saw through the little window that it was time to go, and we stepped down into the passage. Marighal left one piece of the globe in the tester, one in the doorway, one at the head of the stairs one at the foot, one at the doorway to the yard, one in the doorway of the stable, and as we led the horses out with muffled feet, she left the last one in the gateway. As soon as we were deep in the forest she stopped and took a paper packet from her wallet and scattered what it held over the ground at her feet.

'This is grain I have washed well in the juice of certain stinging herbs which my foster-father showed me. My vassals the mice will carry them all about and when my father comes to pursue us with his hounds they will chase a strange scent all over the forest.'

We fled upwards then, and as the sun rose again we travelled fast across the moorland, with our shadows long before us. By the end of the day we were in the forest beyond my master's hold, and there we rested.

Nevertheless by the middle of the next day we looked behind and saw the forest shaking as the giant sped after us.

Afraid, I said, 'Now, wife, we are finished, for I had thought your father had no power in this country, yet here he comes and the forest parts before him.'

'My father's power holds everywhere, for those who wish to see him prevail will always give him way. But I know his limits and I am not afraid, neither should you be. Take the horses down the road till the shoulder of the mountain stands between you and this place, and tether them well. If you wish to see my father bested come back here at once; if not, you had better continue along the road to its end. Remember, though, that you will never be sure of your safety till you see him defeated with your own eyes.'

She dropped from the back of her horse and from the pannier she took a box of black iron about as long as my forearm. I did as she had told me and secured the horses on the other side of the pass, then walked back to see what would follow. She had fixed the black box on to the steep face of a great rock on the hillside by the road, but I could not see how. Now she stood watching the nodding of the trees that marked her father's approach.

'He will be here very soon' she said, 'I had hoped not to use this thing for it will do much to change the face of the forest. Now I see my father will not accept my departure without driving me to the limits of my power. God's will be done.'

With these words she pointed at the black box with a nod and fire gushed out of it with a roar like thunder. The great rock split down the whole of its length and water poured out of it to form a mighty waterfall rushing over the path.

'Wife,' I cried in fear, 'what is this power that changes nature from its course? Surely nothing good can come of it.'

'It is only some scrapings from the byre mixed with charcoal and a yellow rock. Grig, my foster-father showed me what to do. Only nature can change nature, that is the whole truth as I know it. And now it is beyond my power to change it back.'

As she spoke her face grew grim with grief and she waited for her father. Soon we saw him coming through the forest and this time he was alone. When he came up to the side of the new river he stopped and called, 'Well, daughter, you seem to have carried the day between us. I cannot cross this mighty cataract, for the water will carry me away. I could return home for the slaves to build a bridge, but by the time I finished you would be long gone, you, and that long, white-haired creature beside you. I hope you are pleased.'

'I have won, indeed, Father, but do not think that I rejoice in my victory. I am grieved beyond words to think that this marriage will bring your death, but we both know well that there is no remedy for it.' And she wept sorely at that. The sight struck fear in my heart, for I had never seen her weep before.

'Do not grieve for me, daughter,' said the giant, 'my doom will come upon me when it must, whether by your hand or by another's, nor should you be troubled by its coming. I could wish to see you more rejoicing in the fine young man at your side, Marighal, for it seems to me you will not be with him long.'

'Father,' said my lady, angry, 'do not seek to threaten me at this late hour. We are on the road out of your lands now and in the new world you will not have power over us.'

'I speak only the truth, daughter, nor do I seek to threaten. I have lived long on this earth, and I have learned to see a pattern in all events. The man will betray you, to his grief, not by any act of mine, but because it is in the way of things. Do not think I wish you anything but well. Whether we meet again or not, you are still my daughter.'

'I love you, Father, and be sure I know there is no man alive who is your equal. If I could have made my fate fall out another way I would have done so, and if there had been a way to preserve your life I would have found it, but once my foot was upon this road there was no way back.'

'Daughter, I know it well. The price of our power is always higher than we think. Many generations ago I left my immortal bride to seek dominion over mankind. She warned me when I left that what I sought would bring me no joy, but would only increase my emptiness. I would not believe her and left her weeping to find that she only spoke the truth. I never found the road back to her.'

So saying he turned and left us, and my wife wept many strange tears at his parting. At last I said to her, 'Lift up your spirits, my lady, for we are free and life is now starting for us. We are young and very wise, and we can well take up the duties our training has fitted us for. Mount your horse and let us see what fate is waiting for us. The road is open now and we will soon have many chances to win renown, and what is man shaped for if it is not for noble and memorable deeds?'

At this my lady washed away her tears and we rode north and west to the high red moorland, then we turned toward the sea and came to the edge of the plain that surrounds this city. I left my lady there and came to this place to ask for free passage into the city, but when I arrived at the hall I found she had arrived here before me. By some great miracle, all the knowledge of her youth had been taken out of her heart.

It seemed to me, to this very day, that this was her father's work. In a moment of kindness he took her up from the place where I left her and cleansed her of the knowledge which would only have been a burden to her as my wife. I made sure that it was my lady as soon as I saw her there, for I looked at her hand and there I saw that the smallest finger was missing. It was my Marighal, indeed, but not, thanks be to God, as I had known her. That night she came to me a simple maid, happy only to have a fine young chieftain to fight for her people and to rule this kingdom with me for the rest of our lives. Nor has the giant's prediction come true, for in all the years of marriage we have never been apart.

That is my strange history, monk. You see I am by no means clean of sin, but I have seen many strange practices and even destroyed the body of the wife promised to me, but God in his mercy straightaway restored her to me. I am indeed fortunate. Since my baptism as a Christian I have tried to count all my sins as forgiven. Am I not right to do so?

Green Man

MARGARET ELPHINSTONE

Margaret Elphinstone (1948–) was brought up in Somerset and lived in Galloway from 1983 to 1989; she now lives in Ayrshire and lectures in English studies at the University of Strathclyde. The dominant impulse of her work is pastoral; she is also the author of two books on organic gardening. In her novels *The Incomer* (1987) and *A Sparrow's Flight* (1989), the landscape portrayed is a blighted post-holocaust one in need of healing; her *Islanders* (1994) is close to George Mackay Brown's vision in its celebration of twelfth-century life on Fair Isle in the north of Scotland. Ecology, feminism, and hostility to nuclear power feed into these visions.

In her collection of pastoral short stories *An Apple from a Tree* (1991), Margaret Elphinstone puts magic into her landscapes, heightening our sense of nature's otherness. Two stories, 'Conditions of Employment' and 'The Cold Well', describe supernatural guardians of the wild, and a still more enigmatic figure is met in 'Green Man'. Most of the protagonists are female, as throughout her work, and are often portrayed as involved with the rhythms of nature. 'Green Man' is unusual in giving us a woman who learns from a man, albeit a green and possibly non-earthly one. In other stories, 'Islands of Sheep' and 'An Apple from a Tree', alienation from the wilderness of the mind, the inner landscape, is the issue. Many of the stories work by a technique of subversion, making reality ever more alien and dreamlike than the intellect would have it; no longer 'a land laid waste, bound by words, spells, questions, concepts in the minds of men' ('Green Man').

'Green Man' carries this to the level of subverting the reader.

Throughout the extract here, which begins the story, every assumption we make is continually undercut. Thus in the first paragraph the railway seems at first purposeful, but then is disused, only a track-bed; while the sentences drift in from every direction, disorienting us. Then the encounter with the green man is, like that in C. S. Lewis's *Perelandra* (1943) with a green and primally innocent Lady on a pastoral planet, at once familiar and shockingly other. Every time we think we have caught what he is, it is lost in another phrase. Yet the paradox is that out of such ignorance comes a far deeper understanding and a love of the alien: and through the alien, of the landscape of which he is seen as an inseparable part.

❧

Green Man

❧

The most human feature of the valley was the railway. It emerged from a cutting between the hills and swept out above the bogland on a narrow embankment, the loch lying to the north of it. All that was left of the halt was a rusted shed, ramshackle and crazily tilted, by the solid little bridge that spanned the burn. A smaller burn flowed out of the loch, and the two, conjoined, wound their way through heather-tufted marshland, round the long green curve of Airie Hill. Drifts of trees fell across the northern slopes like blown leaves, winnowed away from the bare bones of the hills. There seemed no reason why anyone should have stopped here. Forgotten passengers on the ghost of a departed railway, shooting-parties in tweeds and brogues, solitary salmon fishers in season, shepherds who dropped off here to cover the grazings on these hills which no farm or cottage overlooked. There was nothing else here, nor ever had been. Lochskerrow Halt. A name on a map which lent it meaning only by the dotted line where there was once a railway. The cuttings remained, the long embankments, the grey shingle that crunched under feet that followed the tracks of the departed trains. People once looked out on these hills, incurious eyes strayed over the blank marshland, travellers munching sandwiches glanced out of carriage windows, yawning, and perhaps read a sign that gave a label and a meaning to this place – Lochskerrow Halt. An incident on a journey, a milestone, marking time between Dumfries and Stranraer, a short pause between a beginning and an end.

The only traveller today was a young woman. She walked steadily along the track of the railway, hiking boots scrunching on the clinkers. She had joined the railway at Mossdale, after it crossed the viaduct, and now she walked purposefully westwards towards Gatehouse of Fleet, Creetown, Newton Stewart, Stranraer and Portpatrick. She wore a capacious green anorak with a turned-down velveteen collar of the kind they sell in agricultural stores. In her pockets she carried a map and compass, and in the grey rucksack on her back she had brought food, chocolate, a spare jumper. An efficient and determined person, a person with a destination in view, who had not strayed into this territory idly; a woman who had a day to herself, and who had already decided where she was going.

After Mossdale the railway crossed a small loch by way of another viaduct and then took the traveller by a straight, elevated route over stretches of marshland. Then it enclosed her within a deep cutting, where briars and broom and elder bowed over her from steep banks. The railway emerged again, skirted the long slopes of the hill, with quiet vistas of hillsides to the north blanketed with spruce trees. She passed a track on the left, a last house, but the railway went on regardless and she followed. For a foot-passenger the hill was long, and the curve of the railway, seeking always its own level, described an arc so slow as to be almost imperceptible. The stones were hard underfoot, but here and there other walkers had made little paths on the banks, or the grass was flat and wide enough to walk along beside the tracks. She trudged on and finally the bend was achieved, the hill passed, and the track straightened again, preparatory to crossing over the marsh beside Skerrow Loch. The old railway shed loomed ahead of her. She stopped and consulted the map. Lochskerrow Halt. As remote a station as one could find in Britain, apparently quite pointless. Only a loch, fringed by brown reeds, and hillsides mottled with the browns of autumn and the dark green of the everlasting spruce.

And a tent. A peculiar tent, a round brown tent, like an upturned pot. And a trickle of smoke that curled away into blue autumn air. She stared at it. Someone come for the fishing, or the quiet. Somebody who had a strong desire to be nowhere, and chose here. But the tent was an odd shape, an attractive shape, like a breast. She scowled at the thought which was not one that she had chosen to think, and crossed the track so that she could see better. The person had camped right down by the loch. Whoever it was must be stupid, or immune to midges. She turned to go on.

It was something about the tent, the shape of it, or the colour. It was not quite like anything that she had seen before. It certainly didn't come out of any camping catalogue. She stopped again and stood hesitating on the edge of the railway track. The fire was on the far side of the tent. It must have been hard to make a fire; after the rain everything was soaking. But at least it was safe. There was a gap in the smoke, a hesitation, then it curled up thickly again, like a question mark. Someone had laid more fuel on the fire.

She fingered the map in her pocket. Next stop Gatehouse. She had decided to follow the track. Though the tent was intriguing, demanding her attention, she never spoke to strangers. She was confident but not foolhardy. She had learned self-defence in evening classes last winter. She didn't want to see any campers, they destroyed the illusion of perfect loneliness. But campers had orange tents and neat gas stoves and this tent was neither orange, nor red, nor brown, though it was almost all of them. The smoke rose steadily beyond it. The hills lay bare and autumnal under a gentle September sky. The loch was silent at her feet. It was like a landscape out of a window, magical, for ever out of reach, a place glimpsed once and destined never to be named. But it has a name, and I am standing here, she thought. There is no roof over my head, I breathe the air that belongs to this place. She stood there for another minute, then she stepped off the railway and climbed carefully down the bank.

The tent was pitched on a small green hummock of dry land, a few feet above the edge of the loch. To reach it she had to jump from tussock to tussock of lumpy grass, and brown water oozed and squelched where she had passed. Standing on the shore, she heard no sound but the harsh shiver of a breeze among the dying reed stems and the lap of water on the shore, rippled by a small wind. The tent was big, bigger than it had seemed from above. She felt a pang of sudden anticipation, or fear. All she saw was a tent and smoke, but her stomach registered something alien, another world. She pushed the thought away, and walked quietly round the tent.

The person tending the fire had its back to her; a crouched-down person in what was apparently a cloak of coarse wool, woven into strange intricate patterns of whorls and circles and spirals in curious russet shades, like a maze in autumn. A person – and here she shrank back, with that same pang of anticipation – a person with green hair. She must have moved suddenly, or made some small sound, or possibly the person had been aware of her all the time for, when he looked round, he did not seem at all startled but regarded her with grave interest. Her hands flew to cover her mouth, and her whole body reacted to that sudden fulfilment of fear that seems close to fainting, as if the quiet hills had risen from their foundations and were spinning madly round her. She stood aghast, feeling the blood drain from her cheeks and her heart thud painfully.

He was green.

Completely, uncompromisingly green. The vivid, vibrant green of fresh spinach plants, or bogland grass, or young hawthorn. His hair was thick and green, and hung over his forehead in a green fringe. His skin was green, his eyes were green, even his lips were green. Under the russet cloak he wore strange loose garments of dark green, but his feet were bare – and green. He watched her with gentle interest, and stretched out a green hand to her. She recoiled.

'Sarah,' he said.

I am going to faint, she thought, and even in her terror dismissed the idea as soon as she had found words for it. This was not the moment to faint. She took a deep breath and looked at him. The hills subsided, breathless from their crazy spinning, and relapsed into their comfortable places with the familiarity of a million unmoving years. The water still lapped at the shores of the loch behind her, and across the northern hills a curlew called. Only the man in front of her remained unquestionably green. She stared at him, and slowly her brain adjusted to this new reality. Chlorophyll? she wondered, but the question that came out was different.

'How did you know I was Sarah?'

'When I realised you were on your way.'

Words failed her, an unusual experience for her. His accent was hard to place, a touch of the local softness, laid over clipped English vowels. Just like hers. Perhaps it was hers. Her brain threatened to start reeling again, and she checked it sharply.

'Who? How ... ? What are you doing here?'

'I am meeting you. It's a great pleasure,' he said with maddening formality.

'But you weren't expecting me?'

'Not in so many words, no.'

She couldn't take her eyes off him. It was such an exuberant green, not a pale, subdued green that might by some stretch of the imagination verge on sickly white or pink, nor a very dark green that in a certain light might pass for black or brown. It was the greenest of greens, proclaiming itself almost insultingly as a colour in its own right, a living colour that bore no resemblance whatsoever to any colour that human skin was supposed to be. A green man. Sarah shook her head slowly, and stared at him as if she could never encompass what she saw.

'Who are you?' she asked at last, and was annoyed to hear her voice sounded frail and squeaky.

'Not yet,' he said. 'I hope so, by the end of my journey.'

'Hope to what?'

'Who I am,' he said. 'But perhaps in this country you are already who you are.'

'What?'

'Who.'

'How,' she heard herself say before she could stop, and giggled.

He smiled at her sympathetically. At least his teeth were white. If he were not green, she found herself thinking, he would be extremely attractive. She decided to ask something very simple and specific. 'Is this your tent?'

'Yes. Come in.'

'Not yet,' she said, jumpily. 'I was just interested. It looks different.'

'It would, naturally.'

'Where did you come from?'

'It was the nearest place to here.'

'I don't understand.'

He seemed puzzled. 'It couldn't be otherwise. When you came, you must have come from the nearest place too. There was no other way to pass.'

'When I came,' said Sarah, slowly and thoughtfully, 'I started from my home, which is near Mossdale. Where did you start from?'

'I also started from my home.'

'And how near Mossdale is that?'

'Only a thought.'

'You live a thought away from Mossdale?'

'As we all do.'

'Excuse me,' she said. 'Don't think me rude, but are you being irritating on purpose?'

'I am trying hard,' he said humbly. 'Come and eat and drink with me.'

'I brought my lunch. We can share it if you like.'

'And mine also. It's always the best way to begin.'

Begin what? She didn't bother to ask. She was beginning to feel that it would be pointless. He got up, like a cat uncurling itself, and surprised her again. He was tall, over six feet certainly, but his movements were quite unmanlike, feline and graceful, lacking only a certain power or energy that she had subconsciously expected. He drew back the tent flap and disappeared inside. Sarah came a little closer to the fire. It was very neatly made, and had been packed over with turfs like a charcoal burner's oven, with only the thin spiral of smoke curling out at the top. She gazed down at the uncoiling smoke as if it held an answer.

When he reappeared he held a round pot in one hand, and a plate in the other, both reddish and covered with more of the swirling designs in autumn colours. He laid them down, and spread his cloak on the grass in front of the tent.

'Please sit down.'

She sat down self-consciously, feeling that she was taking her part in some ceremony which had not previously been explained to her, and wondering if her part held any clues of which she was unaware. He spread food out before her, and poured drink into two cups. She watched the liquid as it glugged out of the round pot. It was vivid green. He nodded to her, and offered her a cup. She looked down into it, watching the green stuff still swirling around, frothing a little at the edges. 'It won't turn me ... It won't have any effect on me, will it?' she asked nervously.

'You are already as you are.' It could have been a compliment.

'But this won't ... change me?' she asked delicately, not wishing to be more blunt about it.

'Everything changes. But for one to seek to change another, that would be presumptuous.' He sounded almost angry.

'I'm sorry,' she said quickly. 'I didn't mean to insult you. But this is quite a surprise. It's like walking into a different world.'

'Of course,' he said. 'For you as for me. We each bring a little of our own world with us.'

She swallowed, and took the plunge. 'Have you come from another world?'

'Just as you have.'

'But this is my world.'

He looked around, puzzled. 'Then you belong here.'

'No, this is Lochskerrow Halt. But it's my planet.'

'Lochskerrow Halt. Just as on my planet. But we call it something different.'

'No, wait,' said Sarah, putting down her drink and pressing her hands to her head. 'Do you mean that Lochskerrow Halt is on another planet?'

'It depends which is another.'

'Another from Earth,' said Sarah. 'My planet.'

'I thought you said you lived at Mossdale.'

'Yes. Mossdale, Earth. It's still all one planet.'

'That's certainly true,' he said. 'It's all one.'

'Please,' she said. 'Could you be a little more specific? Did you come from Earth or from somewhere else?'

'Yes.'

'Yes what?'

'Please.'

'I can't bear it,' she said, torn between tears and anger. 'Do you do it on purpose?'

'Drink with me,' he said. 'It will make it much easier.'

Spurred by frustration, Sarah drank. The drink tasted green, like new peas, or the pale hearts of lettuces.

Then she said, 'Will you answer me one straight question?'

'I answer all your questions,' he pointed out. 'Though it's not what I'm accustomed to.'

She thought about that. 'Do you find it rude?'

'Only pointless,' he said. 'But that was in another world. Ask as you please.'

'Do you have a name?'

'Of course.'

He seemed surprised. He'll never answer this, she thought. In no good fairytale or folktale would they ever answer this, but why not try? 'What is your name?'

'I thought you knew,' he said, smiling at her with the utmost friendliness. 'I find it very odd that you don't. My name is Lin.'

'Say that again.'

'Lin.'

'Lin?'

'That's it, more or less. Sarah, will you eat?'

The dish held curious flat loaves which would have appeared more bread-like if they had not been green, and assorted nuts, or berries, or sweets. Whatever they were, Sarah didn't recognise them. She reached for her rucksack and laid out her own food: two cheese and Marmite sandwiches, a tomato, a bar of chocolate and an apple. Lin added her offering to the plate and sat down on the cloak, the dish of food between them. 'Let's eat.'

Cautiously she took one of the green loaves, feeling it would be churlish to stick to her own cheese sandwiches. It was strong and yeasty, as if it were more alive than ordinary food. Lin took a sandwich and chewed it with a puzzled expression. He asked nothing, however, and she resisted the impulse to ask if it were all right. That would merely make another question. The problem was that every sensible remark she could think of was a question. If questions were pointless, then what kind of conversation was left with someone of whom she knew absolutely nothing? Sarah ate in unaccustomed silence, but her companion seemed content. He ate very slowly, and he watched her with an interest which, though disconcerting, was not uncivil or frightening. He looked at her as he might look at the scenery, or a pot plant on the table. She had never, in the presence of a strange man, worried less about being a woman.

'If you never ask questions,' she asked eventually, and realised as she spoke that she was asking a question, 'then how do you find out what you want to know?'

'It depends what I want to know.'

'What do you want to know, Lin?' There was urgency in her voice, as if by supplying him with some motive, or reason for his presence, all would be made explicable.

He appeared to give her question serious consideration. While she waited she unwrapped the chocolate and handed him a piece. 'Nothing,' he said at last. 'The idea is not so much to know as to follow the thought.'

'Which thought?'

'You called it Lochskerrow Halt.'

'I did what? Have some chocolate.'

'The place we have reached,' he seemed to be seeking for words, 'where your thought crossed mine. It's not easy to describe in this language, which travels only in straight lines ... Ugh!'

'What's the matter?'

Lin jumped to his feet and ran down to the loch, where he spat vigorously, washed his mouth out, and spat again.

'Was it the chocolate?'

'I'm very sorry,' he said, wiping his mouth, and coming to sit down again. 'That was extremely uncivil of me. Chocolate, you say. I shall remember that.'

'It's supposed to be sweet. You don't find it so?'

'It tastes like shit,' he said. And then added at once, 'I'm sorry. I forgot. You don't like to have that mentioned.'

'I don't?'

'Taboo,' he said. 'We don't have them. I forgot.'

He seemed absurdly put out. 'Really,' said Sarah, 'it's not important. Who told you about our taboos, anyway?'

'You, of course.'

'Me? I didn't say a thing. And it isn't a taboo with me, particularly.' It seemed important that he should realise she was a fairly liberated person.

'But it is you. There isn't anyone else.'

'But there must be. Where did you learn English?'

He seemed quite at a loss, like a parent trying to find out what a baby wants, wishing the child could only talk and make itself understood. 'Of course I speak your language when I speak to you,' he said patiently. 'How else would you understand what I say?'

'What language do you speak at home?'

'Very little.' She sighed, and he explained with the same air of apology. 'I'm not accustomed you see. That must be why I don't do it to your satisfaction.'

She didn't know whether it was the drink, or the strange food, or his greenness, or the whole incomprehensible situation, but she was beginning to feel ridiculously emotional, as if she were about to experience an earthquake, or a period. He appeared to have come from another planet. An alien from outer space. She looked at him and her face quivered. At that moment he was extraordinarily desirable. The realisation of it swept over her like a wave, leaving her shaken and breathless. Nothing he said made the least sense, and no man on earth had ever treated her with such dispassionate clarity before. He had done nothing, asked her nothing, shown no interest in her whatsoever, unless he knew her perfectly already, as he had known her name. Like an angel. A stupid thought – she pushed it away from her, disgusted. This was not the clean, white, milk-and-water disguise of angels in her child's picture Bible, this was a creature definitely male, attractive, and dynamically green. A fertility god – no, not that either. If he were thinking about sex he would have frightened her by now.

He was still looking at her, his green eyes large with concern or kindliness. Sarah didn't need kindliness from men. Not in her world she didn't. Rebellious emotion surged into her chest so that she could hardly breathe. She felt hot and confused. Something must happen to relieve this tension. Still he said nothing. Despising herself, she burst into tears.

Some Notes On His Departure

JAMES MEEK

James Meek is currently reporter for *The Guardian* in Russia, where his sense of the absurd is continually being gratified. Born in London in 1962 and raised in Dundee, Meek read English at Edinburgh University and went into journalism in Northampton, followed by Edinburgh with *The Scotsman*. In 1991 he drove to Kiev and worked as a freelance journalist, becoming well-known for his reports in both *The Scotsman* and *The Guardian*. He now lives with his wife, Yulia in Moscow. He is the author of the novel *McFarlane Boils the Sea* (1989), set in Edinburgh, *Last Orders and Other Stories* (1992) from which the story here is taken, and recently the mordant novel *Drivetime* (1995), the account of a surreal journey from Edinburgh to Glasgow via Europe.

The stories in *Last Orders* all involve some radical dislocation between the mind and the world, but 'Some Notes On His Departure' is the only one to make the world wholly alien by postulating a reversal of natural law. Gravity is apparently magically suspended, and everything not tied down or inside fixtures falls off the world. The point, it might seem, is that the law that sticks us to the earth is no less bizarre than its absence: we live in an absurd universe either way. This would be a secular version of the use of miracles or the supernatural in more religious fantasies.

But increasingly through the story we do not know that this change has happened to anyone besides the narrator. Only phenomena within his perception have altered. (And of course he may be asleep, drunk, or mad.) His room has upended, and maybe, from the thud, Mrs Dalnaspittal below has also hit her ceiling. He indulges in pictures of life falling off the world, and speculates on who might survive and how. His own ideas become progressively more absurd until he imagines himself flying about with others who remain. Finally, he adds to our questions by not looking out of the window to confirm his vision of the world.

The consequence is that just as the narrator may be a failed interpreter, papering the universe with his mind, so may we be. Just as he speculates, so do we. In which case the story subverts our minds just as it subverts the world. But we do not know either way: and this randomness brings us back to the arbitrary whim that starts the story.

⌁ Some Notes On His Departure ⌁

Sandy lay on the floor of the lounge, listening to music and looking up at the ceiling. The room was full of clutter, whereas the ceiling was empty and smooth. It would be good to walk around there for a while, the floor the ceiling and the ceiling the floor.

At that moment he fell from the floor and landed heavily on the ceiling, bruising his nose and winding himself severely. The furnishings in the lounge crashed around him. A soft thud on the floor suggested Mrs Dalnaspittal downstairs had suffered a similar fate.

Sandy stood up. He was not badly hurt. Betrayed by gravity, there was a turnup, it had always seemed too good to be true that even without special shoes there was no danger of falling off. A serious infringement of Newton's laws had occurred – and why trust an Englishman's guarantee of free gravity for life, no strings attached? Yet the Englishness of the man was not the issue, indeed he had seemed fine, clear-thinking, this shite about apples was typical of the couthy tales they told you to distract you from the nub, the nub of the nub. And here he was, standing on the ceiling. Nubs within nubs. How could Newton explain that? How could Einstein? If you couldn't get at Newton's nub for shite about apples there was certainly no way you could raise Einstein in conversation without some smartarse saying $E = MC^2$ and then slotting a pint in his thrapple as soon as you asked him what it meant. Edward McSquared, the inventor of Einstein.

Everything in the room was now broken. The television was smashed, the record deck cracked, the amplifier box spilling its guts out, the chipboard and melanine bookcases come apart. Total disaster and waste. No, because the books were OK, and the records could be surprisingly tough when dropped. The worst thing was, the ceiling turned out to be all lumps and cracks, and besides it was white and there would be his dirty footprints all over it. He took off his shoes and looked up. The floorboards were solid, beautiful wooden things, daft to even consider leaving them.

So, the car gone too presumably, so much for the wheel lock, just dropped right off the street into the air without a sound, along with all the traffic.

The pros and cons of the situation. Fewer nuclear weapons for one thing, all the nuclear submarines falling out of the sea, and bombers being able to flip over maybe but finding it very difficult to land. A lot fewer people as well, all those folk shopping in the high street just plunging into the sky, the bowling club members observing that what Galileo proved concerning objects falling at the same rate regardless of size was indeed true as the position of the bowls relative to the jack remained more or less unaltered, raising among the more imaginative the possibility of one last game in three dimensions, if you happened to have a bowl close to hand.

Mandatory vegetarianism was inevitable. There, if anywhere, was a lack of foresight, or maybe it had been an injustice to farmers, thinking of them as possessive, conservative, cautious, but anyway imagine not keeping the livestock properly secured to the ground against a gravitational lapse. As it was the fields would have been cleared in seconds, allowing for the odd cow getting tangled up in a tree. The sheep, inoffensive beasts, not fast moving, calm, were most to be pitied. Hurtling from the planet, still chewing grass.

A look out of the window was the thing. God though, imagine missing the exact moment, imagine not looking out of the window at that particular time, though thus more chance of a broken skull, but to have seen everything in the world that was not fixed or held down separating from the planet instantaneously.

What complacency! Just because the ground seemed solid, to think standing on a hill in the open air you could lift one foot, or stand on tiptoe, or even jump so you had no kind of hold at all! Given the number of people there were, some somewhere would have been trying to jump as high as they could. To reach the moment of achievement two feet above the ground, to make a supreme effort of muscle-power to lift yourself a tiny wee fraction off the heavy planet, and feel gravity snap like an overtight guitar string! An instant of ecstasy: you are flying! Followed by the pain, you are falling.

Sandy glanced at the window and looked away again. Moral cowardice. Make no move. What was the opposite of moral cowardice? Immoral cowardice. Therefore his cowardice was the better kind. It was entirely moral. To reach the doorhandle would be hard. Parochial Scottish architecture, just because gravity had always worked before, no provision had been made, i.e. having a handle exactly halfway between the floor and the ceiling. So much for David Hume, though at least he accepted nobody had read his book, let alone faced the consequences.

Sandy sat down on the ceiling and drew the cushions from the settee around him. He put one between his back and the wall and sat on another. What if gravity should return? He put a cushion on his head and the last one on his lap. A prudent measure, keep one step ahead. Was it just luck he had been in the house, or some sharp sixth sense he had, warning him not to go out? Survival of the fittest. Shame about the jungle creatures. Perhaps the big cats had managed to hang on, but for the elephants and the zebras there was no chance. The birds ... fifty-fifty, though some of them could roost OK. But the fish! Jesus! Millions of mackerel and halibut spread out across the sky, another sight he would never see.

Gravity could come back at any moment. The ideal position would be to stand on his head, balancing all four cushions on the soles of his feet. Then nothing could happen to him. This was hardly practical. Better to sit as now, only with all the cushions laid along the length of his body. One way or another, when gravity returned, he would be ready.

Supposing he was the only one. Just him and his furniture somehow picked out. The thud he had heard from downstairs was Mrs Dalnaspittal banging on the ceiling because his music was too loud, she did sometimes do that. He could go outside, get down the stair by somehow working hand over hand on the bannisters, and hang out the doorway. People would gather round, and he would not ask for help. At the right moment he would let go and shoot into the sky. He would move so fast he would not be able to see the surprise on their faces. That was no good, it was the surprise that would make it worthwhile, even for a moment. Instead he would go over to the window and shout. It would take time, but eventually someone would come, and after a few hours everyone in the world would know that in Scotland there was a man who had fallen off the ground. How many interviews would he have to do? A press conference would be organised. There would need to be several, and there would still be more people wanting interviews, thousands. An agent would become involved, there would be plenty of candidates to choose from, try and find a tough but honest one with a good head for figures who would make him a fair bit of money. There was also the possibility of sex with attractive women who would be drawn to his unique gravitational situation by curiosity and the dodgy eroticism that went with novelty, but would not be interested in long-term relationships. Ah, but the freak show. Do you want me for myself, or my lack of gravity? Sex might prove awkward and complicated with two people falling in opposite directions. But the freak show! Appearances on television. As for the scientists. They would cut him into as many bits as there were scientists in the world and send a bit to each, in plastic dishes. How many scientists were there? Let's see, ten people going from school to do science at university every year, say ten from every 20,000 population getting science degrees every year, that's two and a half million in the world, say they all do forty years work, that's 100 million scientists to deal with. Not much to go round. Simpler to lock him up in a large institution behind barbed wire and film him with a video camera and slow-motion film and infra-red and x-rays, try him for various drugs, test his urine regularly, ensure his diet was strictly regimented, strap him into a centrifuge and birl him round at high speeds, connect him up to monitors, try him for word association and what does this shape remind you of? but most important of all, see whether his reverse weight had any military applications.

Avoidance. The low profile, that was the only way. He could not stay in the house. A new habitat was needed, a disused mine, a cave, a forest with exceptionally thick, low branches. Dark places to stop him escaping to the sky. He would have to find a place where food and drink were available, but living off the land was hard enough at the best of times, and what were the best of times but the worst of times with a phoney accent? Setting snares required a certain expertise, not to mention the state of the rabbit when you went back a few days later, still alive but fit only to be killed, and you meanwhile hanging onto the heather for dear life, reaching for the twitching creature with your one free hand, feeling the heather start to come out the ground from your weight. No, no, no, absolutely definitely the only possibility for escape was to reach sanctuary, a place to be found in by a lone man or woman or boy or girl who would be frightened at first yet curious and would understand his need for protection. A church. A barn. A toolshed. An old section of pipe to crawl into and spend the rest of his life in, relying on friendly children to bring him pieces and ice-poles and blankets and reading matter.

It was most unlikely that the thud he heard from downstairs had been Mrs Dalnaspittal wielding the broom handle. The noise caused by his furniture crashing onto the ceiling was a noise that would have provoked alarm and neighbourly concern, possibly a call to the emergency services, not a protest. The chances were good that she had fallen off the floor as well. In these high-ceilinged flats she would have come off badly. Dead perhaps. A cruel prank indeed by the fundamental forces of the universe, to pull an old woman from her chair while she was quietly watching soaps, and bounce her off the ceiling. If Mrs Dalnaspittal had gone, there was every possibility that gravity had failed across the board. A short journey to the window would resolve the question once and for all.

Sandy lay down flat on the ceiling, rearranging the cushions so they covered his body and face in a continuous line. So, two kinds of people, those who had fallen so far and been stopped, like him, and those who had fallen into the sky. Which would be the better group, from the socialising point of view? To stay behind was the obvious choice. This would be survival. The food in the kitchen would last a certain while, and by that time, by signals, by careful trips outside, he would have made contact with others who had avoided tumbling into the unknown. They would band together and form a hardworking, democratic wee community that could fend for itself and knew how to deal with outsiders. After all, who had been cleared off the planet? Who was out in the open? Old women with shopping bags. Tourists. Travelling salesmen. Farmers. Lorry drivers. People walking dogs. Newspaper vendors. Policemen. Tough youths who hung around. Dossers. At the same time many of the old folk, the sick and the disabled and babies would have died like Mrs Dalnaspittal, or wouldn't last long. This would leave healthy working people to carry the torch for human civilization in a world without gravity.

Mind you, certain of the indoor types were not so definitely good. Too many pale unmuscled people who did not like the fresh air and exercise. Agoraphobics. Besides, how could you rely on all the afflicted folk dying. Millions lying or sitting in rooms all day long, kept in the one place by terrible inheritance of wasted limbs, incomplete brains, excess weight. Excess weight! A joyful release. One by one, chocolate bar in hand, the refugees from the fat farms and slimming clubs squeeze out of their windows and vanish without effort into the void. What about the prisons? Convicts also to contend with. Plus the accountants thrown about their offices. There was in the end no telling who would be left to share the vicinity with. And in groups brought together by circumstance, how to maintain law and order? Put it to the vote was fine before, when behind the vote was a man and behind the man was another man and behind the other man was a big office and behind the office were a lot of heavies with big sticks. The same with the ordering around of many big strong men by a wee speccy man with Highers and a degree and a mode of language that enabled him to define the concepts by which he took authority and shared it with others of his kind. There you would be with the assorted remains of human kind, a dozen of you, and who would you be? Sandy; a pair of casuals in labelled cardigans and trainers; a recipient of care in the community; a very drunk man; a thin mother and a loud baby; a ten year-old girl with pigtails and thick spectacles; a man in a raincoat buttoned up to the neck, holding a briefcase to his stomach; a tiny foreign woman who did not speak; a blind pensioner of indeterminate sex; and a night-club bouncer six foot high, weighing fifteen stone, wearing a large beard, who was good at shouting. The possibility did not exist of sitting round in a circle, reaching democratic decisions for the common good of the twelve. The bouncer did not care that the man in the raincoat was blessed with useful scientific foresight concerning the future of life in a world without gravity, or that the tiny foreign woman did not wish to have sex with him, or that Sandy for all his flaws and weaknesses was a good man who warranted protection and assistance. It would come down to a single combat, Sandy and the bouncer wrestling on the oil-soaked ceiling of a derelict factory, the bouncer killing and eating him.

Who would have fallen already, fallen first, fallen ahead, if not hillwalkers? Then open-air swimmers, athletes, sunbathers, shepherds, explorers. The seas and rivers, the soil in the fields, the sand and pebbles on the beach, they would be falling too. Surely the air itself would drift away. Those who hung on would be lost, choking to death, and if they left it too late to leave they would fall out of company, in ones and twos scattered across the world, miles apart, people who had thought about it too much. He had to go now. Could he take something, something to drink, and make his way through the air by flapping his arms to another late decider and share it with them? And if the bulk of the falling world was gone on ahead, they would have gone involuntarily, without control, without a decision, without knowing. Whereas his would be a definite act, a choice, an attempt at discovery, him and his companion. As for the falling, it was an attitude of mind, a mile high and the shape of the earth beginning to show and seeing the planet getting smaller and smaller, it would be flying, surely.

It all depended on the way the planets were set up, but if they kept getting faster and faster they might pass one of the big ones, Jupiter or Saturn, seeing the rings close up, curving from the centre of your vision to the corners of your eyes, if the air to breathe hadn't dispersed by then. The possibilities were endless the moment he stepped out of the window, which he would do very soon indeed.

ᴸIST OF PRE-1900 ᴶOURCES

Robert Chambers, *Popular Rhymes of Scotland*, 4th ed. (Edinburgh: William Patterson, 1870)

F. W. Child, ed., *The English and Scottish Popular Ballads*, 5 vols. (New York, The Folklore Press, 1957)

Robert Henryson, *The Poems of Robert Henryson*, ed. Denton Fox (Oxford: Clarendon Press, 1979)

Gavin Douglas, *The Poetical Works of Gavin Douglas*, ed. John Small, 4 vols. (Edinburgh: William Patterson, 1874)

Patrick Gordon, *The First Booke of the Famous Historye of Penardo and Laissa, other ways callid the warres of Love and Ambitione* (Dort: George Waters, 1615)

James Macpherson, *The Poems of Ossian and Related Works*, ed. Howard Gaskill (Edinburgh: Edinburgh University Press, 1996)

Robert Burns, *The Poems and Songs of Robert Burns*, ed. J. Kinsley (Oxford: Clarendon Press, 1968)

James Hogg, *Selected Poems and Songs*, ed. David Groves (Edinburgh: Scottish Academic Press, 1968)

——, *The Three Perils of Man: War, Women and Witchcraft*, ed. Douglas Gifford (Edinburgh: Scottish Academic Press, 1989)

——, *The Private Memoirs and Confessions of a Justified Sinner*, ed. John Carey (London: Oxford University Press, 1969)

Thomas Carlyle, *Sartor Resartus*, ed. Kerry McSweeney and Peter Sabor (Oxford: Oxford University Press, 1987)

George MacDonald, *Phantastes and Lilith* (London: Gollancz, 1962)

——, *The Princess and the Goblin and The Princess and Curdie*, ed. Roderick McGillis (Oxford: Oxford University Press, 1990)

James Thomson, *The City of Dreadful Night and Other Poems* (London: Reeves and Turner, 1880)

Margaret Oliphant, *A Beleaguered City and Other Stories*, ed. Merryn Williams (Oxford: Oxford University Press, 1988)

Robert Louis Stevenson, *Dr Jekyll and Mr Hyde and Weir of Hermiston*, ed. Emma Letley (Oxford: Oxford University Press, 1987)

—— *Selected Short Stories of R. L. Stevenson*. ed. Ian Campbell (Edinburgh: Ramsay Head Press, 1980)

Andrew Lang, *The Gold of Fairnilee* (Bristol: J. W. Arrowsmith, 1888)

Fiona Macleod, *The Gold Key and the Green Life: Some Fantasies and Celtic Tales by George MacDonald and Fiona Macleod*, ed. Elizabeth Sutherland (London: Constable, 1986)

Sources post-1900 will be found in the Acknowledgments list, with the following exceptions:

Neil Gunn, *The Well at the World's End* (London: Faber and Faber, 1950)
Liz Lochhead, *The Grimm Sisters*, in *Dreaming Frankenstein and Collected Poems* (Edinburgh: Polygon, 1984)
Sian Hayton, *Cells of Knowledge* (Edinburgh: Polygon, 1989)
James Meek, *Last Orders and Other Stories* (Edinburgh: Polygon, 1992)

For permission to reprint copyright material the publishers gratefully acknowledge the following:

Patrick Gordon, *The First Booke of the Famous Historye of Penardo and Laissa* (Dort: George Waters, 1615). By permission of the British Library: shelf mark C34 e.38.
J. M. Barrie, *Peter Pan: A Fantasy in Five Acts* (London: Samuel French, 1988). By permission of Samuel French Ltd and Great Ormond Street Children's Hospital.
David Lindsay, *A Voyage to Arcturus* (Edinburgh: Canongate Press, 1992). By permission of Victor Gollancz Ltd
David Lindsay, *The Haunted Woman* (Edinburgh: Canongate Press, 1987). By permission of Victor Gollancz Ltd
Naomi Mitchison, *The Corn King and the Spring Queen* (Edinburgh: Canongate Press, 1990). By permission of David Higham Associates Ltd
Bruce Marshall, *Father Malachy's Miracle* (London: Collins, Fontana Books, 1962). By permission of David Higham Associates Ltd
James Bridie, *Mr Bolfry*, in *Plays for Plain People* (London: Constable, 1943). By permission of The Agency (London) Ltd
Neil Gunn, *The Green Isle of the Great Deep* (London: Faber and Faber, 1944). By permission of Souvenir Press Ltd and Dairmid Gunn
George Mackay Brown, *Magnus* (Glasgow: Richard Drew, 1987). By permission of John Murray (Publishers) Ltd
George Mackay Brown, 'An Epiphany Tale', from *Andrina* (London: Chatto and Windus/ The Hogarth Press, 1983). By permission of John Murray (Publishers) Ltd
Alasdair Gray, *Lanark: A Life in Four Books* (Edinburgh: Canongate Press, 1981). By permission of Canongate Books Ltd
Iain Banks, *The Bridge* (London: Macmillan, 1984) By permission of Little, Brown and Company (U.K.)
Margaret Elphinstone, 'Green Man', from *An Apple from a Tree* (London: The Women's Press, 1991). By permission of Watson, Little Ltd.